Ruth N Davidar graduated with a Master's degree in Food Service Management and Dietetics from Women's Christian College, Madras, in 1984, and later taught at the Nirmala Niketan College of Home Science in Bombay. While teaching she contributed articles on food and health to a number of popular and women's magazines like *Savvy*, and, *Body and Beauty Care*. But it was only when studying at the Jawaharlal Nehru University in New Delhi that she decided to bring the science of nutrition out of the classroom and into the mainstream of life. The result was *Foodsense*, a column she started with The Pioneer newspaper in December 1993.

Today, Ruth N Davidar is an established columnist and food writer whose specialist columns in the English language and in translation appear in publications as varied as the *Indian Express, Financial Express, Hindustan Times, Sentinel, Aaj, Rajasthan Patrika, Akshar Bharat, Navajyoti, Hindustan, Aryavasta and Dainik Bhaskar* to name a few. She is also on the panel of reviewers for the *Indian Review of Books. Indian Food Sense* is her first book.

Ruth N Davidar lives in Wellington in the Nilgiris in South India.

INDIAN FOOD SENSE

a health
and
nutrition
guide
to
traditional
recipes

Ruth N Davidar

EastWest Books (Madras) Pvt. Ltd.
● Chennai ● Bangalore ● Hyderabad

EastWest Books (Madras) Pvt. Ltd.

No.571, Poonamallee High Road, Aminjikarai, Chennai 600 010.
3-5-1108, Maruti Complex, II Floor, Narayanaguda, Hyderabad 500 029.
Praja Bhavan, I Floor, 53/2, Bull Temple Road, Basavanagudi, Bangalore 560 019.

ISBN 81-86852-79-4

Price: Rs.250.00

Cover design: Spectrum Graphic Studio

Printed by Sri Venkatesa Printing House, Chennai 600 026.

Published by EastWest Books (Madras) Pvt. Ltd.
No.571, Poonamallee High Road, Aminjikarai, Chennai 600 029.

For my grandmothers

Stella Sugirthammal Mathuram and Stella Ahimaz

WHOSE FOOD SENSE I INHERITED

Contents

Preface

I was born a woman and an Indian. The significance of this struck me only many years later. Like most young people in the country, my future goals were rather hazy and I chose to study nutrition because my mother was a home economist herself. When I did get the prospectus to the course, however, I was filled with excitement as I read through the subjects offered in the syllabus. This was, indeed, what I had been looking for and I knew then that I had a vocation for life.

However, I was to learn soon enough that nutrition education and knowledge, as taught to us, was drawn from Western textbooks which were wholly unfamiliar with the Indian scenario. Of course, I am not dismissing outright the efforts of distinguished nutritionists in the country who have taken pains to present their research in papers and textbooks. The principles of sound nutrition, the daily dietary allowances for Indians, the nutrients in foods that make up the Indian diet and the consequences of nutritional deficiencies have all been documented in a number of good books by Indians. But, I believe, the population that benefits from this information is minuscule compared with the many thousands who cannot get a point of easy reference on the subject. Later, when I went on to teach dietetics at the university level, I found an appropriate book which completely identified with the situation on the ground was still not available.

Out of this awareness this book was written. It is not intended as a scholarly thesis but is something anyone wishing to be introduced to nutrition will find useful. This not only includes doctors, nurses, health workers, dietitians and nutritionists, but all the countless men and women, especially women, who have queries about what they eat and why. Needless to say, most people sift through reams of news and reports and advertisements and come to believe what they do not fully understand. Again, it is these people—the misinformed, underinformed and uninformed—who are most susceptible to food selection based on social acceptance, fads, food taboos and superstitious beliefs, and whose ignorance is often exploited by dishonest manufacturers in the food industry and unscrupulous practitioners of the health trade.

What is enormously encouraging is that these attitudes are changing, ironically, in part, because of the plethora of health programmes on television channels invading our living rooms. However, while nutrition information goes into overdrive, the nutrition education it provides is often lost through faulty interpretation. This book, therefore, endeavours to clarify the myriad questions people have on food and health to which the answers have seldom been satisfactory.

It provides nutrition education in the broadest sense of the word. The functions, requirements and sources of each nutrient in food are discussed in easy-to-follow, familiar language, so that the book will not intimidate the uninitiated. The book is extensively cross-referenced within the text to indicate that the process of eating, digestion, assimilation and utilization of food in the body is inter-connected. The latter section comprises a collection of India's most nutritious recipes, representative of each region within the country, but with an emphasis on preparing them with less refined sugar and fat. The appendices at the end of the book are a ready reference and provide almost all the information explained in detail elsewhere in the text.

Finally, though the text was made as up to date as was possible before the book went to press, the book does not claim to be the last word on nutrition. Research is constant, and its findings change with time. It is hoped that nobody who picks up this book will put it down without having benefited in some way.

Wellington   RUTH N DAVIDAR

April 2001

Acknowledgements

While this book is dedicated to my two grandmothers, it really belongs to one other person who, sadly, never lived to see it in its final published form: my mother, Sue Davidar, from whom I inherited whatever basic knowledge of cooking and nutrition I possess.

The process of developing this book involved a number of people whose contributions make this book what it is. My brother David suggested I do this book, and my parents Eddie and Sue Davidar gave me their full support and encouragement. Others helped primarily with the recipe section, though no less important was the assistance I received in preparing the section on nutrition education. To all of them—Mona Ambegaonkar, Dr. G. Azeemoddin, Gool Bhujwala, Doreen Davidar, the late Amy Dhalla, Jyotsna Govil, Jyoti Haldar, Minal Mehta Hazarika, Sharmila Herbert, Rupa Israel, Yasmin Kothavala, Gogi Lal, Aloo Lam, Vera Lam, Cici Mathews, Christine Patham, Jessy Ponnappa, Payal Pujara, Shanti Purushotham, Ratna Raman, Mina Shankar, Dr. Sunita Sharma, Sunita Shastry, Cookoo Suares and Shree Venkatram—my sincere thanks.

I am particularly indebted to three people—my brother, David, Sonjay Kant and Amrita Kumar—whose attitude of nonchalance finally goaded me into completing the book.

I would also like to gratefully acknowledge the nutrition information put out by the Indian Council of Medical Research and the National Institute of Nutrition, Hyderabad (India), which forms the basis of much of the nutrition content provided. I also found the book Normal and Therapeutic Nutrition by C.H. Robinson, M.R. Lawler, W.L. Chenoweth and A.E. Garwick, 17th Ed. (1986), published by Prentice-Hall, Inc., Upper Saddle River, NJ, invaluable in the preparation of this book.

Finally, I would like to thank my publisher, K.S. Padmanabhan, and his wife, Chandra Padmanabhan, besides Kalyani Rajaraman and B. Jayalakshmi, for their warmth and professionalism throughout our time together.

Wellington

April 2001

RUTH N DAVIDAR

Section 1

Nutrients and Nutrition

1. NUTRIENTS

Nutrients are chemical compounds varying in complexity which keep the body adequately nourished. Without them, the body will not be able to carry out the essential functions of growth, development and replacement of tissues, work and activity, and, maintenance of body systems. An excess or deficiency of these nutrients will affect the state of optimal health.

Nutrients are broadly divided into six categories—proteins, carbohydrates, fats, vitamins, minerals and water. Each nutrient has a definite function. Human beings require approximately 45 to 50 nutrients. Today, there is much emphasis on the ill effects of refined sugars, saturated fat and cholesterol, and on the benefits of fibre and unsaturated fat. These are erroneously believed to be in a class by themselves and are cause for much misinterpretation. Hence, a brief look at the various nutrients will give each food its rightful place within each group.

1.1 PROTEINS

Proteins are body builders. They promote growth and are responsible for the building up and repair of tissues. They are the only compounds in the body that contain nitrogen and the wastes that result from their breakdown are excreted by the kidneys. It is, however, important to note that in the event of infection or damage to the kidneys, the quality and quantity of protein intake needs to be carefully regulated in order to reduce the burden of elimination on the kidneys.

Proteins from the diet are broken down into amino acids and these are then built up again or synthesized in the body to give new proteins. Some examples:

Haemoglobin of the blood, insulin that regulates blood glucose levels, keratin found in the skin, nails and hair, myosin of the muscle, collagen of the bones and cartilage, and immunoglobulins (antibodies) that fight infections.

Both sexes need proteins to replace cells that are continuously cast off in the gastrointestinal tract, skin, hair and other tissues, and in the renewal of blood from time to time. Women suffer losses in menstruation.

The amino acids of both animal and plant proteins are of particular significance to human beings. Of the many amino acids known, nine are considered essential. These have to be supplied by the diet as the body has no mechanism to synthesize them. Failure to meet this requirement results in severe impairment to growth and tissue regeneration. These nine are threonine, valine, leucine, isoleucine, methionine, lysine, phenylalanine, tryptophan and histidine. In addition, babies and very young children need arginine. Their infantile livers are unable to synthesize this amino acid at the rate necessary for growth. The other amino acids can be synthesized by the body. If they are not provided in the diet, no function whatsoever will be impaired.

Foods with high quality proteins are almost totally retained by the body and the products of their breakdown, available for excretion, are very small. They are said to have high biological value. Usually, their composition of essential amino acids closely resembles the tissue proteins of the human body. Egg has been accorded the highest value of 100, followed closely by milk, fish, meat and poultry proteins. This, however, does not imply that all animal proteins are superior to vegetable proteins. Gelatin, an animal protein, contributes very little to health. The claim that gelatin strengthens nails is overrated. On the other hand, the proteins in soya beans and wheat germ (that part of the grain that is responsible for the growth of a new plant) compare well with the high-quality proteins of milk and meat. While soya beans can be incorporated in the diet, it is unfortunate that the germ of cereal grains is lost in milling.

Indians, by and large, are vegetarian. This means that the bulk of the proteins in their diet comes from plant sources. Rice, wheat, maize (corn), millets, pulses (dhals) and groundnuts make significant contributions of protein to the Indian diet, although individually these foods lack one or more of the essential amino acids. For example, wheat lacks lysine, rice lysine and threonine, legumes are methionine deficient and low in tryptophan, while maize falls short on lysine, tryptophan and methionine. Therefore, if these foods are consumed separately and exclusively over a period of time, there could be a deficiency. Needless to say, this rarely happens. Indians somehow have the knack of knowing (without instruction) the right combination of foods which will automatically complement each other, both for the best taste and nutrition advantage. Fine examples of this are more than amply demonstrated in the cereal-pulse combinations of iddlis and dhoklas, rice and dhal, and khichidi.

PROTEIN (g per day)		
RDA at a Glance		
M	60	
F	50	
Preg.	+15	
Lact.	0 - 6 months	+25
	6 - 12 months	+18

Indian men and women require approximately 1g of protein per kg ideal body weight, or 60 g of proteins daily for adult men and 50 g for adult women. These values are based on the recommendations of the Expert Group of the Indian Council of Medical Research (ICMR) which suggests that the Indian Reference Man should weigh 60 kg and the Indian Reference Woman 50 kg.

A pregnant woman will need an additional 15 g daily. During the period of lactation, 25 g extra are needed during the first six months after delivery and 18 g more per day thereafter, up to one year. Once the infant is one year and above, the mother can revert to her former (non-pregnant) intake of proteins.

Consumption of proteins in excess of need is often wasteful as the body has no facility to store them. Instead, it is burned as fuel or stored as fat. Conversely, insufficient intake of proteins results in the breakdown of body tissues. Lack of adequate carbohydrates in the diet further aggravates the problem, leading to a condition known as Protein-Calorie Malnutrition (PCM) or Protein-Energy Malnutrition (PEM). Mild forms of PEM may exist even among those with adequate income because of faulty food intake.

1.2 CARBOHYDRATES

Carbohydrates, in-very simple terms, are sugars. They provide energy that enables the body to function smoothly. They range from the very simple to the very complex. The more complex sugars are broken down to simple sugars during the process of digestion.

Carbohydrates are chemically known as saccharides. Single units are called monosaccharides which may exist singly or they may join together to form other carbohydrates. A disaccharide is made up of two monosaccharides. Many monosaccharides when combined together form polysaccharides.

Starch and fibre are the two most common polysaccharides found in plant foods. Starch can be utilized by the human body, but fibre which is not digested in the human digestive tract, is an unavailable form of complex carbohydrate. One of the products of starch degradation is dextrin. This may be noticed in everyday cooking when bread is toasted and flours are browned. This form of "pre-digested" food is especially beneficial for invalids and old people because the first stage of digestion has already been completed outside the body. This could also be the reason why hunger comes on sooner after eating toasted bread.

In many fruits, starch is converted to sugar on ripening. Alternately, sugar is converted to starch as tender vegetables mature. Other sugars that are found naturally, and are perhaps more recognizable, are the disaccharides—sucrose, lactose and maltose. Sucrose or table sugar, when digested, yields glucose and fructose. Lactose or milk sugar provides one molecule of glucose and one molecule of galactose. Maltose or malt sugar is not very common but when grains are allowed to sprout (malting), this sugar becomes available. Maltose, when broken down, gives two molecules of glucose.

Important among the simplest sugars that cannot be broken down any further are the monosaccharides glucose (also known as dextrose, corn sugar or grape sugar), fructose (or laevulose or fruit sugar) and galactose. The sweetness of some fruits like oranges and grapes, and, vegetables like tender corn and carrots, is due to the presence of glucose. Fructose is about twice as sweet as sucrose and is found in honey, ripe fruits and some vegetables. Galactose is present only within the molecule of the disaccharide lactose found in milk.

Glycogen is the storage form of carbohydrates in animals including human beings. It is sometimes called animal starch and is made up of many glucose units. It is synthesized in the liver and muscle, which are also the chief storage sites of glycogen.

Did You Know?
Animal foods are low in carbohydrates

Carbohydrates are the chief source of energy. The body utilizes them for every energy-requiring action including respiration, heartbeat, digestion, work, activity and exercise. The body gives absolute priority to meeting energy needs, indicating that all other physiological and biochemical functions are of secondary importance. Therefore, it is very important that ample carbohydrates are supplied by the diet. Failure to do so will result in proteins being utilized for this purpose. When the diet provides sufficient carbohydrates, then proteins are allowed to carry out their essential functions of tissue building, and, repair and growth. This is known as the protein-sparing action of carbohydrates. The highest concentrations of carbohydrates are found in cereals and legumes, usually in the form of starch. They are also the principal source of carbohydrates in the diet. This is of particular importance in Indian diets since lesser quantities of other foods are consumed. Fruits and vegetables have widely varying levels of carbohydrates, potatoes having a good deal more than, say, cabbage. Lactose of milk is the only source of carbohydrate of animal origin. Glycogen reserves are rapidly depleted the moment the animal is slaughtered.

Since carbohydrates are the single most important nutrient in the Indian diet, low intakes are rare. However, it must be cautioned that unsupervised dieting can lead to a potentially harmful condition called ketosis or acidosis, characterized by excessive fatigue and dehydration, with resultant loss of water and electrolytes. This condition is peculiar to diabetics where insufficient insulin in the blood does not remove glucose from the circulation into the cells where it is utilized. In normal individuals, though adequate insulin is available, any restriction of dietary carbohydrate forces the body to seek alternate sources of energy. First, proteins are broken down (catabolized) and then body fat is oxidized. This is what produces ketosis. Fortunately, in non-diabetics, this condition can be reversed by an intake of as little as 50 g of carbohydrate.

The form in which carbohydrates are consumed has a definite impact on the nutritional status of the individual. Put more simply, it is the difference between consuming carbohydrates that are as close to their natural state as possible, and those that have been subjected to much refining and processing. Whole grain cereals are examples of the former, and refined sugars and flours (all-purpose flour or maida) represent the latter. While experts cannot quite agree on the right balance of different carbohydrates best for human well-being, they are all of the same view that complex, less refined carbohydrates are the most beneficial. On the other hand, highly refined carbohydrates, along with fats and other factors, increase the risk of many chronic illnesses like diabetes mellitus that comes on after middle age and is called adult onset or non-insulin-dependent diabetes mellitus (NIDDM), cardiovascular disease, hypertension (elevated blood pressure), gall bladder disease and gout. The single most important condition linking these chronic states is obesity. Excessive intake of refined sugars also causes an increase in dental caries. Additionally, the use of highly processed carbohydrates, devoid of fibre, is the major contributing factor in problems of the gastrointestinal tract like chronic constipation, diverticular disease (a condition in which decreased muscle tone causes the intestinal wall to form pouches or sacs that trap food thereby permitting greater bacterial activity for longer periods of time with its more undesirable consequences), hiatus hernia, haemorrhoids (piles) and cancer of the colon. Even varicose veins is linked to obesity—a result of refined carbohydrates in the diet.

1.2.1 Fibre

Fibre is known by a variety of names such as roughage, bulk and residue. However, health professionals prefer the slightly more accurate name, dietary fibre. It represents the

Did You Know?
Fibre is not a nutrient

complex, unavailable form of carbohydrate that is found only in plants. It is the indigestible matter in food that makes no nutritive contribution whatsoever but its health benefits are many.

Broadly, dietary fibre may be divided into insoluble and soluble fibres. Insoluble fibres comprise cellulose, hemicellulose and lignin, those substances that give cells their structure and shape. The outer layers of grains called bran, and, the seeds and skins of fruits and vegetables, are good examples of insoluble fibres. Soluble fibres do not have any structural function. Examples are pectins, gums and mucilages. In fruits and vegetables, they are usually found between cells. The jellying properties of pectins are especially valued in cooking. Typically, these fibres do not exhibit any fibre-like characteristics and may be found in legumes (beans and peas), pulses (all dhals), carrots, potatoes, ladies fingers (the sticky, mucilaginous tissue), dried fruits, the endosperm or bulk of cereal grains, maize, flea seeds also known as falooda seeds, onions, and, psyllium seeds and their husk (isabgol).

These two groups of fibres play dissimilar though complementary functions. Insoluble fibres have a high water holding capacity, and this makes the stools soft and bulky, facilitating easy elimination. Therefore, a diet high in fibre necessitates an increased intake of water. Insoluble fibres also increase the rate of movement of food through the intestine, thereby reducing the time available for bacteria to act on it and produce harmful substances. Toxic substances present in foods are also given very little time to cause any damage to the gastrointestinal lining. Hence, insoluble fibres are responsible for the lower incidence of diverticular disease, hernia, cancer of the colon and dental caries.

Soluble fibres, on the other hand, perform two very important functions. First, they form a complex with bile salts, those substances that transport fat from the intestine into the body. By rendering bile salts unavailable, the fat in the meal is carried along with the undigested food and eliminated. Consumption of fresh salads and fruit with very fatty foods helps in this process. The other important function of soluble fibres is to regulate the absorption of sugar from the gut. This in turn reduces blood glucose levels and is of profound significance for diabetics, as lesser than normal units of insulin are required to clear blood glucose from the circulation. Fenugreek seeds, rich in soluble fibre, are known to effectively lower blood glucose and blood cholesterol levels. This dual action of soluble fibres helps to control coronary heart disease, diabetes, obesity, gout, piles, and, gallstones and gall bladder ailments.

However, fibre does not have all positive attributes. Insoluble fibres are known to bind and prevent absorption of essential minerals like calcium, magnesium, phosphorus, iron, manganese and zinc.

Did You Know?
Any dried fruit weighing 100 g provides 300 kcal

If the diet is high in fibre and low in mineral content, this could lead to deficiency states of the concerned mineral. Trace elements are particularly susceptible. Another disadvantage is that not all high-fibre foods are low in calories. Dried fruits like figs, apricots and raisins, and nuts, though very good sources of both insoluble and soluble fibres, are also high-energy foods that contain concentrated sources of calories.

Abdominal discomfort and increased flatulence in some people are the other undesirable aspects of dietary fibre. (See Appendix 5.8).

1.3　FATS

Fats are as important as proteins and carbohydrates and have many very important functions. Foremost among them is the provision of energy since fats are the most concentrated source of energy in the diet. Besides, they supply essential fatty acids (EFA), are the only means by which the fat soluble vitamins A, D, E and K may be utilized by the body, and provide palatability to the foods we eat. Fats keep us warm in the cold weather and protect vital organs like the kidneys against physical injury. In nutrition jargon, fats are known as lipids. They are basically chemical

Structure of a Triglyceride

```
      H
      |
H  —  C — O H   HO OC —R1
      |
H  —  C — O H   HO OC —R2
      |
H  —  C — O H   HO OC —R3
      |
      H

  Glycerol      Fatty Acids
```

compounds made up of fatty acids and glycerol. When the lipid is made up of one fatty acid and glycerol, it is known as a monoglyceride. Two molecules of fatty acid and glycerol form a diglyceride, and three molecules of fatty acid combined with glycerol make a triglyceride. Triglycerides are also called neutral fats and most fat in our food and in our bodies exists in this form.

Minerals and proteins are usually added to fats depending on their function in the body. Phosphorus containing lipids are known as phospholipids, and are found in all the cells in the body, especially those of the brain, nerves and liver. They are essential for the digestion and absorption of fats, and play a vital role in the entry of fatty acids into cells. Lipid-protein complexes are known as lipoproteins and they are the chief means of transportation of fats in the bloodstream.

Fatty acids are not all of one type. This aspect is often played up by manufacturers of fats and their products, so it is relevant to understand their chemical composition.

All fats are compounds of carbon (C), hydrogen (H) and oxygen (O). Here, we will concentrate only on the C and H aspect of each lipid molecule. Normally, C atoms are arranged end to end to form long, straight chains and are joined to each other by the formation of chemical bonds. It is at this point that fatty acids get differentiated into saturated and unsaturated.

In saturated fatty acids, the C atoms have a single bond between them and each C atom in turn will have two H atoms.

$$\begin{array}{ccc} H & & H \\ | & & | \\ -C & - & C- \\ | & & | \\ H & & H \end{array}$$

On the other hand, unsaturated fatty acids have a double bond linking two C atoms, and each C atom is attached to only one H atom.

$$\begin{array}{ccc} H & & H \\ | & & | \\ -C & = & C- \end{array}$$

When there is only one double bond in the fatty acid, it is designated monounsaturated. Oleic acid is an example and is widely distributed in plant and animal foods. Even fats of animal origin like cream, butter and lard which are essentially high in saturated fatty acids contain good amounts of oleic acid. However, the highest concentrations are found in olive oil, groundnut oil, palmolein, gingelly oil, soya bean oil, sunflower and safflower oils, nuts and avocados. Erucic acid is another monounsaturated fatty acid found in mustard and rapeseed oils. Erucic acid is believed to damage heart muscle in animals, but is still unproved in human beings. In certain regions in India, mustard and rapeseed oils are used regularly in cooking, but no toxic effects have been reported, probably because of moderate intake.

As the number of double bonds increases, so does the degree of unsaturation. If there are two or more double bonds in a fatty acid, it is known as a polyunsaturated fatty acid, bearing the much used acronym, PUFA. Linoleic acid with two double bonds, linolenic acid with three double bonds, and arachidonic acid with four double bonds, are examples of PUFA. Fats high in PUFA include safflower oil, sunflower oil, corn oil, soya bean and gingelly oils, groundnut oil, mustard oil and palmolein. Nuts and oilseeds which are expressed to extract these oils are similarly beneficial.

Just as a high-quality protein diet provides essential amino acids, so also a diet of fats must provide essential fatty acids (EFA) because the body cannot synthesize them. These are the unsaturated fatty acids of linoleic acid, linolenic acid and arachidonic acid. However, since linoleic acid is rapidly converted to arachidonic acid in the body, only linoleic acid (found abundantly in vegetable oils, cereals and pulses) and linolenic acid (wheat, bajra, pulses especially black gram, cow-peas and dried French beans, green leafy vegetables, fenugreek seeds, mustard seeds, soya beans, mustard oil, soya bean oil, spices, oily fish and fish oils) need to be supplied by the diet. Walnuts, whole grain cereals, gingelly seeds and groundnuts are packed with EFA. It is particularly important to ensure that infants who receive their nourishment exclusively from mass-produced formulae get sufficient essential fatty acids.

No single fat is made up of only saturated or unsaturated fatty acids. In animal and vegetable fats, a combination of both is present, but one or the other will be predominant. This ratio of saturated to unsaturated fatty acids determines whether the fat will remain liquid at the chilling or refrigeration temperature of 4 degrees Celsius (39 degrees Fahrenheit). Fats that remain liquid at this temperature are known as oils.

Animal fats such as cream, butter, ghee and the fat of meat have a higher percentage of saturated fatty acids, notably palmitic and stearic acids. The fat of beef and mutton (goat) has a higher percentage of saturated fat than pork and poultry. Fish has been known to have high levels of unsaturated fatty acids. Sardines, black pomfret, tuna, mackerel and other fish with dark flesh have more fat

> **Did You Know?**
> Margarine, vanaspati and cocount oil are saturated fats which could contain minuscule amounts of cholesterol

than white fish, but consequently have a higher percentage of essential fatty acids. Chicken too has less saturated fat and some essential fatty acids. The dark meat of poultry has more fat, but also has more essential fatty acids. Much of the fat in chicken lies below the skin, so removing it before cooking reduces the fat content.

On the other hand, vegetable fats are largely unsaturated, and are, therefore, more appropriately called vegetable oils. With the exception of coconut oil which contains saturated lauric acid, and cocoa butter (extracted from the cocoa bean and used in chocolate manufacture), and to some extent palmolein (palm mesocarp oil), vegetable oils have high levels of PUFA and EFA. Interestingly, avocado pears have the highest content of fat among most foods with the exception of nuts, oilseeds and fatty meats. Vegetable oils have been widely exploited by manufacturers to produce hydrogenated vegetable fats, by replacing the double bonds of unsaturated fatty acids with single bonds between the C atoms by the addition of one H atom to the already existing one, in the presence of a metal catalyst like nickel. In this manner, an unsaturated vegetable oil is converted to a saturated vegetable fat. It is possible to control the degree of saturation. If only a few of the original polyunsaturated fatty acids are hydrogenated, the resultant fat will be quite soft and pliable. Soft margarine is a good example of partial hydrogenation. Greater the degree of hydrogenation, the harder the fat. This is the reason why hydrogenated fats remain solid even at high atmospheric temperatures. Vanaspati (margarine without water) is the most common form of hydrogenated fat sold in India. By hydrogenation, the linoleic acid content (essential fatty acid) of the fat is reduced, and also the benefit of a polyunsaturated or monounsaturated fatty acid is greatly diminished.

The use of hydrogenated fats in cooking has been implicated in the growing incidence of heart disease and associated illnesses. This is because all naturally occurring unsaturated fatty acids exist in the "cis" form and during hydrogenation, some of them are converted to the "trans" form, an isomer of the original fatty acid. Once a fatty acid is changed to the "trans" form, it no longer functions as an essential fatty acid because the body's enzymes are not able to recognize the changed configuration. Margarine, formed by the hardening of vegetable oil and water, has 1 to 12 per cent trans fatty acids. Butter, a saturated animal fat, has 5 per cent. Fats that are irradiated to sterilize them also have a low EFA content.

If there is any advantage at all from the nutritional point of view, it is that hydrogenated fats will never get rancid if all the double bonds have been converted to single bonds. Rancidity is an undesirable quality especially seen in fats with a great number of polyunsaturated fatty acids. If these fats are stored uncovered for long periods of time at room temperature and are fully exposed to light, then they will become oxidized. By this it is meant that the oxygen in air breaks down the double bonds in the fatty acid, and the resultant product has an unpleasant flavour and odour. Like hydrogenated fats, saturated fats are also not affected. To some extent, the presence of the natural antioxidant, vitamin E, prevents this action in oils such as corn, soya bean, palmolein, safflower and cottonseed. However, in inhibiting the oxidative process, the real value of vitamin E is lost. Further, in the manufacture of vegetable oils, the addition of vitamin E is widely practised.

Another undesirable attribute of fats is that heating at high temperatures over long periods of time yields a substance called acrolein, due to the decomposition of the glycerol component in the molecule. This action turns the oil dark and viscous and could cause irritation of the mucosal

FAT (g per day)		
RDA at a Glance		
	M	20
	F	20
	Preg.	+10
	Lact.	+25

lining of the gastrointestinal tract. Normal home cooking methods of shallow- and deep-frying have no such effect. However, repeated use of the same oil for frying may bring about this change accompanied by rancidity if the fat is left unprotected from light and air. The decomposed oil will also have reduced polyunsaturated fatty acid and vitamin E levels. In order to prevent harmful chemical changes from taking place, oil should not be held at its smoking temperature for more than 15 minutes at a time, and should not be used over and over again. Corn and olive oils are more stable than other oils, as they can be heated to higher temperatures before they start smoking, and hence take longer to deteriorate.

Fats in the diet may be classified as visible and invisible. Fat that is deliberately added to cooking is known as visible fat and includes ghee, butter, hydrogenated fat and all vegetable oils. Those fats that are consumed as an integral part of foods as in seeds, nuts, fish, meat, whole milk and its products, egg yolk, avocados, cereals, pulses and spices are invisible fats. Almost 50 per cent of the weight of nuts and coconut milk is made up of fat. Any diet planning should take the presence of invisible fat into consideration since it could account for as much as 15 to 20 g of the total fat intake in a typical Indian diet. Indian men and women are recommended an intake of 20 g of fat per day which includes both visible and invisible fat. During pregnancy and lactation, the need rises. An additional 10 g are required by a pregnant woman, and when breastfeeding, the fat intake is to be increased to 45 g daily.

The most obvious consequence of excess fat in the diet is obesity. However, obesity is usually linked to an increased intake of calories, not just of fat. Obesity causes the diseases of the heart, atherosclerosis (thickening of the walls of arteries by fatty deposits); high blood pressure, osteoarthritis, diabetes, gall bladder disease, hiatus hernia, gout, varicose veins, sleep apnoea (snoring which interrupts breathing), low fertility, menstrual problems, poor wound healing, heartburn and cancer. Even a simple operation assumes greater risk if one is fairly overweight. Conversely, fats are needed in the diet to provide the essential fatty acids, and to render the fat soluble vitamins available for absorption. Absence of essential fatty acids results in lesions, scaling and dryness of the skin, and the condition is called phrynoderma. This is easily reversed by the intake of vitamin E and linoleic acid in the diet.

Maintaining fat levels of 18 to 25 per cent of body weight in women and 15 to 20 per cent in men is desirable.

1.3.1 Omega-3 Fatty Acids and Omega-6 Fatty Acids

Omega-3 fatty acids are derived from the essential fatty acid linolenic acid. They are also known as n-3 PUFA. Omega-6 fatty acids, on the other hand, are derived from the essential fatty acid linoleic acid. Another name for them is n-6 PUFA.

Both these fatty acids are found in all cells though Omega-3 fatty acids are concentrated in nerve tissue. However, of the two, Omega-3 fatty acids are receiving more attention because they are believed to protect against cancer of the pancreas, colon, lung, prostate and breast, reduce blood cholesterol levels, bring down high blood pressure, lower the risk of heart attacks and strokes, reduce inflammation in conditions like rheumatoid and osteoarthritis, and help fight fatigue.

Omega-3 fatty acids are found abundantly in oily fish, particularly those found in deep and cold waters like mackerel, tuna, sardines, herring, salmon and trout. Cod and fish liver oils also contain Omega-3 fatty acids. Other sources are walnuts, mustard seeds, soya beans and their oils.

The richest sources of Omega-6 fatty acids are oils derived from sunflower, safflower, maize (corn) and soya bean with groundnut and gingelly seeds providing lesser amounts.

1.3.2 Cholesterol

Cholesterol is the commonest form of sterols or organic alcohols. It is derived primarily from animal sources. Therefore, eggs, butter, ghee, organ meats like brain, kidney and liver, fish roe, seafood especially prawns and shrimps, oily fish, fish oil capsules, and to a lesser extent, whole milk, cream, chicken

> **Did You Know?**
> One egg yolk provides between 225 and 300 mg of cholesterol

and pork, are food sources of cholesterol. In egg, all the cholesterol is concentrated in the yolk. Removing the skin of poultry markedly reduces the cholesterol content. Similarly, the use of skimmed milk drastically lowers the cholesterol intake from the diet. Until recently, it was thought that vegetable sources of food did not have any cholesterol. However, more sophisticated methods of testing indicate that nuts, oilseeds, maize, soya bean, and the oils expressed from them, have negligible amounts of cholesterol. (See Appendix 5.9).

The body itself, chiefly the liver and the intestines, synthesizes cholesterol that is not linked to the dietary supply. The adult body has about 140 g of cholesterol. The production of endogenous cholesterol varies between 800 to 1,500 mg per day and this meets the body's requirement. Cholesterol is an important component of all cell membranes, the brain, nerve cells, bile salts which help in the digestion of fats, the adrenocortical hormones, chiefly cortisol, which regulates carbohydrate, protein and fat metabolism, the male and female sex hormones, and, the substance in human skin called provitamin D_3, which when acted upon by ultraviolet light of sunshine gives vitamin D.

At this juncture, it becomes important to mention lipoproteins and their role in fat transportation. Both cholesterol and triglycerides being fats are not soluble in the aqueous medium of blood. Therefore, they form complexes with proteins for easy transportation. These lipid-protein complexes are known as lipoproteins.

Two classes of lipoproteins exist. Low-density or beta lipoproteins (LDL), and high-density or alpha lipoproteins (HDL). Low-density lipoproteins are the chief carriers of cholesterol. Their triglyceride component is low. When the proportion of triglycerides is greater, they are known as very low-density lipoproteins (VLDL). In both these lipoproteins, the proportion of protein is lower than fat. On the contrary, in high-density lipoproteins the proportion of protein to fat is greater.

Lipoproteins assume enormous significance in the aetiology of heart disease. High levels of HDL are indicative of lower risk as they keep the arteries clear by removing cholesterol from the cells and blood vessels to the liver for recycling or disposal. Hence, HDL do not partake in the formation of plaques that narrow arteries and reduce blood flow resulting in atherosclerosis, heart attacks and strokes. Greater HDL levels are also directly associated with reduced levels of impotence. They are sometimes described as "good" or "beneficial" lipoproteins. Persons who have greater muscle mass in proportion to fat, and who exercise regularly and do not smoke, have higher levels of HDL in the blood. Oestrogen, the female hormone, is also believed to boost HDL levels, thereby greatly reducing the incidence of heart disease in pre-menopausal women. Fish oils are more likely to be converted to HDL in the body. Raw onions (just half a medium one or its juice) and raw garlic (two cloves chopped), consumed every day, boost HDL levels in the body. Moderate alcohol consumption has a similar effect.

However, a high cholesterol diet will show a marginal increase in blood cholesterol. A daily intake of 300 to 500 mg of dietary cholesterol (the amount in one egg yolk) does not appear to adversely affect serum cholesterol levels, nor do shellfish, even those rich in cholesterol. More important is the type and amount of fat in the diet which has a direct bearing on blood cholesterol levels, A diet rich in fat, particularly if it contains more saturated fats than unsaturated, increases the LDL or "bad" cholesterol levels. When the VLDL levels are elevated, it may be assumed that excess carbohydrates in the form of refined sugars or highly processed cereals have been partaken of. In other words, excess fat and sugar in the diet raise blood cholesterol levels. Dietary restrictions of fat and sugar are, therefore, important. Pectin which causes jams to jell and fenugreek seeds have been shown to have cholesterol lowering effects.

The normal total serum cholesterol levels in adults is in the range of 120 to 200 mg per 100 ml. For Indians, total cholesterol levels should average 150 mg per 100 ml. Levels of HDL should be greater than 45 mg per 100 ml. LDL levels of 130 mg per 100 ml or more increase the risk of heart disease. Most importantly, a total cholesterol level of less than 200 mg per 100 ml does not indicate absence of coronary illness. It is the LDL level that matters most.

1.4 CALORIES

Calories basically represent energy. They are not nutrients in themselves. The three major nutrients, namely, proteins, fats, and carbohydrates, provide energy. When food is

> **Did You Know?**
> Calories are not nutrients

consumed, this same energy is utilized by the body to carry out various voluntary activities like exercise and work, and, involuntary physiological, biochemical and biological functions such as heartbeat, respiration, excretion, glandular secretion, digestion, and, metabolism of food and maintenance of body temperature. Even at rest, the body needs energy.

A word about the measurement of energy. The calorie (cal) refers to a unit of heat and finds equal expression in physiology and in the physical sciences. It represents energy in general. At this point, however, the similarity ends.

Physiologically, the term calorie represents a thousandfold increase in energy over the physical unit. It is for this reason that food energy is spoken of in terms of kilocalories (kcal). Moreover, it must be understood that when talking of energy in food and ultimately of the energy

Did You Know?
Physiologically
1 kilocalorie = 1 calorie
(kcal)   (cal)

produced from food in the body, the terms calorie and kilocalorie may be used interchangeably. More importantly, it must be stressed that physiologically 1 kilocalorie equals 1 calorie and *not* 1,000 calories.

Soon the calorie is expected to be expressed in joules which is more universally accepted. The joule is the unit of energy in the metric system, and 1 calorie (cal) or 1 kilocalorie (kcal) equals 4.184 joules (J) or 4.184 kilojoules (kJ)—approximately 4.2.

Proteins and carbohydrates average 4 kilocalories per gram whereas fat yields more than double at 9 kilocalories per gram, regardless of whether they are solid fats like butter and ghee or vegetable oils. Highly refined sugars and fat are called "empty calorie foods". Actually, this is a misnomer since they are packed with calories. Though they contribute carbohydrate and fat beside

Did You Know?	
Energy Yield per Gram	
Proteins	4 kcal
Carbohydrates	4 kcal
Fats	9 kcal
Alcohol	7 kcal

calories, the absence of other nutrients makes high levels of sugar and fat in the diet an important causative factor in the condition of obesity and its related disease states.

Alcohol too provides energy, approximately 7 kilocalories per gram. Casual drinkers are not affected adversely by alcohol but chronic alcoholism can lead to many deficiency states. In cases where energy is not supplied by the diet, the body utilizes its own stores of energy found in the liver and muscle as glycogen, in body tissues (proteins) and fat or adipose tissue.

It is important to know how many calories we need in order to function under normal circumstances for energy, as we know, is required for both involuntary and voluntary action. When the body is at rest, much involuntary work is under way. This involves respiration, heartbeat, digestion and regulation of body temperature. The energy required to carry out these functions is known as resting metabolism or the basal metabolic rate (BMR).

BMR varies from person to person and is chiefly governed by the three factors, age, sex and body size. A number of other factors increase or lower the BMR. Sleep, increasing age, a short and squat figure and lowered thyroid activity are known to slow down the BMR. Needless to say, women have lower BMR rates than men because they have a greater proportion of body fat. Conversely, the BMR is accelerated by fever, a higher ratio of lean body mass (muscle) to fat, tallness, pregnancy, lactation and high thyroid function. Even the climate alters the BMR, with extremes effectively lowering the rate.

By increasing the BMR, more calories are burnt. One invaluable and cheap means of raising the BMR is to exercise regularly. When more calories are burnt, the body fat is reduced and the lean body mass increases. The benefit appears to continue even after the exercise has been stopped for a while. Mental exertion does not raise the BMR.

The other component that decides the energy requirement of individuals is the physical activity they engage in every day which includes both work and exercise. The amount of energy that is required for work usually depends on the habitual activity of the person. Based on this, the ICMR has broadly grouped all persons into three categories—sedentary, moderate and heavy workers. Most urban men and women fall within the first category since they pursue desk jobs, teach or remain at home doing housework. Moderate workers include those skilled and semi-skilled persons who are weavers, carpenters, agricultural labourers and housemaids. The heaviest work is done by men and women employed in construction jobs, stonecutting and mining. Accordingly, it is possible for one's energy needs to shift from one category to another. For example, with increasing age, a moderate worker may lead a more sedentary life. So, it must be recognized that these recommendations are only guidelines to assist in meeting the daily energy requirements of various groups.

The total energy requirement (BMR plus activity) for sedentary men is 2,425 kcal and for sedentary women 1,875 kcal per day. Moderate work increases the requirement to 2,875 kcal for men and 2,225 kcal for women. The heaviest workers need 3,800 kcal and 2,925 kcal daily, for men and women respectively. Pregnancy, which raises the BMR, places an extra burden on the calorie requirement which has to be raised by an additional 300 kcal. Breastfeeding is even more energy expensive. During the first six months of lactation, 550 extra kcal are needed, and from the sixth month to a year after the birth of the infant, 400 kcal more have to be added to the mother's diet. Interestingly, men burn more calories than women for the same activity possibly because of higher muscle mass.

ENERGY (kcal per day)				
RDA at a Glance				
		Sedentary	Moderate	Heavy
	M	2,425	2,875	3,800
	F	1,875	2,225	2,925
	Preg.		+ 300	
	Lact.	0 - 6 months	+ 550	
		6 - 12 months	+ 400	

Adult Energy Expenditure Chart

Activity	Kcal per Hour	
	Women	Men
Sedentary Office work including typing; writing; sewing; eating; watching television; listening to the radio; playing cards; driving	80	100
Light Work Cooking; dusting; ironing; personal grooming; rapid typing; walking dog; shopping	110	160
Moderate Work Housework like machine laundering; sweeping; doing minor repairs about the house; light gardening; moderately fast walking; yoga	170	240
Vigorous Work Scrubbing and polishing floors; laundering by hand; brisk walking; gardening; golfing	250	350
Strenuous Work Swimming; playing tennis; dancing; steady running and jogging; bicycling; weight training (not weightlifting); step exercises; moderate effort exercise machines	350	More than 350
High Intensity Work Skipping; aerobics; high effort exercise machines	More than 500	
Sleep	50	50
Sexual Activity [kcal expended per minute]	8	12

Normal Therapeutic Nutrition, 17/E by Robinson, ©0.

Adapted by permission of Prentice-Hall, Inc., Upper Saddle River, NJ.

With the extensive use of television and the automobile, chances of engaging in a physically active lifestyle have been severely affected. Most of us will probably find the example given below typical of our lives:

Activity	Hours	Kcal per Hour		Total	
		Women	Men	Women	Men
Sleep	8	50	50	400	400
Sedentary	11	80	100	880	1,100
Light	4	110	160	440	640
Moderate	1	170	240	170	240
			Total	1,890	2,380

Exercise is erroneously believed to cause fatigue and increase one's appetite. Instead, it helps to raise the BMR making the person more alert. That is why experts recommend that all exercise be stopped three hours before bedtime. if a sound night's sleep is to be guaranteed. However, plunging into an intense exercise regimen from a sedentary way of life is inadvisable. A medical check-up and a gradual increase in activity would be more beneficial and lasting.

1.5   FATS AND FIGURES

Though much has been said on the subject of calorie requirement, it may be noticed that the overwhelming emphasis is on activity and rest. The factor of body size and calories has not been dealt with so far. The universal homily that we are what we eat is not well defined. It does not take genetics into consideration. There is a story told among South Indians that if a man wished to marry a woman, he had better take a look at her mother first. Not without reason, though largely through observation, ancient wisdom recognized what genes do.

Basically, everyone falls within one of three body types. Tall, slim people have a lower percentage of body fat and they are described as ectomorphs (16 to 22 per cent body fat with shoulders and hips almost the same width). At the other end of the scale are the short, squat people who have a higher proportion of body fat. Their body build is described as endomorphic (28 to 34 per cent body fat with hips as wide as shoulders or wider). In between falls the group who have mesomorphic figures (22 to 28 per cent body fat with shoulders wider than the hips).

Numerous charts are available that give indications of ideal weight. Their two most important considerations are height and body frame. However, the ICMR has only now formulated ideal height and weight charts for Indian boys and girls aged 5 to 18 years (See Appendix 5.11). Reference standards for Indian men and women have yet to be determined. So far, the ICMR has only established scant guidelines for healthy and active adult Indians aged 20 to 39 years. They are the Indian Reference Man who should weigh 60 kg for a height of 163 cm, and the Indian Reference Woman who should weigh 50 kg for an average height of 151 cm. Until such time as standard weights for adult Indian men and women of different heights are available, the basis for desirable body weight is the Indian Reference Man and the Indian Reference Woman.

In the absence of a standard height-weight guide for Indians, two methods, widely recognized as safe and reliable all over the world, can be used to determine ideal weights for heights. The first is called the Body Mass Index (BMI) or Quetlet's Index. The other is the Waist-Hip Ratio. Both standards are equally relevant for men and women.

Body Mass Index (BMI) is based on each individual's physiology. Though it is not a guide to give the ideal weight of a person, the BMI will indicate whether one is overweight within the limits of heredity. One's actual weight in kilograms is divided by the square of one's height in metres.

Example

Actual weight = 55 kg

Actual height = 1.65 m

Therefore, BMI = $\dfrac{55}{1.65 \times 1.65}$ = $\dfrac{55}{2.7225}$ = 20.20

> **Did You Know?**
>
> Body Mass Index
>
> = $\dfrac{\text{Weight in Kilograms}}{(\text{Height in Metres})^2}$

A BMI in the range 18.5 to 25 is considered the healthiest, especially if one is a non-smoker. Weight gain in this category can be controlled by merely altering one's eating habits and combining it with a bit of exercise.

Between 25 and 30, the BMI would suggest increased risk from heart ailments and adult-onset diabetes. These persons should exercise regularly and eat a low-fat diet.

A BMI of 30 or more would indicate obesity, while below 18.5 would suggest undernourishment.

However, even with a normal BMI, the risk of developing heart disease and the other complications associated with obesity is high. Body shape or where body fat is stored is an important criterion for determining one's health status. Epidemiological studies seem to suggest that people of apple shape who carry more weight on the upper half of their bodies, including the stomach (a paunch, for instance), are most at risk. People whose lower half is heavier, with the hips and thighs bearing more weight, are described as pear-shaped and are less prone to illness. Women have a tendency to put on weight around the hips and thighs, and men around the middle. So, merely having a normal BMI is not sufficient. The Waist-Hip Ratio, based on body shape, has to also be within acceptable limits.

To calculate Waist-Hip Ratio, divide the waist measurement in centimetres by the hip measurement in centimetres.

Example

Waist measurement = 64 cm

Hip measurement = 95 cm

Therefore, Waist-Hip Ratio = $\dfrac{64}{95}$ = 0.7

> **Did You Know?**
>
> Waist-Hip Ratio
>
> = $\dfrac{\text{Waist Measurement in Centimetres}}{\text{Hip Measurement in Centimetres}}$

For men, the Waist-Hip Ratio should not exceed 0.9.

For women, the value should not exceed 0.8.

The cornerstone of reducing weight is to adopt sensible eating habits since all excess calories, regardless of source (whether from proteins, carbohydrates or fats), are converted in the body to fat. Recent research suggests, however, that calories derived from carbohydrates are better utilized for work and are less likely to be stored. Moderation in the use of highly refined foods like refined flours and sugars, and, fats and alcohol will keep the calorie count in check.

The "sweet tooth" excuse, proffered to justify indulgence, is not an inherited phenomenon. It is an acquired taste, a learned response from childhood, when food rewards often take the form of high-carbohydrate, high-fat foods. This attitude is carried well into adulthood where the rewards for good behaviour and achievement are often high-calorie treats.

Moreover, good and pleasurable occasions such as birthdays and religious festivals call for a celebration, and the food served usually takes the form of sweets and fatty foods. In India, the vast array of Indian sweetmeats (undoubtedly unmatched in variety, colour and flavour by any other nation in the world) are virtually heavy-duty fat and sugar concoctions. And, given the diversity of religions in this country, we have no dearth of reasons to overload on calories.

Snacking has been variously condemned and praised. At one level, many small and varied meals are preferable to three big meals a day because the body is better able to cope when a smaller amount of food is presented for digestion. However, if snacks are consumed *in addition* to the main meals, then it becomes important to watch those calories. Here again, it is the content that matters. Pure sugar foods are absorbed quickly, leaving the person hungry and wanting more food in a very short time. Fatty snacks, on the other hand, delay the passage of food through the gastrointestinal tract, thereby reducing the intake of nutritious food at mealtimes.

In India, snacking is a common feature, and is accepted as a part of daily life. In many homes in South India, the mid-morning snack or tiffin is compulsory. However, mealtimes are especially important for children as they may not make the right choices left to themselves, leading to inadequate intake of important nutrients. Mealtimes also provide the occasion to inculcate good food habits.

It is especially important that women watch their weight. Women who are overweight could have an irregular monthly cycle, and if they are considering pregnancy, may have trouble conceiving a child. However, once pregnant, many Indian women believe that weight gain is inevitable and a sign of good health. This probably explains why many women are comfortable with their ample proportions and make no effort to get back into shape even after the child is born.

True, a pregnant woman gains weight. By the last trimester, this weight gain should average 11 kg, the total of the growing foetus, the expanded circulation, development of maternal tissues and fluids, and, the building up of reserves. Dieting during pregnancy increases the probability of low birth weight and premature babies, congenital defects and stillbirths. Therefore, it is necessary to have greater food intake, and consequently

> **Did You Know?**
> To produce the daily average of 850 ml of breast milk, 750 kcal are required

more calories. Lactation is energy expensive, and whenever possible, breastfeeding should be encouraged. For the six months after childbirth, 550 extra kcal are to be provided in the mother's diet, and 400 kcal, in addition to the regular intake, during the subsequent six months. The extra energy that is required is released from the reserves built up in the mother's body. Failure to breastfeed will firmly install all those extra calories in adipose tissue. It must also be stressed that even in infancy, feeding foods rich in fat and refined carbohydrates should be discouraged. Too often mothers anxious to have bonny babies tend to overfeed, often with high-calorie foods. Not uncommonly, milk preparations and cereal mixes that contain added sugar are used, and even milk is sweetened. Fat cells are thereby increased unwittingly, and if these feeding trends continue into childhood and up to adolescence, more and more fat cells are added to the body where they are fixed for life. Subsequent attempts to reduce weight only deplete the fat cells, reducing their size but *never* eliminating them completely. Thus, a lifelong task to keep trim begins. However, a word of caution. Do not resort to feeding children under the age of five commercial foods prepared from skimmed milk.

Ultimately, the aim should be better health not just weight loss. Heredity, sex, age and, very often, factors such as one's job and environment are immutable. Therefore, a moderate change in lifestyle is the workable alternative. Contemplating a change is not without its problems. With the growing number of working women, and with people travelling great distances to their place of work, it is often that the heaviest meal in the day is eaten after sundown. And what was said many years ago still holds good today—eat breakfast like a king, lunch like a prince and supper like a pauper. This is the surest way of seeing calories burn. For most people, the morning hours are the busiest, and chances are that very little of the calories from breakfast will be converted into fat. The opposite is true of eating huge suppers. As it may not be possible to get a good lunch away from home, almost everyone looks forward to a satisfying evening meal. The solution may lie in advancing suppertime. Try to finish supper by 7 pm which will still make quite a difference in the number of calories put away as body fat.

Moderation in alcohol consumption, a lower intake of coffee and carbonated beverages, reduction in smoking (if it cannot be given up altogether), regular sleep and exercise are other factors that can be controlled.

> **Did You Know?**
>
> In India, a bottled or soda fountain-dispensed soft drink of 200 ml capacity gives approximately 100 kcal

Certain medications need to be approached with caution. Steroids build muscle mass. As the use of certain drugs cannot be avoided, and especially if the illness is chronic, it may be a good idea to check with your doctor about possible side (adverse) effects. The oral contraceptive pill is being increasingly accepted. Some women report weight gain but it is more likely in women whose general state of health is poor.

1.6   VITAMINS

Vitamins are very important for the growth of the human body and are viewed as a panacea for all ills. Deficiency of a vitamin in the body usually spells trouble. Generally speaking, if you are feeling irritable, depressed, weak, dizzy and have symptoms like headaches, diarrhoea, skin irritation, anaemia, loss of

Did You Know?
Micrograms may be abbreviated as mcg *or* µg 1,000 mcg = 1 mg

appetite, sleeping problems and forgetfulness, it just may be possible that one of the numerous vitamins is lacking or in short supply in the diet. However, with regular intake, these symptoms will be reversed promptly and completely. Vitamins are usually required in such small quantities that a well-balanced diet supplies all of one's needs. Their primary function is to partake in biochemical reactions in the body that convert the major nutrients of proteins, carbohydrates and fats into their various components, and, finally, into energy. Broadly, vitamins are divided into two categories—fat soluble and water soluble. Of the 13 vitamins identified so far, vitamins A, D, E and K are classified as fat soluble, and they are retained by the body if the intake exceeds requirement. The other nine are water soluble, with eight of them forming the B complex group. Vitamin C is the other water soluble vitamin. Excess of vitamins B and C is excreted.

1.7   FAT SOLUBLE VITAMINS

Vitamin A or Retinol (Retinyl Esters, Retinaldehyde, Retinoic Acid)

In Nature, vitamin A is found in two forms—as the vitamin itself, called retinol, and as carotene. Carotene is known as the precursor of vitamin A or provitamin A, because on conversion in the body it yields vitamin A. Many forms of carotene exist but the one considered most useful to human beings is beta carotene.

The main function of vitamin A is to improve vision in dim light. An important signal of vitamin A deficiency is night blindness (nyctalopia). Drivers whose eyes are unable to adapt to the dark after facing the glare of headlights lack sufficient vitamin A and expose not only themselves but others as well to the possibility of serious harm. With progressive deficiency, the outer layer of the eye (conjunctiva) will become dry and thickened (xerophthalmia), and later, corneal scarring or xerosis results with loss of sight. Vitamin A is also responsible for the integrity of epithelial tissue which is the lining of mucous membranes within the body, and the skin externally. Lack of vitamin A leads to keratinization that leaves the skin dry, rough and scaly due to shrinkage and degeneration of cells. Vitamin A also helps to maintain normal growth and development of the skeletal system and teeth. Further, vitamin A boosts the immune system and builds resistance to infection. Additionally, foetal growth is normal with adequate vitamin A.

More recently, beta carotene is believed to reduce the risk of heart attacks and strokes, cancer of the lung, throat, oesophagus, stomach, colon, prostate, breast and cervix, and, to delay the onset of cataracts and retard macular degeneration, thereby maintaining visual acuity in the elderly.

Since it is fat soluble, vitamin A, as retinol, is found only in animal fats. Fish liver oils are the most outstanding source of this vitamin especially if the fish is harvested from deep, cold waters. Other sources are whole milk, cream, butter, liver and egg yolk. In India, the practice of clarifying butter to produce ghee causes a 25 per cent loss of vitamin A. The hydrogenated fat vanaspati is fortified with vitamin A and vitamin D. Other commercially prepared fats also contain these vitamins.

But beta carotene, which is more abundant in Nature, is derived largely from vegetable sources. Yellow and orange fruits and vegetables, and green leafy vegetables, make important contributions of beta carotene. In green leafy vegetables, the green pigment chlorophyll masks the bright yellow of carotene. Spinach, the greens of beetroot, radish, turnip, drumstick and fenugreek, mint and coriander leaves, curry leaves (though sparingly used), carrots, ripe mango and papaya, oranges, apricots and cape gooseberries, are all outstanding sources of beta carotene. Tomatoes, the orange variety of yam, pumpkin and sweet potato, green chillies and capsicum are good sources of the vitamin. Much of the beta carotene in palmolein is lost in the refining process. The colour of cow's ghee may be attributed to the presence of carotene. Though deceptively yellow, pineapple is a poor source. The various pulses (dhals), jackfruit, and, vegetables like bitter gourd and some beans also make a fair contribution to the diet. Regular consumption of high carotene foods like mango, particularly when it is in season, can lead to a build-up of vitamin A stores in the body sufficient for the whole year. Rancidity in fats destroys vitamin A.

The daily allowance provides for the intake of *either* vitamin A *or* beta carotene. Accordingly, the intake should be 600 mcg of vitamin A (retinol) or 2,400 mcg of beta carotene for both adult men and women. Only lactation increases the need for this vitamin. The intake of a woman who is breastfeeding her child must be 950 mcg of vitamin A or 3,800 mcg of beta carotene daily up to one year.

Another unit of measure employed for vitamin A is the international unit (IU). One IU of vitamin A is equivalent to 0.3 mcg of retinol or 0.6 mcg of beta carotene. However, to avert the need for repeated conversions of related elements, vitamin A and beta carotene will soon be expressed in retinol equivalents (RE) to bring uniformity to the system. Accordingly,

1 RE = 1 mcg retinol (3.33 IU)

1 RE = 6 mcg beta carotene (10 IU)

The recommendations for beta carotene are higher because only a third is absorbed in the gastrointestinal tract whereas retinol is completely utilized. For efficient absorption, sufficient fats and proteins should be included in the diet. Malabsorption syndromes like coeliac disease (allergy to the protein gluten found in wheat, rye and barley), tropical sprue and irritable bowel syndrome, where there is rapid passage of food through the gut allowing little time for absorption, protein-calorie malnutrition, and illness that interferes with fat metabolism, lead to the manifestation of deficiency symptoms. Consequently, all tissues are laid open to infection.

VITAMIN A (mcg per day)		
RDA at a Glance		
		Retinol or Beta Carotene
M	600	2,400
F	600	2,400
Preg.	600	2,400
Lact.	+350	+1,400

While it is almost impossible to overdose on vitamin A, the body stores any excess which could lead to toxicity. If the intake is from natural sources, this may result only after many months or years of high intake. Artificial supplementation with megadoses of vitamin A, such as unnecessary consumption of huge amounts of vitamin pills, will precipitate this condition sooner. Initially, there will be pressure on the brain leading to symptoms of toxicity like enlargement of the liver, the chief storage site of vitamin A, loss of appetite (anorexia), vomiting, headaches, drying and peeling of the skin, blurring of vision, drowsiness, hair loss and bone fragility. Large doses of vitamin A during the first three months of pregnancy could be the reason for miscarriages and congenital defects of the foetus.

Conversely, huge amounts of carotene are not toxic. Carotene will accumulate below the skin giving it a yellowish-orange tinge distinguished from jaundice as the eyes remain clear. It gradually dissipates when the intake is reduced.

Vitamin D or Cholecalciferol (Ergocalciferol, Calciferol, Viosterol)

The principal function of vitamin D is the formation of strong bones and teeth. The presence of vitamin D permits adequate absorption and deposition of calcium and phosphorus which are necessary for good skeletal and dental development.

The chief source of vitamin D is the human body itself. Vitamin D_3, also known as cholecalciferol, is manufactured in human skin when it is exposed to the ultraviolet rays of sunlight. Foods that are fortified with this vitamin are an excellent dietary source. Milk and butter are easily fortified. In India, the hydrogenated fat vanaspati and table margarine are usually fortified with vitamins A and D. Otherwise, foods are poor sources of this vitamin. Except for fish liver oils, animal foods like liver, fatty fish (which bones may also be consumed) and egg yolk, supply small amounts. Processed cheese, butter and milk contain comparatively low levels of vitamin D. It is essential that fats are also present. Bile, which is produced by the liver and stored in the gall bladder, is necessary for absorption.

Vitamin D_2 or ergocalciferol is produced when ultraviolet light acts on ergosterol which is found in yeast and fungi like mushrooms.

However, the vitamin D produced in the skin or derived from foods has to be converted to its active form before it becomes functional, a process that takes place in the liver and kidney. The inactive form of vitamin D is also stored in the liver. When there is a drop in the calcium and phosphorus levels in the blood, this storage form of vitamin D is released into the circulation and carried to the kidneys where fully active vitamin D is formed.

Indian diets which are largely vegetarian provide very little vitamin D. Hence, especially among vegetarians, exposure to sunlight is the only significant means of getting sufficient vitamin D. Even sunshine on the face and hands for five minutes daily is adequate. Muslim women, who are burkha-clad, a garment that keeps out all light, are most susceptible to deficiency of this vitamin, as are the elderly and the disabled who venture out infrequently. Malabsorption syndromes, and, liver and kidney ailments can precipitate and prolong the condition.

The daily requirement of vitamin D for adults in the *absence of sunlight* is 10 mcg (400 IU) daily. (One IU of vitamin D is equivalent to 0.025 mcg). Pregnant and lactating mothers need an additional 5 mcg (200 IU). Higher levels, say 1.5 mg per day, is lethal.

Vitamin D is also known as the anti-rachitic factor because it prevents rickets, a disease characterized by soft and fragile bones, bow-legs and other skeletal deformities. The child might otherwise appear healthy but will lack muscle tone and will take its first steps much later than other children. The appearance of both the milk and permanent teeth may also be delayed. If the symptoms are detected early enough, timely treatment can reverse mild deformities. However, for the large part, these malformations are permanent.

In adults, the result of vitamin D insufficiency is osteomalacia or adult rickets. In this condition, the mineral content of bone is reduced without loss to its size. Women who have repeated pregnancies and inadequate nutrition are particularly prone. Kidney and liver dysfunction are other causative factors. One consequence of osteomalacia is the tendency to spontaneous fractures. Others include weakness and pain in the muscles, and softening of bones leading to the bending of the entire skeletal framework.

VITAMIN D *(per day)* (without sunlight)		
RDA at a Glance		
	mcg or IU	
M	10	400
F	10	400
Preg.	+ 5	+200
Lact.	+ 5	+200

Since vitamin D can be stored in the body, excessive intake is toxic, causing symptoms of nausea, vomiting, thirst, excessive urination, diarrhoea and weight loss, anorexia, paralysis and even stupor. Kidney stones may also be formed. In severe cases, the tissues of important organs such as the heart, lungs, kidneys and even the arteries may be calcified because too much vitamin D raises blood calcium levels. When the excess is withdrawn, the symptoms disappear, but the damage to the soft tissues is irreversible.

Recently, vitamin D is being researched for its role in the production of insulin and fertility in women. Vitamin D could possibly help prevent osteoporosis, kidney disease, and, cancer of the breast and colon.

Vitamin E or Tocopherol

This vitamin has attracted much interest because it is known as the anti-sterility factor, instilling hope of enhanced sexual prowess. However, its main function is as an antioxidant, which prevents the oxidation of fats both within the body and without. Vitamin E is also involved in the formation of red blood cells.

VITAMIN E (mg per day)	
RDA at a Glance	
M	10
F	8
Preg.	+ 2
Lact.	+ 3

Vitamin E is found widely in Nature, chiefly in vegetable oils, like corn, soya bean, cottonseed and safflower. The high concentration of polyunsaturated fatty acids (PUFA) in these fats makes them very susceptible to oxidation, and vitamin E is their natural protection. Whole grains, nuts especially groundnuts and walnuts, seeds like gingelly, legumes and green leafy vegetables are other good sources. Milling of grains without parboiling (called "conversion" in the West) removes the vitamin E present. This also indicates that the germ of wheat and rice are those parts of the grain that store vitamin E. Sprouting cereal grains increases their vitamin E content substantially. Animal sources, with the exception of fish liver oils, are low in the vitamin.

Men need about 10 mg and women 8 mg of vitamin E daily, which is comfortably met by the diet. Pregnant women need an additional 2 mg while lactating mothers will benefit from an extra 3 mg daily. Some recommend up to 30 mg per day. Deficiency is rare, and may be seen only in premature and low birth weight babies. The oral contraceptive pill lowers vitamin E levels. Like all fat soluble vitamins, any disruption in the lipid metabolism, particularly in the secretion of bile salts, besides bowel problems, leads to impaired absorption. The symptoms are anaemia and nerve damage causing tingling, numbness, pain and muscle weakness.

Excess intake has proven relatively non-toxic except probably in causing a deficiency of vitamin K. Recent research shows that vitamin E being an antioxidant is able to avert the damaging effects of chemicals produced by cell metabolism called free radicals, tobacco smoke, car exhaust and environmental pollutants. Among its benefits—cataract formation is prevented (if the problem exists, it retards the progress to opacity of the lens); macular degeneration is slowed down; the risk of heart disease is reduced and extensive damage to the heart muscle following a heart attack is prevented; lung, oral and pharyngeal cancer and chronic conditions like bronchitis are kept in check; and, sufferers of Parkinson's disease may enjoy more comfort with the delayed onset of tremors, twitching and loss of balance. Vitamin E may also prevent spinal cord damage in patients with cystic fibrosis.

Vitamin K or Phylloquinone (Menaquinone, Menadione)

Vitamin K is the clotting factor. The liver synthesizes prothrombin and other important clotting proteins that prevent haemorrhaging. Without vitamin K, this function will not be possible. Vitamin K also maintains the tissues and bones in the body.

VITAMIN K *(mcg per day)* (dietary intake only)		
RDA at a Glance		
	M	70 to 140
	F	70 to 140

Vitamin K is found in green leafy vegetables, cabbage, cauliflower and pork liver. It is also formed by bacteria present naturally in the intestine. Corn and soya bean oils also contain some vitamin K. Whole milk and its products, and meat, are fair sources of the vitamin. All other foods are poor sources of vitamin K.

The recommended intake of this vitamin falls in the range of 70 to 140 mcg daily for men and women. The upper value should read as the maximum required, if the whole amount is to be supplied by the diet. This situation may arise when the use of powerful drugs and malabsorption syndromes drastically reduce the ability of the human intestinal bacteria to synthesize the vitamin.

Deficiency of vitamin K causes lowered levels of the clotting factors in blood. Usually the cause is not due to insufficient dietary intake. More likely it is the ill effect of either impaired absorption or liver dysfunction. Liver dysfunction, particularly, is of great importance, as bile is necessary for absorption.

People who have a tendency to heart attacks and strokes are prescribed the regular use of drugs that prevent clotting (anticoagulants). They should be aware that this therapy carries the risk of haemorrhage. Prior to surgery of the gall bladder or liver, vitamin K is administered so that prothrombin is maintained at levels necessary to ensure that healing progresses smoothly.

Today, the possibility of utilizing vitamin K in the prevention of cancer and to retain calcium in the bones to avert osteoporosis is being explored.

1.8 WATER SOLUBLE VITAMINS

Vitamin C or Ascorbic Acid

This vitamin, highly soluble in water, and, sensitive to light and heat, is also known as the anti-scorbutic vitamin since it is the only vitamin that can prevent scurvy.

VITAMIN C (mg per day)	
RDA at a Glance	
M	40
F	40
Preg.	40
Lact.	+40

Its role in a number of essential body functions is undisputed. Chief among them is the formation of collagen, a protein that forms the ground substance of bone and cartilage, dentin that builds teeth and the building of tissues that line blood vessels. In the stomach, vitamin C helps convert iron from its complex ferric state into simpler ferrous salts which is the form of iron that is readily absorbed. Besides, it assists in a number of biochemical reactions and helps to prevent haemorrhages.

Some Indian foods like Indian gooseberry and guava are outstanding sources of the vitamin. The West Indian cherry (acerola), an uncommon fruit, which is available in some gardens and farms in India, has the highest content of vitamin C. This fruit alone provides 1,000 mg of vitamin C per 100 g of the edible portion.

Green leafy vegetables like cabbage, drumstick leaves, the greens of turnip, radish and knol-khol, coriander leaves, the cashew fruit, green chillies and capsicum are good sources of vitamin C. Citrus fruits, papaya, potatoes, cauliflower and bitter gourd are other good sources. All meats, milk, fish and seafood are poor sources of the vitamin.

Since vitamin C is easily destroyed, though widely available, foods containing vitamin C should be handled with care. All vegetables should be washed *before* cutting, and do not chop them too finely. Larger pieces conserve more of the vitamin. Also, cooking should be done in the shortest possible time. Suggested cooking methods are shallow-frying (stir-frying used in Chinese cooking) and steaming. Keeping the lid on the vessel also helps to retain the vitamin but the green colour of vegetables may be discoloured by volatile organic acids that are not allowed to escape. Pressure-cooking does appear to be the best method to keep the vitamin. Adding baking soda to preserve the colour of green vegetables further destroys vitamin C.

In tubers like potatoes much of the vitamin C present is found just below the skin. Therefore, it is advised that the whole potato be cooked in its jacket *without* peeling. This allows the vitamin to move into the centre of the vegetable causing little loss when the peel is eventually removed.

Since vitamin C is also readily oxidized when exposed to air, cut vegetables and fruits should be used as soon as possible. Storing cooked foods and fruit juices under refrigeration does not prevent the loss of this vitamin. However, it is very interesting to observe that if vitamin C-rich foods are stored in an acid medium, say, if they are combined with tamarind, lime juice or vinegar, then the vitamin loss is considerably reduced.

Pulses and legumes have little vitamin C content in their dry form. However, soaking them and allowing them to sprout (malting) greatly increases their vitamin C content. On an average, 24 hours after germination, the vitamin C content is about 8 mg per 100 g of the pulse. By the end of 72 hours, the level rises to 14 mg per 100 g. Pulses that are most commonly sprouted are whole bengal gram and whole green gram. Sprouted grams are also known to promote the removal of wastes by the kidneys.

The recommended dietary intake of vitamin C is 40 mg per day for adults. Pregnancy does not raise the demand for this vitamin but a lactating mother needs 80 mg per day up to one year after childbirth.

Deficiency of vitamin C causes improper formation of bone and cartilage which results in bone displacement, faulty calcification and sharp pain in the joints. Frequently, the gums are sore and bleed easily. Poor wound healing and susceptibility to infection are the more common symptoms.

Since vitamin C is not stored in the body, a regular, daily supply of the vitamin has to be assured. Smoking, high alcohol consumption, diuretics (prescribed to relieve premenstrual bloating in some women) and the oral contraceptive pill cause loss of vitamin C. However, excess intake is excreted, placing heavy stress on the kidneys. Kidney stones may be formed because of increased acidity of the urine. Gastrointestinal disturbances like stomach-aches and diarrhoea have also been reported. Much worse, excess vitamin C may promote increased uptake of iron from the stomach which interferes with the process of wound healing. Other problems include destruction of red blood cells and obstruction of anticoagulant activity in the circulation.

The ability of vitamin C to ward off colds and reduce their severity has its critics and devotees. One's general state of health is a more decisive factor in lowering susceptibility to infection.

Research today points to vitamin C as a possible deterrent in the development of cataracts and macular degeneration (as it concentrates in the eye), heart disease and cancer.

The Vitamin B Complex

Though these water soluble vitamins are interrelated, they perform individual functions in the metabolism of proteins, fats and carbohydrates. Therefore, it becomes important to discuss them separately.

Vitamin B₁ or Thiamine

Thiamine is mainly involved in carbohydrate metabolism, particularly with the oxidation of glucose in the brain and nervous tissue. By Nature's perfect design, this vitamin is usually present in high-carbohydrate foods like cereals. Cereals, if consumed unrefined, are an important dietary source, since thiamine is concentrated in the bran (outer layers of the grain) and the germ. With milling, much of this benefit is lost unless the grain is first parboiled. Rice is more commonly parboiled than wheat. In this process, paddy is steeped in water and then subjected to steam treatment. Next, it is dried and milled. Parboiling helps to draw the thiamine from the bran and germ and distribute it throughout the endosperm which forms the bulk of the grain. In India, parboiled rice is sold as "boiled rice" and the one

VITAMIN B₁ *(mg per day)*				
RDA at a Glance				
		Sedentary	Moderate	Heavy
	M	1.2	1.4	1.6
	F	0.9	1.1	1.2
	Preg.	+ 0.2		
	Lact.	0 - 6 months 6 - 12 months	+ 0.3 + 0.2	

that is not is called "raw rice". Parboiled rice with its higher thiamine content is used infrequently. The habit of excessive washing of cereal grains "to remove starch", and cooking by the drainage method (as against the absorption method), further adds to the loss of thiamine. In the days when hand-pounded, unpolished (red) rice was the only rice available, this problem was unknown.

Although yeast and wheat germ have the greatest abundance of this vitamin, their consumption is limited and we get very little thiamine from them. Other good sources are pulses, dried peas and beans, and nuts like groundnuts. Addition of baking soda, a practice common in India to soften grams (pulses) and to reduce cooking time, destroys thiamine. Cooking in an acid medium protects it. Pork is an outstanding source of thiamine. So is liver. Some shellfish, like clams, shrimp and crab, also contain thiamine. Eaten raw, this vitamin is of little use since the enzyme thiaminase present in the flesh of seafood inactivates the vitamin. However, cooking destroys the enzyme. Raw betel-nut and red cabbage also contain thiaminase. Milk is a fair source, and normal pasteurization temperatures do not destroy thiamine. However, rigorous boiling of milk in the home destroys the vitamin. Lean meat and mushrooms have some thiamine. Chicken, fish and fruit are poor sources.

The daily dietary allowance for thiamine depends on the intensity of work. Sedentary men and women require 1.2 mg and 0.9 mg respectively. Moderate and heavy male workers need 1.4 mg and 1.6 mg, and female workers in these categories, 1.1 mg and 1.2 mg. During pregnancy, the allowance rises by 0.2 mg. While breastfeeding her infant, a woman will require an extra 0.3 mg for the first six months, and, thereafter, only 0.2 mg more up to one year.

This vitamin is also known as the anti-neuritic vitamin, and therefore, its deficiency is marked by muscle weakness, and, burning and tingling and numbness (paraesthesia) of the calf muscles and feet. Other symptoms include fatigue, depression, and, loss of appetite and weight. Gradually, the optimum functioning of the gastrointestinal and cardiovascular systems is disrupted. This leads to indigestion, headaches and abnormally high heart rate (tachycardia). At this stage, the disease is called dry beriberi. As the disease progresses, there is palpitation, breathlessness and severe oedema (fluid accumulation) that precipitates heart failure. This stage of the disease is known as wet beriberi.

High alcohol consumption and diets where only highly milled rice and foods rich in tannins (those compounds that give tea and coffee their rich hue) are consumed with limited diversity in food selection precipitate deficiency states.

Treatment involves administration of the whole vitamin B group rather than thiamine in isolation.

Vitamin B₂ or Riboflavin (rarely Vitamin G)

Along with vitamin B₃ or niacin, in the body, riboflavin plays a major role in the generation of energy from the three major sources, namely, carbohydrates, proteins and fats. Riboflavin also sustains niacin in its role as an antioxidant vitamin.

Organ meats like liver and kidney, yeast and wheat germ contain very good amounts of the vitamin. Milk and milk products, meat, eggs, crab, green leafy vegetables and mushrooms also contribute riboflavin. Cereals and pulses are fair sources, but rice is practically devoid of the vitamin. Fruits and fats are poor sources. Consumption of

VITAMIN B₂ (mg per day)			
RDA at a Glance			
	Sedentary	Moderate	Heavy
M	1.4	1.6	1.9
F	1.1	1.3	1.5
Preg.	+0.2		
Lact. 0 - 6 months	+0.3		
6 - 12 months	+0.2		

predominantly cereal diets, especially of rice, leads to deficiency states, if vegetables and milk are completely absent. Though this vitamin is water soluble and unstable in the presence of light and alkalis, acids have a protective effect.

Deficiency of this vitamin is characterized by a smooth and greasy dermatitis at the angles of the nose and chin, cracks and fissures appearing at the corners of the lips (cheilosis), sore and purplish-red tongue (glossitis), and, the thighs and genitals become inflamed and itchy. The initial signs of the deficiency are usually burning and itching and watering of the eyes with blurring of vision. Later, cataracts may develop. Upper respiratory infections may complicate an existing condition. Heavy drinkers may lack riboflavin.

Based on whether an individual is a sedentary, moderate or heavy worker, the daily allowances of riboflavin for men range from 1.4 to 1.9 mg, and for women, the range is 1.1 to 1.5 mg. Pregnancy and the first six months of lactation call for an additional 0.2 mg and 0.3 mg respectively, with the requirement reverting to 0.2 mg extra from the seventh to the twelfth month of lactation.

Vitamin B₃ or Niacin (Nicotinic Acid, Nicotinamide, Niacinamide)

Niacin is involved in the metabolism of proteins, carbohydrates and fats. Vital enzymes containing niacin partake in antioxidant activity in the body. The essential amino acid tryptophan is converted to niacin in the body. This is the most stable of all the B vitamins and is unaffected by heat, light, acids or alkalis.

A diet rich in protein ensures that sufficient niacin is also consumed. The best sources are organ meats like liver, and groundnuts. Poultry, meat and other protein foods are good sources, besides yeast. Whole grain cereals, pulses, nuts and oilseeds also contain a small amount of niacin. Beetroot greens, dates, potatoes and cauliflower are especially important as low-protein sources of tryptophan. Milk and its products, maize, jowar (a millet), and, most fruits and vegetables contain negligible amounts of this vitamin. However, though milk and egg are poor sources of niacin, they are

VITAMIN B₃ (mg per day)				
RDA at a Glance				
		Sedentary	Moderate	Heavy
	M	16	18	21
	F	12	14	16
Preg.		+2		
Lact.	0 - 6 months	+4		
	6 - 12 months	+3		

abundant in tryptophan, a factor that cannot be ignored in meeting the body's requirement of niacin.

In cereals, a compound called niacytin combines chemically with niacin making it unavailable to the body. However, treatment with alkali destroys the bond and niacin in its available form is released. This is a peculiar feature of maize which contains this vitamin in the bound form. When treated with slaked lime *(chunna)*, niacin is released.

Deficiency of this vitamin affects the skin, and, the gastrointestinal and nervous systems. Initial symptoms are fatigue, headaches, and, loss of appetite and weight. Glossitis (soreness and inflammation) extends throughout the alimentary canal with the tongue turning scarlet. As the disease progresses there is severe diarrhoea, symmetric dermatitis that appears equally on both sides of the body but only on the exposed surfaces of the skin, and symptoms of dementia. In extreme cases, death follows. Hence, it is also known as the disease of the 4 Ds. Pellagra, as the disease is called, is prevalent in parts of India where maize and jowar form the staple diet. This condition can be averted by even small intakes of milk or groundnuts. A high alcohol intake and generally poor diet could lead to niacin deficiency.

The recommended dietary intake of niacin for men is in the range of 16 to 21 mg, and for women, 12 to 16 mg daily, based on their habitual work and activity. During pregnancy, a woman will need an additional 2 mg per day. The demand for niacin is greater during lactation—an extra 4 mg daily for the first six months of breastfeeding and 3 mg extra per day for the next six months.

In the West, doctors prescribe huge doses of supplemental niacin to lower cholesterol levels in the blood. Unless closely monitored, this could cause liver damage. Niacin is also considered a possible cancer inhibitor.

Vitamin B$_6$ or Pyridoxine (Pyridoxal, Pyridoxamine)

This vitamin essentially helps in the metabolism of proteins. Its other functions include the maintenance of the nervous and immune systems, and the production of red blood cells. Vitamin B$_6$ is assisted by vitamin B$_2$ to carry out these tasks.

The supply of vitamin B$_6$ is linked to the proteins found in foods, notably, meat, liver, pork, egg yolk, poultry and fish. Though whole grain cereals are good sources, much vitamin B$_6$ is lost in milling. In fact, wheat germ along with yeast would contribute a fair amount of vitamin B$_6$ if included frequently in the diet. Avocados, bananas, pulses, legumes, groundnuts and dried fruits are very good vegetable sources

VITAMIN B$_6$ (mg per day)	
RDA at a Glance	
M	2
F	2
Preg.	+ 0.5
Lact.	+ 0.5

of the vitamin. Carrots, cauliflower, cabbage, mushrooms, onions, potatoes, spinach and sweet potatoes also provide vitamin B_6.

Deficiency states are rare, but when they occur, irritability, dizziness, anaemia and skin irritation, manifested by a form of scaly dermatitis on the face, are the main symptoms.

Drugs used in the treatment of tuberculosis and high blood pressure are antagonistic to vitamin B_6 activity. Hence, deficiency may result if supplements are not taken. High alcohol consumption, smoking and the use of the oral contraceptive pill are also known to interfere with vitamin B_6 functioning in the body.

High supplemental doses of vitamin B_6 also have their problems. They cause numbness of the mouth and hands, and difficulty in walking.

Indian men and women are recommended a daily intake of 2 mg of pyridoxine. Pregnancy and lactation increase the need for this vitamin to 2.5 mg per day.

Some women are helped by vitamin B_6 supplements to overcome the discomfort of premenstrual syndrome (PMS) and morning sickness during pregnancy. Vitamin B_6 may protect against neural tube defects in the foetus.

Folic Acid or Folacin (Folate, Pteroylglutamic Acid, Vitamin M)

This vitamin together with vitamin B_{12} regulates the formation of red blood cells in the bone marrow. Folic acid is also necessary for the synthesis of genetic material and proteins.

Folic acid is widely distributed in foods. Organ meats, yeast, egg yolk, unsplit bengal gram, cow-peas, groundnuts and gingelly seeds, green leafy vegetables, ladies fingers and parsley are excellent sources of folic acid. Whole grain cereals and nuts are good sources. Milk and milk products, meat, chicken, tubers and fruits are poor sources. Folic acid is destroyed by prolonged cooking.

Mild deficiency is characterized by depression, weakness, headaches, forgetfulness, sleeping problems and anaemia. It may result from factors such as pregnancy, breastfeeding, the use of the oral contraceptive pill and diuretics, medication taken for epilepsy, and high alcohol consumption. Severe deficiency leads to megaloblastic anaemia where large red blood cells (macrocytes) with reduced oxygen-carrying capacity are released into the circulation. These cells are immature and are known as megaloblasts. Malabsorption syndromes, where the predominant symptoms are vomiting and diarrhoea, are

FOLIC ACID (mcg per day)	
RDA at a Glance	
M	100
F	100
Preg.	+300
Lact.	+ 50

the major cause of this form of anaemia. Poor dietary intake of folic acid, particularly among the elderly, may be another causative factor. However, folic acid deficiency alone does not manifest any neurological disturbances common in vitamin B_{12} (pernicious) anaemia. Treatment with oral (by mouth) and parenteral (intravenous) doses of folic acid reverses this condition.

Research today is focused on the possible benefits of folic acid and vitamin B_{12} therapy as protection against heart disease, nerve damage and neurological defects in the unborn such as spina bifida. Folic acid if taken during pregnancy lowers the incidence of cleft lip and palate in the foetus. It is also believed that folic acid reduces the risk of cervical and colonic cancer.

The recommended dietary intake for Indian adults is 100 mcg of folic acid daily. During pregnancy, women will need an additional 300 mcg and during lactation, only 50 mcg extra every day.

Vitamin B_{12} or Cyanocobalamin

Vitamin B_{12} has a function closely related to folic acid and is much less associated with the other vitamins of the B complex group. It is needed by all the cells for protein and gene synthesis, but, above all, it has two primary functions. The first is its singular function of promoting the maturation of red blood cells in the bone marrow in collaboration with folic acid. The

> **Did You Know?**
>
> Vitamin B_{12} is synthesized by intestinal bacteria. Bacteria that enter the gut through poor hygienic practices also manufacture vitamin B_{12}

second function is the formation of the myelin sheath composed of complex phospholipid that surrounds every nerve fibre.

Vitamin B_{12} is found only in animal foods. Organ meats like liver, sardines, and, most seafood like crab and shrimp are very good sources. Other sources include egg, especially the yolk, meat, milk and fish. In milk, vitamin B_{12} is bound to the whey proteins. Hence, the importance of utilizing the whey in curries or to prepare dough when milk is curdled to make chenna or paneer. Strict vegetarians who consume neither milk nor egg may not need vitamin B_{12} supplements because this vitamin is produced by the activity of the microbial flora in the gut. Vitamin B_{12} is destroyed by large doses of vitamin C if taken simultaneously. High alcohol consumption and smoking also reduce its availability. Calcium is necessary for the absorption of vitamin B_{12}.

Vitamin B_{12} deficiency from dietary insufficiency is extremely rare because the liver stores are sufficient for many years. It is more often the result of a genetic condition where the intrinsic factor, a substance that is necessary for the absorption of vitamin B_{12}, is absent. The intrinsic factor is secreted by the lining of the stomach and it forms a complex with vitamin B_{12}. When the intrinsic factor-vitamin B_{12} complex reaches the large intestine, the vitamin alone is released into the bloodstream. Inability of the stomach lining to produce the intrinsic factor brings about the condition known as pernicious anaemia. In this anaemia too, immature red blood cells are released into the circulation. Other symptoms, typical of this anaemia, are pallor, fatigue, loss of appetite, loss of weight, abdominal discomfort and prolonged bleeding time. Also, since vitamin B_{12} is responsible for the integrity of nerve fibres, neurological disturbances like unsteady gait and mental depression are present. In this problem, examination of the gastric secretion will reveal a marked absence of acid (achlorhydria). This may be distinguished from iron deficiency anaemia, where hypochlorhydria or little hydrochloric acid is present in the gastric juice. Sadly, lack of the intrinsic factor is primarily an autoimmune disorder, where the body views the substance as an intruding alien and blocks its production with antibodies.

However, the condition of pernicious anaemia is not without a cure. Injecting small amounts of the vitamin will bring about a reversal of symptoms. Moreover, if this is not possible, it has been found that when large amounts of synthetic vitamin B_{12} are taken orally, some of it is absorbed by simple diffusion. This suggests that because the supply of vitamin B_{12} in a normal diet is small, the intrinsic factor is necessary to capture all of the vitamin present. Therefore, when more of the vitamin is available, it does not need to wait in queue to complex with the intrinsic factor. This situation is also evident when large amounts of liver are consumed regularly. Treatment is to be continued for life if pernicious anaemia is diagnosed.

VITAMIN B_{12} (mcg per day)	
RDA at a Glance	
M	1
F	1
Preg.	+0.5
Lact.	+0.5

Surgery of the stomach where the site of intrinsic factor production is removed, and of the ileum, where vitamin B_{12} is absorbed, and malabsorption syndromes, result in megaloblastic anaemia from vitamin B_{12} deficiency and is usually treated with folic acid and vitamin B_{12} therapy. Folic acid is also known to reverse the symptoms of pernicious anaemia. However, it is dangerous to believe it is an adequate substitute, let alone a cure, because the neurological problems of vitamin B_{12} deficiency will get progressively worse if only folic acid treatment is given.

The recommended intake of this vitamin for adult Indians is placed at 1 mcg per day. Pregnant and nursing mothers will require an additional allowance of 0.5 mcg of vitamin B_{12} daily.

Recent research seems to suggest that vitamin B_{12} may protect against heart disease and nerve damage. Also, vitamin B_{12} possibly prevents neural tube defects in foetuses during the first six weeks of pregnancy.

Pantothenic Acid (rarely vitamin B$_5$)

This vitamin, like many of the other B vitamins, is necessary for the numerous functions in the body that bring about the release of energy from food. It is also involved in the formation of cholesterol and haemoglobin. As the name suggests, this vitamin is abundant in most foods, especially in those of animal origin. Egg yolk, liver and chicken, yeast, wheat germ, avocados, dried peas, cow-peas, groundnuts, cauliflower and mushrooms are excellent sources. Whole grain cereals, pulses and potatoes, meat, pork and fish are also good sources. A redeeming feature is that this vitamin is also manufactured by the bacteria naturally present in the intestine. Therefore, deficiency in human beings hardly occurs at all. Moreover, deficiency symptoms are hard to isolate because this vitamin is usually associated with the others of the B complex group. A deficiency of pantothenic acid is sometimes linked to chronic alcoholism. This vitamin helps to protect the human body against pollutants especially pesticides. In particular, it is believed to prevent the accumulation of DDT in body tissues.

PANTOTHENIC ACID *(mg per day)* (dietary intake only)	
RDA at a Glance	
M	4 to 7
F	4 to 7

No allowance has yet been determined for Indians but a daily intake of about 4 to 7 mg of pantothenic acid should be ample, and safe.

Biotin or Vitamin H

Without biotin all the energy producing mechanisms in the body will suffer irregularities, especially the metabolic processes involving fats and carbohydrates.

This vitamin is present in all the organ meats, yeast, egg yolk, pulses, legumes and nuts. Small amounts are present in whole grain cereals, milk and meat. Like pantothenic acid, the intestinal bacteria also produce this vitamin, so deficiency is rare. Alcoholics are one group with a tendency to deficiency. The symptoms typically include dermatitis, falling hair, loss of appetite, nausea, and, muscular aches and pains.

BIOTIN *(mcg per day)* (dietary intake only)	
RDA at a Glance	
M	100 to 200
F	100 to 200

However, the presence of a substance in raw egg white called avidin can prevent the absorption of biotin. Cooking destroys avidin.

There is no recommendation for the intake of biotin for Indians. A daily allowance of 100 to 200 mcg is considered safe and adequate.

1.9 MINERALS

Minerals are very important for the body and exist in a variety of compounds—as enzymes, in the fluids within and without cells, in the blood, tissues and hormones, and, even in vitamins. Of the approximately 25 mineral elements present in the body, about 17 are considered essential which means they have to be supplied in the diet. These include calcium, phosphorus, sulphur, magnesium, iron, zinc, iodine, copper, fluoride, manganese, molybdenum, selenium, chromium, cobalt, nickel, sodium and potassium, besides vanadium, boron and silicon. The other minerals, though present, appear not to have any special function, until research proves otherwise.

Calcium

More than any other mineral, calcium is the one element that is found in the greatest abundance in the human body. Along with phosphorus, it is the major component of bones and teeth. The role of calcium in the body is not restricted to this structural function alone. Calcium is also needed for the relaxation and contraction of muscles, to regulate the heartbeat, for clotting of blood and transmission of nerve impulses, for absorption of vitamin B_{12} from the large intestine, and for a number of enzyme activities.

CALCIUM (mg per day)		
RDA at a Glance		
	M	400
	F	400
	Preg.	+600
	Lact.	+600

Calcium is found only in a few foods, with milk and its products, and green leafy vegetables providing the bulk of calcium in the diet. Fish in which the bones may be eaten, crab, shrimp, ragi the millet, unsplit bengal gram, black gram dhal, dried French beans, gingelly seeds, mustard seeds, almonds, soya beans, dry coconut and jaggery are good sources too. Chewing betel leaf with slaked lime (calcium hydroxide) adds to the calcium intake. Some spices and condiments like cinnamon, cumin seeds, cloves, coriander seeds, carum seeds, asafoetida and poppy seeds contain good amounts of calcium, and though their use in cooking is limited, their contribution of calcium cannot be overlooked. Cereal grains, meat (except mutton), tubers and fruit (except dried fruits) are poor sources of calcium. Discarding cooking water causes a loss of calcium.

The absorption of calcium from the small intestine is dependent on a number of factors and they include (a) vitamins D and C (b) an acidic environment, and (c) lactose in milk. The presence of phosphorus and protein also increases calcium absorption.

Just as some factors promote calcium absorption, there are others that are antagonistic. Chief among them is the presence of certain inhibitory substances in vegetable foods. Oxalates in green leafy vegetables, and phytates (phosphorus compounds), commonly present in the outer layers of cereals, pulses and nuts, prevent absorption. These substances bind with calcium to form insoluble calcium oxalate and calcium phytate that cannot be absorbed and are thus eliminated. To some extent, these effects may be averted. Vegetarians may be advised to eat a little curds or other milk product with their greens. As the oxalate in the greens will be bound largely to its own calcium, it will spare the calcium from the alternate source which should be absorbed readily. Yeast fermentation of whole grain cereal products such as wholemeal wheat flour is especially beneficial. Yeast contains an enzyme, phytase, which is capable of breaking down phytic acid (phytate). The human intestine also contains phytase which probably explains why oxalates pose a bigger threat to calcium sufficiency (and of other mineral elements) than does phytate.

Diarrhoea and kidney failure (where vitamin D is not converted to its active form) also decrease calcium absorption.

If the diet does not provide sufficient calcium, it is supplemented from the bones leading to osteomalacia or bone softening where the bone is depleted without loss to its size. During pregnancy, if the additional calcium needed is not met by the diet, the mother's bones will be depleted to meet the demands of the growing foetus. The mother will eventually suffer spontaneous fractures. Lactation also increases the requirement for calcium. A common fallacy exists that the mother's teeth are lost with each pregnancy. Once teeth are mineralized, they do not lose their calcium easily. Therefore, low blood levels of calcium lead to loss of the mineral only from the bones.

Initial symptoms of calcium deficiency will include muscle cramps, weakness and heart palpitations. As the condition advances to osteomalacia, there is extreme rheumatic-like pain, bending and distortion of the bones of the spine, ribs and pelvis leading to crippling and fracturing of bones. Cataracts could also form in the eye.

Osteoporosis, on the other hand, is commonly seen in middle-aged women who have passed their childbearing years. The demineralization of bone is symptomless, and can be detected only by X-ray when the bones will have a moth-eaten appearance (X-rays of bones demineralized by osteomalacia will show a lighter shadow). The bones become extremely brittle and fractures, especially of the femur (thigh bone), are common. The primary cause of this condition is a low oestrogen level. Younger women who experience premature menopause because of removal of the ovaries, hysterectomy or sterilization as a means of contraception, and those who smoke, drink excessively, diet constantly and seldom exercise are also at risk. Coffee and aerated (fizzy) drinks also leach calcium from the bones making them less dense. There is no effective cure, only further damage can be prevented. Calcium and vitamin D therapy is standard recommended treatment.

The recommended dietary allowance for calcium is 400 mg per day for men and women. Pregnant and nursing mothers will need an additional intake of 600 mg daily.

Phosphorus

Phosphorus, like calcium, is the main constituent of bones and teeth. Apart from this, phosphorus is necessary for a number of other body functions. Among its more important roles is the regulation of the glucose metabolism including the absorption of glucose, its storage and ultimately its release as energy. It also influences the metabolism of proteins and fats. Phosphorus is also found in cell membranes and in the genes.

Phosphorus is naturally present in milk and meats. Whole grain cereals contain phosphorus in the form of phytate that interferes with calcium absorption. Some vegetables and fruits contain phosphorus. Chicken, pork, fish, egg, pulses (dhals), carrots, oilseeds and nuts, especially groundnuts, are other good sources. Some baking powders may have phosphorus salts.

The recommended dietary intake of phosphorus is 400 mg daily for Indian adults, and 1 g for women during pregnancy and lactation. Ideally, a 1:1 calcium-phosphorus ratio promotes optimum utilization. Although phosphorus is available in higher quantities in most natural foods, this does not create an imbalance in the uptake of calcium. Problems could arise only if phosphorus-containing food additives are used frequently. Deficiency is rare.

PHOSPHORUS (mg per day)	
RDA at a Glance	
M	400
F	400
Preg.	+600
Lact.	+600

Sulphur

Sulphur is present in all body cells, especially in connective tissue, skin, nails and hair. Sulphur compounds are also found in the liver, kidney, heart valves, salivary glands and brain. Insulin and heparin, a substance that prevents clotting (anticoagulant), contain sulphur too.

Sulphur in the diet is provided by sulphur-containing amino acids like methionine, an essential amino acid (See Proteins), cystine and cysteine. Important food sources, therefore, are meat, fish, poultry, pork, milk, cheese, egg, cereals, pulses, dried peas and beans, drumstick leaves, fenugreek leaves, nuts, oilseeds, jackfruit seeds, cauliflower, knol-khol and drumstick.

The recommended dietary allowance of sulphur is yet to be determined.

Magnesium

Magnesium is found in bones along with calcium and phosphorus, and in the fluids surrounding the cells (extracellular fluid), thereby helping in muscle contraction and transmission of nerve impulses, even heartbeat. It is also required for a number of metabolic reactions within the cell.

If magnesium is consumed with calcium, particularly in large amounts, each may interfere with the absorption of the other. Excess phosphorus also has a similar effect. As in calcium absorption, the presence of phytates and oxalates prevents magnesium uptake from the intestine. An acid medium, on the other hand, promotes absorption.

Good sources of magnesium are wheat germ, yeast, green leafy vegetables, dried peas and beans, pulses, nuts, whole grain cereals, fresh ginger, green chillies, ripe mango and plums. Most spices have magnesium in significant amounts but their contribution to the diet is limited because of the small quantities used. Refining of cereals causes huge losses, and discarding cooking water further reduces the level of dietary magnesium.

Deficiency is encountered only when chronic disease states like malnutrition and diabetes besides severe diarrhoea and vomiting are present. Chronic alcoholism also precipitates deficiency states because of increased excretion of magnesium. Regular use of diuretics (in the treatment of high blood pressure, heart and kidney disease) and the oral contraceptive pill increases the loss of this mineral element.

MAGNESIUM (mg per day)	
RDA at a Glance	
M	350
F	280
Preg.	+170
Lact.	+170

Depression, muscle cramps, irritability, nervousness, high blood pressure and palpitations are symptomatic of magnesium deficiency. If the deficiency is not corrected, convulsions can occur. Lack of magnesium has been implicated in cataract formation. Magnesium is invaluable in reducing the risk of heart irregularities following a heart attack. As magnesium increases bone density, it plays a crucial role in preventing osteoporosis.

In the absence of a recommended dietary allowance of magnesium for Indian adults, internationally accepted values of a daily intake of 350 mg for men and 280 mg for women can be applied. Pregnant and lactating women need 450 mg. Anticancer drugs increase the requirement for magnesium.

Iron

All cells contain iron. But haemoglobin, the essential component of red blood cells, ferritin in the intestinal mucosa, and, haemosiderin in the liver, spleen and bone marrow, have the highest concentration. Smaller amounts are present in the muscle protein, myoglobin, and, in iron-containing enzymes that assist in the formation of collagen and genetic material, and in the conversion of beta carotene into vitamin A.

To meet the iron needs of the body, ten times the daily requirement has to be provided in the diet because utilization of iron from foods is dependent on two factors, namely, iron availability and iron absorption.

Purely vegetarian diets are usually poor in available iron. Further, the form in which iron is present in foods also determines its availability. Iron in foods is found in two forms—heme and non-heme. Heme iron closely resembles the iron in haemoglobin and myoglobin. This form of iron is readily absorbed in the human gut and is found only in animal foods. Non-heme iron is made up of the inorganic salts of iron, namely, ferric salts. These are absorbed into the body only after conversion into ferrous salts. More foods contain non-heme iron. Even in animal foods, the ratio of heme to non-heme iron is about 40:60. The presence of inhibitory substances like tannins in tea, and, phytates in cereals and vegetables reduces the availability of iron. Phytates form insoluble complexes with iron in the presence of calcium and magnesium. By using iron vessels in cooking, the food levels of iron can be increased. While the availability of this iron can never be fully researched, at least the dietary intake goes up.

IRON (mg per day) RDA at a Glance		
	M	28
	F	30
	Preg.	+ 8
	Lact.	30

Absorption of iron in the gut is never very satisfactory. Therefore, the right environment for iron absorption has to be created. This can be done by keeping the following simple points in mind:

a) Inclusion of vitamin C in the diet, a natural reducing factor, helps convert ferric iron to its ferrous form, thus rendering it available for immediate absorption.

b) Consuming fermented foods with a good acid content favours iron absorption. For instance, if curds are eaten with spinach it greatly enhances the utilization of iron found in spinach even though curds are a poor source of iron. Lactic acid in curds is responsible for this action.

c) Acid foods like tamarind, mango powder and raw mango, vinegar, lime juice and tomatoes when used in cooking promote iron absorption besides mobilizing iron from iron vessels.

d) Provide enough protein with the iron in the diet. Since iron is both transported and stored as a iron-protein complex, sufficient protein can only improve the chances of greater absorption.

e) Constant use of antacids neutralizes the acid in the stomach and interferes with iron absorption.

f) Germinating grains reduces their phytate content.

Heme iron, which is readily available to the body, is found in liver, lean meat, seafood, fish, egg yolk and poultry. The non-heme, inorganic salts of iron are also present in animal foods besides green leafy vegetables, cereals, pulses (dhals), dried peas and beans, and dried fruit. A number of spices have high amounts of iron but since they are used in small quantities their iron contribution to the diet is insignificant. Most fruits, vegetables and milk (even though it is an animal food) are poor sources of iron.

The measure of iron deficiency which causes anaemia is determined by the level of haemoglobin and the number of circulating red blood cells. Women and growing children are more prone to anaemia than men. Women suffer a loss of elemental iron through menstruation which averages 15 to 30 mg per month. However, if the diet is wholesome, the problem is not grave, and the body stores of iron will compensate. Men, on the other hand, start storing iron from their twenties onwards.

In fact, it is being increasingly acknowledged that menstruation is an important factor in preventing heart disease in pre-menopausal women. Generally, narrowing of arteries is due to plaque formation (deposits of lipids in arterial walls) which reduces blood flow and could ultimately lead to heart attacks and strokes if the artery is blocked altogether. Iron is known to interact with low-density lipoprotein (LDL), the undesirable form of cholesterol, to form these plaques. The loss of iron through menstruation in women is beneficial in that less of it is available for plaque formation. This also explains why the incidence of heart disease in women rises sharply upon the onset of menopause.

During pregnancy, because of the great demand on the mother to build foetal and maternal tissues, and the increase in blood volume (in relation to the lesser number of red blood cells present), even a very healthy diet may not provide sufficient iron and supplementation is necessary. Early signs of iron deficiency are fatigue, listlessness, shortness of breath, irritability and sleeping problems. An examination of the gastric juice will show low levels of hydrochloric acid (hypochlorhydria) which is corrected by the administration of histamine. In severe cases, the nails will become spoon-shaped which is called koilonychia in medical parlance.

The values for normal haemoglobin in India are 13 to 18 g per 100 ml of blood for men and 12 to 16 g per 100 ml for women.

The recommended dietary allowance of iron for Indians is 28 mg daily for men and 30 mg for women. During pregnancy, women need an additional 8 mg of iron per day. No additional iron is recommended for nursing mothers since milk is a poor source of iron. Solely breastfed infants have sufficient body stores to meet the demands of growth and development up to the age of six months. Beyond six months of age, supplementation with iron-rich foods must be started.

Excess iron is stored in the liver with seemingly no ill effects. However, if the iron overload is greatly increased, then the symptoms of cirrhosis will appear. This is very, very rare. Excessive supplementation of iron interferes with the absorption of zinc which plays a role in wound healing and regulating the immune system.

Zinc

Zinc is found in all the cells in the body and is an integral part of a number of enzymes, even those with antioxidant function. The mineral is particularly concentrated in the eye, liver, blood, bone and prostate. Zinc is vital for the efficient functioning of the genes, the immune and reproductive systems, and, for growth and maturation.

ZINC (mg per day)		
RDA at a Glance		
	M	15.5
	F	15.5
	Preg.	+ 5
	Lact.	+10

Seafood, meat, liver, egg yolk, pork, poultry, processed cheese, wheat germ and whole grain cereals are very good sources of zinc. However, phytates found in whole grain cereals will interfere with absorption. Fish, pulses, dried peas and beans, nuts and oilseeds are also good sources. Roots, tubers, green leafy and other vegetables contain some zinc. Milk and most fruits are poor sources. Vegetarian diets, therefore, are generally poor in zinc. The simultaneous presence of calcium and vitamin D in the gut further interferes with the uptake of zinc, as does high supplemental doses of iron.

The early signs of zinc deficiency are poor appetite, diarrhoea, hair loss, slow wound healing (diabetes also causes poor wound healing but for altogether different reasons) and a weakened immune system. The white flecks on nails are wrongly attributed to calcium deficiency (nails contain no calcium, only keratin, the same protein found in hair). Other factors considered, this may in fact indicate that more zinc should be included in the diet. Zinc deficiency in adolescence can cause growth retardation and delayed sexual maturity. A low dietary intake of zinc is associated with cataract formation. Taste and night vision are also affected by a lack of zinc. An increase in zinc sometimes helps to alleviate the symptoms of premenstrual syndrome.

A daily intake of 15.5 mg of zinc is recommended for Indian adults. Pregnant and nursing mothers need an extra 5 mg and 10 mg respectively, every day.

High alcohol consumption, diabetes, the oral contraceptive pill, viral hepatitis, malnutrition and kidney disease are factors that precipitate deficiency states.

Symptoms of toxicity appear when the zinc intake is excessive. It is not common but could appear when acid foods are stored in zinc containers.

Iodine

The principal function of iodine is the formation of thyroxine and tri-iodothyronine, two hormones produced by the thyroid gland. They are involved in growth and the general metabolic activity of the body. Much of the dietary iodine intake is by way of plants grown in iodine-rich soils. Animals get their iodine by consuming plants that contain the mineral. If the iodine content of the soil is poor, then it is highly likely that people in that area will develop endemic goitre, a condition that is most noticeable by the enlarged thyroid gland in the neck. It indicates the gland's efforts to produce thyroxine despite the lack of iodine in the body. However, it must be emphasized that this condition has no effect on the general functioning of the person. Even the basal metabolic rate or BMR will be normal.

A more serious condition occurs when a woman whose own body stores of iodine are severely depleted gets pregnant. As dietary iodine is also non-existent, the growing foetus gets no iodine at all and develops cretinism. The child is born with severe mental retardation, impaired physical development, growth failure and drastically low basal metabolism. If the infant is given thyroid treatment early on, the physical condition may improve but the mental damage is irreversible. Spontaneous abortions and stillbirths are also common among iodine-depleted pregnant women.

In regions where the iodine intake is poor because of iodine-deficient soils, endemic goitre leads to endemic cretinism. The only solution to this problem is to provide iodized salt to people who cannot obtain iodine from any other source. The Government of India in a concerted bid to provide iodized salt to the entire population has banned the production and sale of non-iodized salt in the country. This is the only way by which both endemic goitre and endemic cretinism can be prevented. Rock salt (mined) and solar salt (produced by the evaporation of sea water and salt brines) are *not* better alternatives to non-iodized salt.

IODINE (mcg per day)		
RDA at a Glance		
	M	150
	F	150
	Preg.	+ 25
	Lact.	+ 50

Generally speaking, the land bordering the sea coast has adequate iodine. Salt-water fish, seafood and shellfish are, therefore, very good sources of iodine for non-vegetarians. Dairy products, eggs and meat have an iodine content that is in proportion to the iodine intake of the animal, which in turn is dependent on the iodine levels of the plants it consumes, and ultimately, on the soil which supports their growth. Inland soils are usually poor in iodine. The people living in the sub-Himalayan regions of India are particularly vulnerable. Cooking lowers the iodine content of foods.

A group of substances called goitrogens found in plants of the Brassica family, namely, cabbage, cauliflower, radishes and turnips, if eaten uncooked, can interfere with the uptake of iodine. Groundnuts and oilseeds are also known to have goitrogens (See Appendix 5.10). However, it has not been proved that they are the cause for endemic goitre.

The daily recommended intake of iodine is placed at 150 mcg for men and women. Pregnant women are advised to increase that intake to 175 mcg and nursing mothers to 200 mcg per day. Low iodine intakes do not cause hypothyroidism, but excess could precipitate hyperthyroidism.

Copper

Copper has a very important role in the formation of haemoglobin as it helps to absorb iron from the gut besides transporting stored iron to the sites of synthesis. Copper is also active in taste sensitivity, in maintaining the integrity of the myelin sheath which envelops nerve fibres, in the formation of connective tissue and the melanin pigment, and in bone development. Copper is also a constituent of a number of enzymes, including those with antioxidant activity.

COPPER (mg per day)		
RDA at a Glance		
	M	2.2
	F	2.2

Nutritional deficiency of copper is rare since most diets provide adequate copper. Organ meats and shellfish among animal foods, and pulses (dhals), legumes, whole grain cereals, oilseeds especially gingelly seeds, nuts and mushrooms among plant foods, are good sources. Milk, meat, rice and fruit are deficient in copper. Copper ions are present in foods stored in copper (and brass) vessels. However, it must be cautioned that cooking in copper vessels can cause excessive deposition of the metal in the liver leading to jaundice and cirrhosis especially in children below five years. Kidney damage is also likely.

Indian adults require about 2.2 mg of copper daily. The presence of vitamin C and zinc, cadmium and molybdenum increases the requirement of copper since they interfere with its absorption. Ancient wisdom suggests that drinking water stored in copper vessels alleviates the pain of arthritis and rheumatism. Low copper levels in the body can lead to cataract formation.

FLUORIDE (mg per day)		
RDA at a Glance		
	M	1.5 to 3
	F	1.5 to 3

Fluoride

The benefit of fluoride as a prophylactic of dental caries in children and of osteoporosis in adults is well established. It exists as a calcium salt of fluoride in the body.

In India, 1 part per million (ppm) (1 part fluoride per million) or 1 mg fluoride per litre of drinking water is considered safe and adequate. The permissible limit for ground water is 0.8 ppm. Where the level is in the range of 2 to 3 ppm, fluorosis results, a condition marked by arthritis-like symptoms. The afflicted suffer from skeletal fluorosis, dental fluorosis and gastrointestinal problems. Muscle weakness and anaemia could also result from excess fluoride. This happens only over many years of high intake. It is endemic in most parts of the Indian subcontinent with Uttar Pradesh, Rajasthan, Gujarat, Andhra Pradesh and Tamil Nadu being the worst affected. High molybdenum and low copper intakes further aggravate this problem.

Chronic dental fluorosis is the result of drinking water having flouride levels in excess of 2 ppm. The enamel becomes dull and pitted and the teeth appear mottled. Pregnant and nursing mothers who live in endemic areas are likely to have children who suffer from dental fluorosis. Dental caries are absent in this condition. Most importantly, water with high fluoride levels does not look or taste different. Ordinary home methods of boiling and filtering water do not remove fluoride.

Since fluoride is found in all soils, all dietary sources, especially drinking water and tea, contain sufficient levels of this mineral to ensure that even an adult requirement of 1.5 to 3 mg per day is met.

Manganese

Manganese has an important enzymatic function in the utilization of carbohydrates, proteins and fats. It is essential for cartilage formation, bone growth and development, regulation of nerve impulses and reproduction. It also functions as an antioxidant in the body.

MANGANESE *(mg per day)*		
RDA at a Glance		
	M	5.5
	F	5.5

Foods such as ragi, spices, condiments, oilseeds and nuts, pulses (dhals), dried peas and beans, whole grain cereals, green leafy vegetables and some fruit are good sources. Animal foods have lower levels.

The requirement of manganese for Indian adults is 5.5 mg daily. This is met adequately if highly refined foods are consumed in moderation.

Molybdenum

Molybdenum participates in the uric acid metabolism, in the synthesis of genetic material, in the release of stored iron and in providing energy from fat.

A high molybdenum intake interferes with copper absorption. Moreover, it also causes a gout-like condition (acute arthritis due to excessive accumulation of uric acid in the blood).

Molybdenum is found abundantly in pulses (dhals), dried peas, coriander leaves, nuts and oilseeds like groundnut and gingelly, and organ meats. Whole grain cereals also provide some molybdenum.

It is recommended that Indian adults have a daily intake of 500 mcg of molybdenum. Deficiency is rare.

Selenium

Selenium is found in all tissues but is concentrated in organs like the liver, kidney and testes. Selenium along with vitamin E plays an important role as an antioxidant in reducing the risk of cancer and heart disease, and for sustaining the liver in its numerous activities. Selenium is also needed for normal growth and development, hormone production especially of the thyroid gland, and, for healthy hair, skin and eyes.

The concentration of selenium in foods is closely related to the protein content, and hence, it is found largely in meat, organ meats, seafood and fish. The level of selenium in cereals depends upon the selenium content of the soil in which they are grown. Ragi is rich in selenium. Milled cereals suffer huge losses, so raw rice has very low levels of selenium. Whole grain cereals and parboiled rice have some selenium. Milk provides the bulk of selenium in Indian diets, and butter, particularly, is rich in selenium. Pulses (dhals), and, dried beans and peas also contain selenium. Selenium is lost when cooking water is discarded. Fruits except avocado pears, and vegetables are poor sources. Vitamin C interferes with the absorption of selenium whereas vitamin E promotes it.

A low intake of selenium can lead to liver, fertility and and hormonal problems. If endemic, a heart condition could develop in children. Excess selenium is toxic, and causes dental caries, hair loss, skin changes and fatigue.

Indian adults are advised 55 mcg of selenium per day. Pregnant women will need an additional 10 mcg daily.

MOLYBDENUM (mcg per day)		
RDA at a Glance		
	M	500
	F	500

SELENIUM (mcg per day)		
RDA at a Glance		
	M	55
	F	55
	Preg.	+10

Chromium

Chromium is present in the kidney, spleen, testes and hair, and in lower concentrations in the heart, pancreas, lungs and brain. It activates a number of enzymes. Chromium is closely linked to the utilization of insulin, and is absolutely essential for the removal of glucose from the blood. It also controls the level of fat and cholesterol in the blood.

Important food sources of chromium are liver, yeast, meat, cheese, nuts and oilseeds, spices, condiments, poppy seeds, pulses (dhals) and whole grain cereals.

Cereals lose most of the chromium present on milling. Milk, chicken, fish, most fruits and vegetables (except bottle gourds and green leafy vegetables) are low in chromium.

A daily allowance of 65 mcg of chromium is recommended for Indian adults.

CHROMIUM (mcg per day)		
RDA at a Glance		
	M	65
	F	65

Cobalt

Cobalt is the mineral element in vitamin B_{12}. Therefore, cobalt and vitamin B_{12} have similar functions. It is also believed to assist in the utilization of iodine.

Food sources of vitamin B_{12}, therefore, provide cobalt in the diet. Liver, seafood, egg yolk, meat and fish are good sources of cobalt. Other animal foods like chicken, milk and pork also contain cobalt. Plant sources do not provide any. Bacteria in the human gut, and bacterial contamination of foods, are other sources of vitamin B_{12}, i.e. cobalt.

Megadoses of Vitamins and Minerals—Help or Hazard?

High doses of vitamins and minerals are looked upon as a means of maintaining good health. The common belief is that the higher the dosage, the healthier it is. While it is possible to supply all the major vitamins and minerals in a tablet, the relevance of numerous minor elements, both known and unknown, to human existence has yet to be established. Moreover, it is unlikely that the precise balance of nutrients for human beings will ever be available in pill form. If refined and highly processed foods are any guide, the more we make advances in food technology, the more we are likely to suffer losses of one kind or the other. Further, despite scientific progress, the recommendations for the intake of minimum levels of vitamins and minerals to avert deficiency symptoms are fraught with controversy, as age, sex, activity, physiological status, habitual diets, cooking practices, and even stress, can alter the requirement. There is really nothing that can replace a well-balanced, nutritious meal. Fruits, vegetables, whole grain cereals, pulses, nuts, meat, fish and milk are among the most reliable sources to meet our daily requirement of vitamins and minerals. Furthermore, pills will never satiate hunger nor can they replace the pleasure of tasting fine food. And there is always the danger of pills not being made to specification, to contain and release nutrients at the rate and in amounts intended. In fact, heavy doses of some nutrients can be quite harmful and could cause nausea, vomiting, diarrhoea, hair loss and nerve damage. Others such as the water soluble vitamins put a heavy strain on the kidneys because any excess is excreted.

However, pills have their uses too. This is particularly true when food restrictions, for whatever reason, make balancing a meal difficult. Severe allergic reactions triggered by the ingestion of certain foods, children in boarding schools, old people with poor incomes and disability, or who are unwilling to shop and prepare food, long journeys where mealtimes are erratic and meals far from wholesome, are all good reasons to take extra vitamins and minerals in manufacturer's packaging.

Generally speaking, the body is robbed of vital nutrients when alcohol, tobacco, caffeine, refined sugar, processed foods and diuretics (to relieve fluid retention) are taken indiscriminately.

1.10 ELECTROLYTES

The name electrolyte derives from the fact that these substances are capable of transmitting an electrical current when in solution. When electrolytes are dissolved in water, they split up or dissociate into their components which are known as ions. This process is called ionization. Ions carry an electrical charge which may be either positive or negative. The positive ions are called cations, examples of which are sodium (Na^+), potassium (K^+), calcium (Ca^{++}) and magnesium (Mg^{++}). The negative ions are called anions, and chloride (Cl^-), bicarbonate (HCO_3^-), phosphate (HPO_4^{--}) and sulphate (SO_4^{--}) fall within this group. Therefore, when a substance like common salt or sodium chloride (Nacl) is in solution, it will dissociate into positive sodium ions (Na^+) and negative chloride ions (Cl^-). The balance of ions (equal number of cations and anions) in the solution keeps it in perfect equilibrium.

In the body, this same principle applies. The fluids in the body may be divided into the fluids within the cell and those outside the cell. Those fluids that are found within cells are described as intracellular fluids and those outside as extracellular fluids. The extracellular fluids are blood plasma, lymph and the intercellular (interstitial) fluid which bathes every cell.

Sodium and chloride are the principal ions outside the cell, and, potassium and phosphate within the cell. However, lesser amounts of all the other electrolytes are found in the intracellular and extracellular fluids. By the constant movement of ions between cells and the surrounding fluids, the body is kept in perfect osmotic (fluid and electrolyte) balance.

Beside this important function, electrolytes have other uses in the body. Sodium assists in the contraction of muscles, even heart muscle, promotes the peristaltic movement of the gastrointestinal tract and facilitates the transmission of nerve impulses. Potassium has a role similar to sodium in muscle and nerve functions. It also regulates blood pressure. Further, potassium is necessary for enzyme reactions within the cell. Chloride has important digestive functions. It is the chief anion in gastric juice. Chloride is also found in amylase or ptyalin, the enzyme in saliva that digests cooked starch.

Sodium

Sodium is obtained largely by the addition of salt (sodium chloride) to food. One teaspoon of salt provides about 2,000 mg of sodium. (Even an adult needs only between 1,100 and 3,300 mg of sodium per day.) Baking powders, soup cubes, preservatives (sodium benzoate, sodium citrate and sodium propionate) and monosodium glutamate (MSG), a flavour enhancer, many of which do not necessarily taste salty, contribute large amounts of sodium when added to foods. Sodium cyclamate, the sweetener, is also a source of sodium. It is best to keep the daily intake within 2,000 mg.

Sodium occurs naturally in meat products, milk, egg white, fish and shellfish, and among vegetables, mainly those of the green leafy kind. However, cabbage, drumstick leaves and curry leaves are poor sources of sodium. Most other vegetables have moderately high sodium levels with the exception of knol-khol which has a very high sodium content. Fruits except musk melon, roots and tubers, and cereals are low in sodium. Pulses (dhals) have varying amounts of sodium. Sodium is lost when cooking water is discarded. This knowledge is particularly important in the planning of low-sodium diets recommended in the management of hypertension or high blood pressure, cirrhosis of the liver, cardiac and renal diseases, and other conditions which require the elimination of oedema.

Besides being the chief source of sodium in the diet, the use of iodized salt is advocated to provide essential iodine as well.

There is a problem of uncontrolled intake of salt in India, by way of pickles and other preserved foods like pappads, vattals and vadagams (fresh vegetables like green chillies or leftover rice are mixed with salt, sun-dried, then fried in hot oil and eaten). High consumption of sodium can, among other factors, cause hypertension, fluid retention, heart and kidney failure, and stomach cancer. The use of vinegar, tamarind, mango powder and lime juice helps to improve palatability without increasing sodium intake.

Low levels of sodium could cause muscle cramps, dehydration, low blood pressure, vomiting and loss of appetite.

Chloride

Most of the chloride intake is from sodium chloride or common salt. Sodium and chloride are lost through perspiration in very hot climates and from physical exertion, or through gastrointestinal disturbances like diarrhoea and vomiting. Generally, the level of these ions is regulated by the kidney, and, sodium and chloride are normal constituents of urine. However, if the losses are heavy, dehydration results. In this condition, water is drawn out of cells to dilute the concentration of sodium outside the cell. When this happens, the thirst mechanism is activated, and the intake of fluids restores the balance. However, salts are required to be added if equilibrium is to be maintained. A daily intake of 1,700 to 5,100 mg of chloride is adequate for adults.

Potassium

Potassium is widely distributed in foods. Animal sources include meat, milk, chicken and fish. Legumes and pulses (dhals) provide rich amounts of potassium from plants. Carrots, potatoes, tomatoes, nuts, oilseeds and especially whole grain cereals are also good sources. All fruits with the exception of grapes are abundant in potassium. Most vegetables have moderate amounts of potassium. Cooking water contains potassium that has leached out, so it is important not to discard it. The recommended intake for adults is in the range 1,875 and 5,625 mg per day.

Potassium deficiency may occur as a result of prolonged vomiting, diarrhoea, severe malnutrition due to chronic alcoholism, anorexia nervosa (abnormal dislike for food) and low-carbohydrate regimens. Surgery, burns, prolonged fever, the use of diuretics and hormonal imbalances can also bring about low potassium levels. Potassium deficiency is characterized by sluggishness, weakness and extreme thirst. Excess potassium causes lethargy. Both conditions affect the heart.

Oral Rehydration Therapy—Home Treatment

In India, one of the most fatal effects of insanitary conditions or just plain carelessness in feeding infants is uncontrolled diarrhoea leading to dehydration and death. Since hospitals and specialized care are often so hard to reach in an emergency, the difference between life and death may simply lie in preparing a rehydration drink at home.

Take 1 litre water (preferably boiled) and add to it 2 level tablespoons (30 g/1 oz) sugar, 1/4 teaspoon salt and 1/4 teaspoon baking soda (bicarbonate of soda). If baking soda is not available, add another 1/4 teaspoon salt. Taste the drink after dissolving all the ingredients together. It should not be saltier than tears. Follow the feeding schedule given below or as often as thirst demands:

Age	Total Consumption in 24 Hours
Below 6 months	1/4 to 1/2 litre
6 months to 2 years	1/2 to 1 litre
2 years to 5 years	3/4 to 1 1/2 litres
Above 5 years	As much as the child will consume

It is very important to continue breastfeeding along with the oral rehydration therapy even if the child is very ill.

In addition, orange juice, tender coconut water, well-mashed ripe banana, buttermilk, rice and dhal water or even mashed potatoes, if tolerated, will help greatly in restoring the electrolyte balance.

This drink is also recommended for adults who have bouts of severe vomiting and diarrhoea, or even during summer when profuse sweating, especially when combined with strenuous exercise, causes loss of water and electrolytes.

1.11 WATER

No life is possible without water. It is a universal solvent and is the environment in which all biochemical and physiological reactions take place in the body.

The human body is made up of about 60 per cent water which is around 40 litres. As described earlier, body fluids are divided into two categories—intracellular and extracellular fluids. Intracellular or the fluid within the cell accounts for about 25 litres. The remaining 15 litres make up the extracellular fluids found outside the cells which include blood plasma, lymph and the secretions of all glands. Of this, plasma alone accounts for three litres.

Every day water is lost from the body. About 2.5 litres are lost through the lungs, skin, kidneys and faeces daily. These are called obligatory losses, which means that these losses will occur regardless of intake because the metabolic equilibrium of the body has to be maintained. For example, unless the kidneys excrete urine, the waste products of metabolism like urea, the end product of protein metabolism, will not be removed. Similarly, even though it is not very apparent, every single one of us sweats all the time. This is known as insensible or invisible perspiration. As against this, visible perspiration occurs when the environmental temperature is high, in fevers, and, when physical activity and work is intense. This is the means by which the body temperature is regulated.

This constant loss of water has to be replaced throughout every day. The most obvious means of replacement is by the activation of the thirst mechanism that ensures that water and other fluids are consumed. Some water is also provided by food. If the intake of fresh fruit and vegetables is increased, consequently, the intake of water also goes up. The third source is the body itself, involving the metabolic process. Though the contribution is small, it cannot be ignored. Water is usually one of the end products in every metabolic (oxidative) process. To ensure that sufficient fluids are consumed every day, match the intake of fluids with the intake of calories. Adults will need about 1ml per kcal and infants about 1.5 ml per kcal (See Calories).

Athletes and those engaged in intense physical activity for long periods of time, might lose as much as four litres of water *per hour*. They must consume small amounts of fluids continuously every few minutes (say at 15-minute intervals) to restore the fluid balance. This is preferable to consuming large amounts at one time. Even after strenuous activity has ceased, it is important to drink more than the daily average for the next 24 to 48 hours.

An adult losing four litres of water could be very dehydrated and will show symptoms of disorientation if the fluids are not replaced immediately. Loss of more than eight to ten litres through bleeding, vomiting or diarrhoea can lead to death.

1.12 NUTRIENT INHIBITORS

Nutrient inhibitors are also known as antinutrients. As the name suggests, they interfere with the utilization of nutrients present in foods. There are, however, many ways by which their effects can be overcome, the most obvious being to consume a mixed diet. However, when lack of purchasing power restricts the choice of food to a few staples, and if these contain the offending substances in abundance, then deficiency symptoms will be manifested. Fortunately, most of these substances are destroyed by cooking or by the fermentation process. Since a typical Indian diet contains very few foods that are eaten raw or have not undergone any preparation at all, this problem is well within control.

The most common nutrient inhibitors are oxalates (or oxalic acid) and phosphorus compounds called phytates (or phytic acid). Oxalates bind the calcium abundant in green leafy vegetables, so that the body cannot utilize calcium. Other oxalate-rich foods are plantain flower and green plantain (used as a vegetable), nuts, oilseeds especially gingelly seeds, Indian gooseberry, drumstick (the vegetable), rhubarb, Indian olive, cocoa and chocolates, and tea. Cereals have a relatively low oxalate content. Magnesium is also adversely affected by oxalates in the diet and is poorly absorbed if they are present in the same meal. Moreover, high-oxalate diets are probably causative in the formation of kidney stones.

On the other hand, phytates bind the metal elements of iron, zinc, magnesium and calcium, and interfere with their uptake from the gut. These are especially abundant in the outer layers (bran) of whole grain cereals, in legumes and pulses (dhals), and, in nuts and oilseeds. Spices also contain phytates. Refining cereals eliminates this problem. The use of yeast to ferment foods prepared from whole grain cereals or their products greatly reduces this effect. This is because yeast contains phytase, an enzyme that breaks down phytic acid. The human gut also contains some phytase. Phytates are broken down enzymatically when cereals, legumes and pulses are germinated.

Goitrogens are substances that prevent the body from utilizing iodine by blocking the uptake of iodine by the thyroid gland even though the intake may be adequate. Foods that commonly contain goitrogens belong to the Brassica family and include radish, turnip, cabbage, cauliflower and Brussels sprouts. Groundnuts and some oilseeds (mustard, for example), soya beans, legumes and lentils, maize, ragi and tapioca are also known to contain goitrogens. Normal consumption of these foods has no adverse effect, and cooking destroys goitrogens.

Other detrimental substances are the trypsin inhibitors. They inhibit the activity of trypsin, a protein-digesting enzyme that is active in the small intestine. These are found in soya beans, legumes and egg white. Trypsin inhibitors are easily destroyed by heat, especially at pressure-cooking temperatures (121.5 degrees Celsius/250.7 degrees Fahrenheit at 15 pounds pressure for 15 minutes).

Tannins, commonly associated with tea, are also implicated in nutrient non-availability. Heavy tea drinkers who eat poorly may suffer from thiamine deficiency. Tannins also bind iron. They are found abundantly in the seed-coats of legumes, spices and tamarind, and, in millets like ragi and bajra. Since most of these foods are not consumed in isolation, the inhibitory effects of tannins are not felt.

Niacytin is a nutrient inhibitor that binds niacin or vitamin B_3 found in cereal grains, and in particular, maize. Treatment with alkali (slaked lime) breaks this bond and frees niacin.

Among animal foods, the most troublesome appears to be avidin, a protein found in raw egg white. Avidin binds biotin of the vitamin B complex group and prevents its absorption in the digestive tract. Another enzyme, thiaminase, found in shellfish like clams, shrimp, betel-nuts and red cabbage inactivates thiamine or vitamin B_1. Both avidin and thiaminase are sensitive to heat and are destroyed by ordinary cooking temperatures. (See Appendix 5.10).

1.13 FOOD TOXINS

The poisons we may ingest, albeit unwittingly, could do much harm particularly if the food is consumed regularly.

In parts of India, kesari dhal *(Lathyrus sativus)* is a staple, and it contains a water-soluble toxin called beta-N-oxalylamine-I-alanine (BOAA) which can cause a crippling, neurological disorder called lathyrism. The toxin can be removed by steeping in water and discarding the soaking water or by parboiling for one hour or more. Most Indian diets do not employ this dhal, though it may be added as an adulterant to other dhals. The only known treatment for this condition is the withdrawal of the offending pulse. Sadly, among the poor classes where this is not always possible, the symptoms are often severe, affecting the spinal cord, and consequently, leading to paralysis of the lower limbs.

Broad or fava beans *(Vicia faba)*, a favourite ingredient in sambhars, could cause a form of haemolytic anaemia called favism in persons deficient in the enzyme glucose-6-phosphate dehydrogenase (G6PD), responsible for the integrity of red blood cells. This is a genetically inherited condition, and, in India, it has been recorded among minority groups such as the Parsees and Jews. A simple blood test will confirm the absence of the enzyme. Symptoms of sensitivity include fever, abdominal pain and headaches, besides the anaemia. However, the broad beans have to be uncooked or lightly cooked and included habitually in the diet in order to pose a problem. Young children, aged two to five, are most likely to be affected.

Gossypol in cottonseed is not of much significance since it is not consumed in Indian diets.

Potatoes with green patches are dangerous to consume. They contain a powerful alkaloid called solanine. Solanine is found just below the skin of, especially germinating, potatoes. Ingestion of this substance causes pain, vomiting, diarrhoea and jaundice. To prevent the greening of potatoes, they should be stored away from bright light, and those that have already turned green should be discarded. Cultivating potatoes requires constant vigilance as the developing tubers have to be kept covered with soil in order to prevent them from turning green on exposure to sunlight.

Another toxin is related to groundnuts. In damp conditions, the nut tends to encourage the growth of a mould called *Aspergillus flavus* which produces a powerful toxin called aflatoxin. These toxins are carcinogenic and are known to damage the liver. Careful physical examination and elimination of infected nuts, and storage in dry conditions, are the practical means of tackling this problem. Also, never eat a spoilt nut. Cooking temperatures do not destroy aflatoxin.

1.14 FOOD ADULTERANTS

With so much profit to be made with demand outstripping supply, producers of food are very often tempted to take advantage of the situation. Substituting unwholesome substances for food becomes common practice, denying the consumer good nutrition and value for money. Some of the most commonly adulterated foods are spices, tea, coffee, flour, honey, fats and oils.

Dried papaya seeds are added to black pepper, and, exhausted tea and coffee grounds are dried and recycled. Roasted bran and sawdust are added to a number of masala powders. The bright colours of turmeric, chilli and coriander powders, and pulses (dhals) may be attributed to coal tar dyes.

Kesari dhal is often added to bengal gram dhal and few are aware of the poison it contains. Physical removal of the offending dhal is almost impossible, since it closely resembles the food it adulterates. Tapioca flour, which is cheap and available in abundance, is added to bengal gram flour and wheat flour.

Coloured cane sugar syrup is frequently sold as honey. Fats and oils are probably the most abused. Mineral oil is purified and added to most vegetable oils. This can cause gastrointestinal disturbances, besides damaging the liver and heart. Butter and ghee are often a mixture of hydrogenated fats and lard.

Country eggs that satisfy health faddists are often no more than battery-produced eggs dipped in a weak solution of tea.

Looking at the growing list of adulterated foods, one might conclude that nothing we eat is wholesome. However, there are numerous standards that have to be met before foods reach the consumer.

In India, the AGMARK is used for agricultural products that meet with the standards set out in the Grading and Marketing of Agricultural Products Act of 1937.

The Prevention of Food Adulteration Act (PFA) of 1954 has stringent rules which govern the Fruit Product (Amendment) Order (FPO) of 1961 that sets standards of quality for fruit and vegetable products and the Meat Product Order (MPO). All processed foods have to follow the guidelines set out by these two supervisory bodies. Unfortunately, the testing of food samples outside the large cities and towns is inadequate because of ill-equipped laboratories and poorly trained personnel.

The Indian Standards Institution (ISI) mark issued by the Bureau of Indian Standards (BIS) is also a guarantee of quality, and standards for over 700 food products have been formulated.

Buying reputable brands from reputable stores, even if it is marginally more expensive, is well worth the extra money because adulteration is less likely.

1.15 FOOD CONTAMINATION

Food contamination includes toxic chemicals present in foods (pesticides), and, bacteria and other micro-organisms that cause disease.

Pesticides

One cannot deny the importance of pesticides. Without their use, much of the food produced will be lost to disease and infestation. However, indiscriminate application of pesticides is common, and the residues present in the food at the time it reaches the table are not even considered.

In India, regulation exists, but enforcement is lax. Of the 119 pesticides and their 6,500 formulations registered under the Insecticide Act (1971), some 70 per cent are either banned or limited to restricted use in the West because they are poorly degraded. Dichlorodiphenyltrichloroethane (DDT) is among them (banned in the United States in 1972), as are BHC (benzene hexachloride) and methyl parathion. Indians have the highest concentrations of DDT (between 12.8 ppm and 31 ppm) and other toxic chemicals in their bodies, more than most people in the world. Pesticides are used freely in India because of constant pressure to achieve impressive growth of both foodgrains and cash crops in the agricultural sector.

Farmers are seldom trained in safe methods of application. Many pesticides are meant to be used during sowing or transplantation and not before harvesting. Besides lack of knowledge regarding the time of application, indiscriminate use is rampant, often in excess of need, leading to yet another problem. Pests develop resistance which then requires altering tried and tested formulae to develop more effective insect control.

Food-borne Illness

Food-borne illness is usually understood by the layperson as food poisoning. However, this generalization may be differentiated into food infections and food intoxications.

Food infections result when disease-causing bacteria present in the food are ingested. In food intoxications, the toxins or poisons that are produced by the bacteria are consumed. The organism by itself poses no threat of illness.

In bacterial food infections, food acts merely as a carrier of germs. The bacteria that cause typhoid and paratyphoid fevers (Salmonella), Shigella that causes bacillary dysentery or shigellosis, and cholera (Vibrio), are examples of bacteria that are merely carried by food to the gut of a person where they multiply and cause illness. Other bacteria find food a suitable medium for growth, and their numbers are greatly increased before the food is ingested. The gastroenteritis caused by Clostridium perfringens and Bacillus cereus fall in this category.

Toxins produced by the growth and activity of bacteria in food cause food intoxication. The bacteria Staphylococcus, found in infected wounds, boils and pimples, can cause staphylococcal poisoning. The enterotoxin (causing illness in the gut) that is produced is not destroyed by temperatures normally employed in home cooking. The food which contains this toxin will not taste, smell or appear spoiled.

More dangerous is the presence of the toxin produced by the bacteria Clostridium botulinum that causes botulism, an acute illness affecting the nervous system. The afflicted person usually dies from paralysis of the respiratory system and cardiac failure if the antitoxin is not administered in time. The activity of these bacteria is restricted to canned foods since C. botulinum favours the absence of air and low-acid foods like meat, fish, maize and peas for growth. The toxin is destroyed by heating to about 100 degrees Celsius/212 degrees Fahrenheit for at least 15 minutes.

Basically, many of these illnesses can be avoided if a little cleanliness and hygiene is observed in the kitchen. Since much of the water used in the cultivation of crops is untreated, and for which certification by the municipality as safe is not available, the only control that can be exercised is by the person preparing food.

Fruits and vegetables should be washed in flowing water (if possible), then rendered safe for consumption by using the sterilizing agent potassium permanganate ($KMnO_4$), which is available in most chemist shops in India under the brand name "Pinky". Dissolve a few crystals of potassium permanganate in water until it turns a pleasant shade of magenta, and submerge the fruit or vegetable in it for one hour will clean it adequately.

Meat, poultry and fish are more likely to be responsible for food-borne illness. The scalding water that is used to facilitate the plucking of poultry is a fine breeding ground for the Salmonella organism. After plucking, many of the birds are held in cold storage. This slows down bacterial activity if the freezing temperature (minus 18 degrees Celsius/0 degrees Fahrenheit) is kept constant. However, power failures and power cuts accelerate the process of deterioration as the repeated thawing and freezing not only damage the tissues making them soft and flabby, but also give the bacteria a chance to grow again. Excessive handling of meat, fish and poultry before refrigerated storage also encourages spoilage. The only alternative is to clean, wash and cook flesh foods with a little salt before refrigerating them. This is both convenient and safe.

Cooked foods should not be stored for long periods of time without refrigeration. And, once cooked food is removed from the refrigerator, it should be used as soon as possible, so that the bacteria present in it do not get a chance to multiply.

Canned foods do not automatically contain the organism *Clostridium botulinum,* but as a safety measure, check the dates of manufacture and expiry before purchase of any processed food. Reject any rusted, damaged, leaky or bloated tins and do not be tempted to taste the contents. Canned foods need some form of heat treatment before use, if botulism is to be avoided. Particularly those that are not acidic must be boiled vigorously for 15 minutes. If the food does not lend itself to this treatment, open the top of the can and stand it in a vessel of boiling water which reaches almost up to the lip of the can. Allow the *contents of the can* to bubble for a minimum of 15 minutes before consumption.

Parasitic Infestations

Many protozoa and worms (helminths) gain entry into the human body through food. Amoebic dysentery or amoebiasis, caused by the organism *Entamoeba histolytica,* is especially prevalent during the rainy months when improper drainage of the monsoon waters provides the perfect medium for the mixing of sewage and drinking water supplies. This happens because the pipelines of both systems run parallel to each other and even a microcrack can allow entry of contaminated water. The condition may be acute or chronic. In the acute form, diarrhoea of varying severity is the predominant symptom. The danger of chronic amoebiasis is that except for mild discomfort and occasional bouts of diarrhoea alternating with constipation, the person may not be aware that the problem exists at all. This could lead to infection of tissues and to the formation of abscesses in vital organs like the liver. Recurrent stomach upsets should always be taken seriously, and stool tests become necessary to confirm infestation and to commence timely treatment.

Worm infestations are not uncommon either. Since Indians are basically vegetarian, the vast majority are spared the possible infestation with the minute roundworm *Trichinella spiralis* found in raw or partially cooked, infected pork which causes trichinosis. The larvae of this worm form cysts in pork, and if this meat is consumed, they are released in the gut during the process of digestion. These larvae then attach themselves to the mucous lining of the intestines where they grow and mature. The females produce more larvae which migrate in the bloodstream to muscles in all parts of the body, where they encyst once more. If they lodge in important organs like the brain, tumours may form and death can result. Tapeworm infestation also comes from meat. Cysticercosis, a condition that affects the brain, is caused by tapeworm found in improperly cooked pork. Beef tapeworm, once within the body, if it does not migrate in the bloodstream, tends to reside in the intestines, growing to many feet in length.

The reasons for these infestations are easily identified. Insanitary methods of faecal disposal is the chief cause. Vegetables, especially greens cultivated in village plots, are frequently irrigated with raw sewage. Additionally, in India, pigs meant for human consumption are not reared in a controlled environment. Therefore, personal hygiene and cleanliness in the kitchen is the only means of prevention (See Food-borne Illness).

Cysts of *Trichinella spiralis,* for instance, cannot be easily spotted even if they are not deeply embedded in the meat. Cutting them out and discarding them before cooking is good practice, but not always possible. It is, therefore, wise to use whole cuts of meat and minced meat products such as sausages, luncheon meat, kebabs and cutlets sparingly, since cysts will not be readily visible in them. Further, this organism is destroyed if pork is cooked until it is no longer pink. Pressure-cooking is recommended. Freezing at minus 18 degrees Celsius/0 degrees Fahrenheit or lower for at least 72 hours (three days) also inactivates most organisms and renders meat safe.

Water, too, should be sterilized before use. Though the city's municipal supplies are chlorinated before distribution, particularly during the rainy season, the load of impurities increases, lowering its efficacy. Moreover, amoebic cysts are not affected by chemical treatment. Only boiling for ten minutes (the water should be allowed to bubble vigorously) followed by filtration (if possible) destroys most bacteria and protozoa. Mere filtration is not sufficient since filters do not hold back viruses, notable among them being the hepatitis Type A virus, transmitted in water (and food) contaminated with faecal matter.

For filtration to be effective, a method has to be followed. First, determine that the filter candle washers fit snugly, so that the water does not run through to the chamber below, without filtering through the candle. When there is a build-up of slime and impurities, the

> ### Did You Know?
> Ultraviolet radiation and halogens do not kill bacterial spores

filter candle should be cleaned with a soft brush in plenty of running water and detergent. Then the cleaned candle should be immersed in a vessel of water and brought to the boil. The water should be allowed to bubble for ten minutes. Then the candle is to be cooled and fitted in the filter. For best results, establish a routine for cleaning and sterilizing the filter. Ignoring the cleaning of the filter chambers and bottles used to store sterilized water is a common mistake. These too should be washed in detergent and rinsed in boiled water to prevent the bacteria lurking in them from starting up new colonies.

Newer methods of sterilization involve ultraviolet radiation and treatment with halogens. For effective sterilization with ultraviolet water purifiers, the exposure time should not be less than five seconds—unlikely if there are frequent power failures and power cuts. It is, therefore, prudent to repeat the radiation process twice before drawing off the water. And irradiated water should always be stored in sterilized bottles. If the ultraviolet filter is fitted with a carbon filter, it will have to be changed from time to time, and voltage fluctuations could damage the ultraviolet lamp. So, in practice, a continuous supply of power and frequent changes of the filter are necessary for this form of sterilization to effectively protect against water-borne diseases.

Halogens, like iodine, are very effective sterilizing agents. They kill bacteria but not their spores. The most common halogen filters available in the market sterilize water by killing bacteria held back in a filter pad saturated with iodine. This means of water purification is not recommended for regular use in the home because during the sterilizing process the iodine in the filter is depleted, and it is not possible to determine when it is completely exhausted. What is known, however, is that the iodine depletion is hastened when the water has a heavy load of physical and bacterial impurities, and that the filter will have to be changed to ensure a continuous supply of clean water. This method of water sterilization is best restricted to long journeys and picnics.

In rural areas, wells replace the municipal water supply. If sewage disposal is also within the same precincts, then the water source needs to be protected. Most importantly, a minimum of 40 feet (12 metres) must separate septic tanks and the water supply. At this distance, the layers of soil act as a filter. Wells must, additionally, be protected with sufficiently high, seepage-proof walls with the land sloping away from them so that rain water does not drain into them directly.

1.16 FOOD TABOOS

Scientific knowledge encourages us to eat foods based on their nutritive value. Yet, in India, religious, social and cultural taboos and superstitions govern our food intake.

All communities throughout the country believe foods are either "cold" or "hot (heaty)". This refers to the inherent quality of the food which either promotes retention of moisture resulting in colds, coughs and chills, or causes excessive drying of body fluids. "Cold" foods which are retentive, therefore, are to be avoided at night or during the cold and rainy months. This means that curds, many fruit especially citrus fruit and bananas, and some varieties of greens, are taboo in the cooler months. "Heaty" foods like ripe mangoes are believed to cause boils, sores and nosebleeds, and are hence not beneficial to the body in summer. However, it must be remembered that when fruits and vegetables appear in a particular season, they are meant to be eaten at that time, if we are to derive any benefit at all. For instance, ripe mangoes, which are abundant only in summer, are a rich source of beta carotene (the precursor of vitamin A), and a whole year's supply of beta carotene can be obtained from eating mangoes in just one season. Indian wisdom suggests that you have a little milk with ripe mangoes to offset their "heaty" effect. Similarly, fenugreek leaves, which are freely available during the cold winter months of North India, are recommended for arthritis sufferers to relieve the pain and discomfort which gets worse in this season.

Another popular assumption is that milk and sour fruit if taken together will curdle milk. Though milk is alkaline, once in the stomach, it stimulates the production of gastric juice just like any other protein food. (All protein foods need gastric juice for their breakdown.) Gastric juice is largely made up of hydrochloric acid, the potency of which is many times that of even the most acid fruit. So, the curdling of milk in the stomach will take place, regardless of whether or not acid or fermented foods are consumed at the same time. Curdling is also an important step in the digestion of milk and separating milk from other foods will not spare it from this effect.

No situation offers so much opportunity to impose taboos on food intake than pregnancy and lactation do. During pregnancy, when most nutrients are needed in greater quantities, food restrictions place heavy stress on meeting even the regular (non-pregnant), daily requirement. For example, even the best nourished pregnant woman will probably show signs of anaemia due to iron insufficiency without supplements. In India, where the iron intake is almost solely dependent on vegetable sources like greens, these are restricted to satisfy the Indian preoccupation with producing a "fair-skinned" child. All dark-coloured foods, like green leafy vegetables, are restricted, and light-coloured ones are favoured.

Another more dangerous outcome of traditional beliefs is restricting the intake of food of pregnant women in the hope that the delivery will be easier if the size of the growing foetus is contained. Since difficulty during delivery is related to the size of the infant's head, there is no concrete evidence that limiting the mother's food intake reduces the baby's head circumference. Instead, the nutritional status of both the mother and child (including significantly lower birth weight) is adversely affected. For instance, if the increased need for calcium during pregnancy is not met by the diet, calcium will be drawn from the mother's bones to compensate. This has two effects. Not only will the skeletal system of the foetus be poorly developed, but the mother will suffer from a condition called osteomalacia or bone softening which is characterized by much pain and distortion of the bones of the spine, ribs, legs and pelvis, leading to spontaneous fractures. A pregnant woman in many parts of India is also encouraged to consume great quantities of warm ghee and other fats. Unnecessarily, additional calories are added, and, besides, these are the least nutritious foods to include at this time.

Colostrum or first milk after delivery is also restricted in the belief that the mother's wastes are excreted through it. However, colostrum contains immune bodies called immunoglobulins which are meant to compensate for the infant's fledgling immune system. Withdrawal of this milk will deprive the child of this natural protection against illness, particularly gastrointestinal disturbances, that are common in bottle-fed babies.

The dictum, "Starve a fever and feed a cold", survives on the fallacy that food stokes fevers. Fever, on the contrary, burns body tissues causing progressive loss of strength. A high-calorie, high-protein diet is necessary to spare them, particularly the delicate tissues of the brain.

1.17 FOOD FADS

Young people are especially vulnerable to trends in society and peer preferences of their groups. This is reflected in the foods they consume too. Adolescence is that age when the last and final growth spurt before adulthood takes place, so there is an increased need for calories, proteins and other nutrients, which often *equals* or *exceeds* adult requirements. Adolescents must be made to realize that their diet influences their growth and development, and that this stage in their lives affords the last opportunity to set down the foundations for a healthy future.

Not all fad diets are bad. When they contribute valuable nutrients, it may not be detrimental to indulge in them. The danger in following such a diet pattern is that when the food fashion changes, the new substitutes may bring about a worse state of nutrition.

Fast foods and junk foods are terms used to describe foods in vogue. Most of them provide more calories, fat and sodium than any other nutrient. They are especially low in vitamins, minerals and fibre. If they regularly replace wholesome meals, their nutritive adequacy is in doubt.

Indian junk foods like bhel puri, sev and pani puris, and pav bhajji could be quite nutritious, except that they are deep-fried, and therefore, are high in fat and calories.

1.18 HEALTH FOODS

The terms organic and natural are sometimes used to describe health foods.

The term organic is usually ascribed to foods that are grown in soils enriched exclusively with animal dung and humus, and not by the use of artificial fertilizers. This nomenclature also implies that no pesticides have been used in the cultivation of crops, and that pest control is by natural predation only.

Natural foods are those health foods that contain no chemical preservatives or additives. Little do people realize that common salt and table sugar, the most commonly added chemicals to food, are also additives, since they are used to prevent spoilage in the preservation of foods. Consumption of foods like pickles that are concentrated sources of salt is, in fact, more harmful than healthful.

Honey, brown bread, sprouts, yoghurt (curds), and, wheat germ and bran are another category of health foods that are strongly recommended to improve one's general health, revitalize flagging spirits and to delay the onset of ageing. Anyone will recognize that many of these foods are common to the Indian diet. Curds are probably the only form of milk that adults habitually consume in India, and, wheat germ and bran are present in unrefined wheat products like wholemeal wheat flour. Sprouted grams (pulses) also have a place on many regional menus.

A word about honey. It is often taken as a slimmer's alternative to sugar, refined or otherwise. However, if consumed by volume—the most common application of this food—honey actually contains more calories than sugar. To clarify: one tablespoon of honey (21 g) provides 67 kcal whereas one tablespoon of sugar (15 g) provides only 60 kcal. No doubt, if the *same weight* of each food is taken, i.e., 15 g, then honey will provide the lesser number of calories—only 48. The point of this argument is to show that since volume as a measure is used more frequently than weight, honey being the heavier, contributes more calories.

Health faddists help sustain a spurious food industry which does not provide value for money. Very often in India, brown bread is white bread coloured with caramelized sugar, and honey could be coloured cane sugar syrup.

It may be observed that the term health foods is really very misleading since no evidence exists to suggest that they are more nutritious than other foods. Neither are they more beneficial or less harmful than the foods we normally eat. Health foods should thus be viewed in this more balanced perspective.

1.19 FOOD SELECTION—SOURCES OF NUTRIENTS

So much has been said about nutrients and their intake. However, it can be a bewildering experience for those confronted with making the right choice when it comes down to food selection. There are two sets of guidelines that will help.

First, there are the Recommended Dietary Allowances (RDA) for Indians that are standards which have been established by the Indian Council of Medical Research (ICMR) to meet every nutritional need, every day, for men and women. Additional allowances, wherever necessary, are provided to accommodate the increased demands of pregnancy and breastfeeding in women (See allowances given against each nutrient in the text).

The first step in meal planning is to determine the nutritional target to be achieved by every member of the family, at least for the major nutrients. Usually, all else follows, if the major dietary requirements are met daily.

Second, for greater convenience, there is the system in which foods have been grouped together based on the essential nutrients they provide. This system is known as the Basic 5 in India. (In the US, there are only four categories, called the Basic 4 Food Groups.) All the foods within a group will provide similar nutrients, and, therefore, they can easily be substituted for one another to provide the same benefit. Moreover, for a standard weight, foods of the same group will provide the same number of calories. Using this system, all that needs to be done is to include foods from every group, every day, in greater or lesser quantities to ensure a perfectly balanced meal (See also Appendices).

1.19.1 Basic 5

The five major food groups are:

1) Cereal Grains and Their Products

All cereals like rice, wheat, maize and their products, and, the millets like ragi, bajra and jowar are included in this group.

About 80 per cent of the energy requirements of Indians is met by this group of foods. Their contribution of other nutrients is also equally important. Chief among them are proteins. However, the proteins found in cereals lack the essential amino acid, lysine, and to a

> **Did You Know?**
>
> By rule of thumb, 1 oz/30 g/2 table-spoons dry weight of cereals provides approximately100 kcal, 20 g of carbohydrate and 2 g of protein

lesser extent, threonine. Maize, particularly, is deficient in many essential amino acids. (See Proteins). This deficiency can be compensated for by a judicious combination with pulses. Rice protein is of a higher quality than any of the other proteins of this group except wheat germ, whose protein compares favourably with animal proteins.

The consumption of whole grain cereals is more beneficial than refined cereals. This is because the bran and germ are retained. The minerals of iron and phosphorus, magnesium and manganese, selenium, zinc and copper, chromium, molybdenum, sodium, potassium and chloride, and, the B vitamins of thiamine, pyridoxine, folic acid and pantothenic acid, and, vitamin E, are especially abundant in these parts of the grain, particularly the germ. Parboiling is one means of ensuring that some of these benefits are retained in the endosperm after milling and polishing. Use of unrefined, unsifted, wholemeal flours like atta also contribute these minerals and vitamins to the diet.

However, even in unrefined cereals, inhibitory substances called phytates interfere with the availability of iron, zinc, magnesium and calcium. Yeast fermentation of unrefined cereal products appears to release these minerals from their bound form because of the presence of the enzyme phytase which breaks down phytic acid (phytate) (See Nutrient Inhibitors).

Excessive washing of cereals and discarding the cooking water causes a loss of vitamins of the B complex group especially thiamine and niacin, besides the minerals calcium, magnesium, selenium, sodium and potassium.

Ragi is a rich source of calcium. The bran of whole grain cereals is an undisputed source of insoluble fibre. Cereals are poor sources of fat though small amounts are present in the bran and germ.

2) Pulses and Legumes

Into this group may be classed all the pulses, whole (known as grams) or split (called dhals), such as bengal gram, black gram, red gram, green gram and lentils, and, all the legumes like dried peas and beans, cow-peas, dried French beans, field beans and soya beans.

This group also provides energy. For Indians who are largely vegetarian, this is the single most important source of protein besides milk. They do not provide all the essential amino acids but in combination with cereals, which is usual, this balances out. For example, rice

> *.Did You Know?*
>
> On an average, 1 oz/30 g/2 tablespoons dry weight of pulses or legumes provides 100 kcal, 18 g of carbohydrate and 7 g of protein

or wheat with dhal is a staple in most parts of the country (See Proteins). The B vitamins of thiamine, pyridoxine, folic acid and pantothenic acid, and, vitamin E, are found in pulses and legumes. Though the vitamins A and C are lacking, sprouting pulses increases their vitamin C content significantly.

Of the minerals, calcium, phosphorus, iron, magnesium, sulphur, copper, manganese, molybdenum, chromium, potassium, chloride, sodium and zinc are obtained from this source.

Soluble fibres are also abundant in this group.

3) Vegetables and Fruits

This group is particularly valued because it is a virtual storehouse of vitamins and minerals, besides providing the benefit of vast amounts of fibre. Fat is negligible in this group, and hence free consumption of these foods should be encouraged.

Vegetables may be divided into three classes based on their water content. The higher the water content, the lesser the load of calories. Accordingly, these classes are:

a) Vegetables with a high water content and the least calories. About 200 g of this group will provide only 50 kcal. Foods included in this group are all the green leafy vegetables, snake and bottle gourds, cucumber, bitter gourd and ash gourd, knol-khol, parwar, brinjal, radish, turnip, cabbage, lettuce, cauliflower, vegetable marrow and chow-chow marrow, drumstick, French beans, capsicum and pumpkin. This group provides vitamins A (as carotene), E and K, vitamin C, the B vitamins riboflavin, pyridoxine, folic acid and pantothenic acid, and, the minerals of calcium, magnesium, sulphur, manganese, iron, molybdenum and chromium, and the electrolytes of sodium, potassium and chloride. Unfortunately, much of the mineral content of these vegetables is not available for absorption since they are bound to oxalates and phytates (See Nutrient Inhibitors). Cabbage, cauliflower and broccoli have the amazing property of inactivating food toxins. Bitter gourd is beneficial for lowering blood sugar levels.

Green leafy vegetables have been much researched as an alternative and cheap source of protein. However, its relevance in human nutrition has to be established.

b) The vegetables ladies fingers, beans, mushrooms, carrots, beetroot, onions and plantain stem will give about 50 kcal per 100 g of the vegetable. This group contributes vitamin A, pyridoxine, folic acid and pantothenic acid, and, of the minerals, phosphorus, sodium and potassium. The fibre content of the diet is also augmented. Plantain stem is much valued in South India for its preventive and curative properties in the treatment of gallstones and kidney stones.

c) Fifty grams of starchy vegetables, namely, fresh peas, colocasia, potatoes, yam, sweet potatoes and jackfruit seeds will each provide approximately 50 kcal. Their most valuable contribution to the diet is energy and soluble fibre. Besides, they provide pyridoxine, folic acid and pantothenic acid—B vitamins, and, sulphur

> **Did You Know?**
>
> Vegetables consumed in these amounts will provide about 10 to 12 g of carbohydrate, with the protein content varying from about 6 to 10 g for green leafy vegetables and between 1/2 and 1 g for the rest

and potassium. The orange variety of these vegetables is an important source of beta carotene, the precursor of vitamin A.

Fruits may also be divided into two groups based on their calorie content. Very sweet fruits like ripe bananas, fresh dates, sapotas, grapes, ripe jackfruit and mangoes average 100 kcal per 100 g of fruit. The rest provide about 50 kcal for every 100 g of fruit.

Fruits are an invaluable source of vitamin A (as carotene), vitamin C, pyridoxine, potassium (the very best), magnesium, manganese and chromium, and, fibre.

Though fruits contain almost no fat and protein, avocado pears are one of the best sources of both. The fat is largely oleic acid, a monounsaturated fatty acid. Avocado pears are also an outstanding source of the B vitamin, pantothenic acid, which confers protection against pollutants.

Dried fruits are believed to be more nutritious than fresh fruit. They contain no more nutrients than fresh fruit, but, for the same weight, provide five times as much. This is particularly true of iron which, when concentrated in the dried fruit, is many times that which is found in fresh fruit. Dried figs, dates and grapes are good examples of this. However, vitamin C is lost totally by drying. Dried fruits are an excellent source for both soluble and insoluble fibre (See Fibre). They are also calorie-rich, providing about 300 kcal per 100 g.

Grapes, particularly the purple variety, fight fungi naturally by producing a substance called resveratrol which helps to control blood fat and cholesterol levels. Raisins contain resveratrol too, but, must necessarily be artificially dried, as this compound is destroyed by sunlight.

4) Milk, Meat and Their Products

This group has particular importance for Indians since only a small number include meat and its products in their diet.

Most vegetarians consume milk in one form or the other. However, lacto-ovo-vegetarians, those who include eggs as well as milk in their diets, are the best off.

Milk is a source of very high quality protein, especially the liquid whey, which separates out when milk is curdled. In the making of paneer or cottage cheese, every effort must be made to utilize the whey instead of the usual practice of discarding it. The fat of milk is also easily digested.

The carbohydrate in milk is lactose. Its positive attributes include promoting the bacteria in the gut to manufacture the B complex vitamins of vitamin B_{12}, biotin and pantothenic acid, and suppressing the activity of the putrefying bacteria. Moreover, the presence of lactose favours the absorption of calcium and phosphorus in the digestive tract. When lactose is present as lactic acid, the absorption of iron is facilitated. Therefore, milk, if consumed as curds along with iron-rich foods, will greatly assist in the absorption of the latter. Human milk is more than twice as sweet as cow's milk.

Did You Know?

One small cup (1/4 pint/150 ml) of whole milk (cow's) provides about 100 kcal. Skimmed milk of the same quantity will give around 50 kcal. The carbohydrate content of both whole and skimmed milk is approximately 6 g and the protein content about 5 g for this amount. Curds prepared from whole milk will have the same levels of nutrients. However, buttermilk provides only 25 kcal for 1/4 pint/150 ml, and, 1g each of carbohydrate and protein. Fat levels vary with the extent to which milk fat (cream) is retained. Whole milk will provide 6 g fat approximately, buttermilk 2 g and skimmed milk less than 1/2 g per 1/4 pint/150ml

---

Milk is an outstanding source of riboflavin, but it is quickly lost if exposed to light. It is a poor source of niacin, but a rich source of its precursor tryptophan, an essential amino acid (See Proteins), which is converted to the vitamin in the body. It provides some vitamin A (especially whole milk and its products) and vitamin B_{12}. It is a fair source of vitamin K, thiamine, pantothenic acid and biotin.

Milk is by far the most beneficial source of calcium and phosphorus, and, contains sodium and potassium as well. Other minerals also present in milk are sulphur, selenium and cobalt. However, it is a very poor source of iron. Breast-fed babies are able to obtain sufficient iron from their liver stores up to the age of six months, after which iron-rich foods should be included in their diets (See Iron).

Buffalo milk contains more protein, fat and carbohydrate than cow's, and, consequently, more calories.

Cheese is an outstanding source of vitamin A (if prepared from whole milk), calcium, phosphorus, iodine, zinc and protein. It also contains good amounts of vitamin B_{12} and cobalt. However, most cheeses are high in fat and contain cholesterol.

Many adult Indians tend to give up drinking milk saying that it does not "agree" with them. In reality, few people are truly allergic to milk. The problems that arise from the ingestion of milk may be due either to the protein or the sugar (lactose) in milk.

Though milk has three predominant proteins, namely, casein which forms the curd, and the proteins in whey, lactalbumin and lactoglobulin, the latter (particularly β-lactoglobulin) appears to be responsible for any allergic reaction to milk protein. This condition is called milk sensitivity, and will be manifested in early infancy. Special care is required as the child will fail to thrive if the cause is not detected early on. It is quite possible that the condition will clear between 18 and 24 months of age.

Lactose intolerance, what most people complain of, is really not a true allergy to milk. It is brought about by the inadequate production of lactase, the enzyme that splits lactose into glucose and galactose. Thus, lactose remains undigested and is fermented by intestinal bacteria causing abdominal distension, stomach pain, flatulence and diarrhoea. One of the chief reasons for lowered lactase production is the abrupt removal of milk from the diet. Once children grow up, they graduate to adult beverages like tea and coffee. With less and less lactose to act upon, lactase production is consequently diminished.

It must be emphasized that low levels of milk are still well tolerated. From this point, it is possible to increase the intake gradually. Moreover, since only lactose is the causative factor, many fermented milk foods like curds, buttermilk and cheese, where the lactose has been converted to lactic acid, can be freely consumed without fear of intolerance. This strategy will ensure that the calcium and other benefits of milk are not lost by restricting it.

Other conditions that can reduce the secretion of lactase are gastroenteritis, some antibiotics and anti-inflammatory drugs, and complications of the gut. This is called secondary lactose intolerance. Their effects are reversed once the disorder is rectified, usually in three to six months.

Many researchers have tried to establish a genetic link to the problem of lactose intolerance, as it is more prevalent among Asians, including those from the Arab States, Africans, Europeans from the Mediterranean region and South Americans. However, it may be noticed that these races are also known to have the lowest levels of habitual milk intake.

The meat group is a valuable source of excellent protein and iron. As most of the iron from animal sources is heme iron which is very similar in form to

Did You Know?
Animal foods contain no fibre

iron present in the human body, its value is greater than iron from vegetable sources because it is very easily absorbed and utilized. The other nutrients found in meat are zinc, phosphorus, sulphur, selenium, chromium, cobalt, sodium and potassium, and, the B vitamins of riboflavin, niacin, pyridoxine, vitamin B_{12} and pantothenic acid. The organ meats like liver and kidney in particular are especially abundant in iron, zinc, copper, molybdenum, selenium, chromium, cobalt and sodium, and, the vitamins A and K, besides the vitamins thiamine, riboflavin, niacin, pyridoxine, folic acid, vitamin B_{12}, biotin and pantothenic acid of the B complex group. Chicken contains phosphorus, iron, zinc, sulphur, sodium, potassium, and the B vitamins of niacin, pyridoxine and pantothenic acid. The fat of chicken is softer than most animal fats except fish, hence poultry is recommended over other meats.

Of all foods, pork is the best source of thiamine. Other nutrients found in pork are pyridoxine and pantothenic acid, and, zinc, sulphur, iodine and phosphorus. Lean pork is preferable to fatty pork.

Fish and seafood are very good sources for a number of nutrients. The protein of fish is of a high biological value, and the fat is more beneficial than that found in meats. Fish liver oils are excellent sources of vitamins A, D and E. However, seafood contains relatively high levels of cholesterol, particularly shrimp and sardines (See Cholesterol). Fish and other seafood are also good sources of calcium, phosphorus, sulphur, copper, sodium, potassium, iron (particularly dried fish), zinc, iodine (especially salt-water fish), selenium and cobalt, and, the B vitamins niacin, pyridoxine, vitamin B_{12} and pantothenic acid. Oily fish like mackerel, sardines and tuna contain substances called Omega-3 fatty acids which protect against conditions like arthritis and heart disease. Seafood like clams, shrimp, crab and some fish contain an enzyme, thiaminase, that makes the small amounts of thiamine present in them unavailable. The enzyme is destroyed by cooking.

The protein of egg has the highest biological value of all natural proteins (See Proteins). Besides, eggs are a good source of phosphorus, sodium (egg white), sulphur and iodine, and, the vitamins riboflavin and niacin (as tryptophan). The egg yolk is a storehouse of a number of other nutrients—

> **Did You Know?**
>
> One medium-sized egg (1 1/2 oz/ 45 g) provides 6 g each of protein and fat, and approximately 80 kcal

zinc, iron, cobalt, pyridoxine, folic acid, vitamin B_{12}, biotin, pantothenic acid and vitamin A (carotene and retinol).

The white of egg contains a substance called avidin which complexes with biotin and renders it unavailable for absorption. Cooking destroys avidin.

Though all animal foods contain cholesterol, egg yolk and organ meats like liver have the highest content. All the cholesterol and fat in egg is concentrated in the yolk. One egg yolk contains about 225 to 300 mg of cholesterol. Fish and shellfish, except shrimp, have lower levels of cholesterol. Removing the fat from meat does reduce some cholesterol but not drastically, since the lean and fat in meat contain about the same levels of cholesterol. Skimming milk and removing the skin of poultry before cooking reduces their cholesterol content (See Appendix 5.9—Cholesterol in Foods).

5) Fats and Sugars

Fats and sugars furnish energy in the diet, with fats providing over double the calories of sugars.

Besides, fats from animal sources like butter and ghee also provide vitamin A. In the making of ghee, some vitamin A is lost. Vegetable oils are good sources of vitamin E. Some vitamin K is found in corn and soya bean oils. Palmolein (palm mesocarp oil) has some beta

> **Did You Know?**
> Vegetable oils have negligible amounts of cholesterol

carotene but much of it is lost by the refining, bleaching and deodorizing processes which render the fat edible.

Fats that do not harden on cooling to refrigerated temperatures are particularly beneficial. They contain polyunsaturated fatty acids (PUFA) which are known to reduce the risk of heart disease. Good examples of these oils are safflower, sunflower, corn, soya bean, gingelly, groundnut and mustard.

Other vegetable oils like palmolein essentially contain monounsaturated fatty acids, though almost 50 per cent of palmolein is saturated, comprising largely of palmitic acid. Coconut oil is an exception and is made up of the saturated fatty acid, lauric acid.

Animal fats are high in saturated fats and cholesterol and should be used in moderation. Vegetable oils are converted to saturated fats by a process called hydrogenation. Vanaspati or margarine without water is an example. Together with animal fats, vanaspati is equally responsible for heart disease because it is made up of trans fatty acids. However, it contains virtually no cholesterol.

Fats and edible oils are concentrated sources of energy and provide 45 kcal and 5 g of fat for every 5 g or 1 teaspoon.

Nuts and oilseeds from which oils are extracted may be added to this group. They are also packed with energy and fat, providing about 55 to 60 kcal and 4 to 6 g of fat per 10 g (2 teaspoons). Nuts and oilseeds are an excellent source of vitamin E. They also provide the B vitamins of thiamine, niacin, pyridoxine, folic acid, biotin and pantothenic acid, besides the minerals phosphorus, calcium, magnesium, sulphur, copper, manganese, zinc, molybdenum, chromium and potassium. Groundnut, and, oilseeds like gingelly and mustard, which are used in cooking practically all over the country, either as the nut/oilseed or its oil, are of particular significance because it is now known that compounds with great antioxidant activity are found in them. For centuries in India, gingelly oil was the preferred medium for preserving pickles. Today, it is acknowledged that gingelly oil deteriorates more slowly than other oils when exposed to heat, light and air.

Mustard seeds and the oil extracted from them have the property of preventing cancer.

· Besides refined sugar, jaggery and honey are also included in the sugar group.

One teaspoon of sugar (5 g) gives 20 kcal. Jaggery provides marginally fewer calories at 19 kcal per teaspoon, but its real value is that it contains some calcium, phosphorus, iron and potassium which are lacking in refined sugar. However, more jaggery is needed to bring about the same degree of sweetness as sugar.

Honey is overrated in the claim as an efficient slimming food. Weight for weight, honey contains less calories. For example, 5 g of sugar give 20 kcal and 5 g of honey give 16 kcal. But since these foods are used largely by volume, 1 tablespoon of honey, in fact, provides 67 kcal against 60 kcal from sugar. But, honey provides some phosphorus as well.

Increasingly, a number of artificial sweeteners are available in the market. They may be divided into two categories—those which contain calories and those that do not. Caloric sweeteners include glucose, fructose, sorbitol, xylitol and mannitol. Purely synthetic, low or non-caloric sweeteners are saccharine (sold in India as *Sweetex, Sweet N Low),* aspartame (APM) (currently marketed as *Equal* and *Sugar Free),* cyclamates especially sodium cyclamate and acesulfam-K(ASK—K for potassium).

These sweeteners are important as sugar substitutes specifically in the management of insulin-dependent diabetes mellitus (IDDM) where total calorie intake is restricted. For dieters, this is the worst possible means to watch their weight. It is far better to limit the intake of refined carbohydrates and fats.

Of the caloric sweeteners, glucose and fructose are subunits of sucrose or table sugar. Glucose has about half the sweetness of sugar and fructose is 1.7 times sweeter. Fructose is found naturally in honey and sweet fruits. While fructose may be used in the control of diabetes, its use should be professionally managed, since it metabolizes to glucose during fasting and in poorly controlled diabetes, raising blood sugar levels.

Sorbitol is half as sweet as sucrose. Sorbitol is naturally present in apples, plums and cherries. It yields as many calories per gram as sugar, but raises the blood glucose level more slowly. In the body, sorbitol is first degraded to fructose, causing

> **Did You Know?**
> Sorbitol and sugar yield 4 kcal per g

speculation about its effectiveness in diabetic control. Some people are troubled with abdominal discomfort and diarrhoea after using sorbitol. Therefore, the daily consumption of sorbitol or fructose should not exceed 25 g.

Xylitol, like fructose, is used in the control of insulin-dependent diabetes mellitus and requires the same care in its application. It is as sweet as sucrose, but is not responsible for dental caries because the bacteria in the mouth do not ferment it. Hence xylitol finds favour in the food industry, particularly as a sugar substitute in the manufacture of sweets and chewing gum. Plums and strawberries contain xylitol. Mannitol is 0.7 times as sweet as sucrose.

The non-caloric sweeteners are useful in improving the palatability of foods by providing the desired degree of sweetness even in very small amounts.

Saccharine is the best known, and has a sweetness 300 times that of sucrose. Some users have complained of a bitter aftertaste which has never been conclusively resolved. It breaks down on heating, so it is not used extensively in the food industry.

Aspartame, 200 times sweeter than sucrose, moved in to replace saccharine in the sweet and soft drink industries because it was neither overshadowed with an aftertaste nor was it known to cause cancer in laboratory experiments on animals given high doses. However, it contains the amino acids aspartic acid and phenylalanine. Phenylalanine has to be restricted in persons suffering from a rare, genetically inherited condition called phenylketonuria, so knowledge of foods containing aspartame is essential. Up until 1994, the Prevention of Food Adulteration Act (PFA) of the (Indian) Union Health Ministry had not approved its use in the food industry.

Sodium cyclamate is 30 times as sweet as sucrose and it is not degraded by heat. However, it is believed to be carcinogenic in experimental animals. Acesulfam-K, half as sweet as saccharine, is widely used and has no aftertaste. The existing regulations (up to 1994) of the PFA have yet to include this sweetener in its permitted list.

1.19.2 Spices and Condiments

Outside the Basic 5 grouping are the spices and condiments. Indian food without spice is unimaginable. Most spices, notably, poppy seeds, cumin seeds, asafoetida, coriander seeds, mango powder, fenugreek seeds, black pepper, tamarind and turmeric provide phosphorus, calcium, iron, zinc, magnesium, copper, manganese, chromium, sodium and potassium. Even though their use in cooking is limited, this contribution is not insignificant. However, availability of some of these minerals is in doubt (See Nutrient Inhibitors). Green chillies are among the best sources of vitamin C, providing about 111 mg per 100 g. Green chillies are also rich in riboflavin and copper. Onions contain pyridoxine and potassium, while garlic provides riboflavin and phosphorus.

Besides, spices and condiments have a number of non-nutritional benefits. Root ginger, garlic and onions are known to reduce elevated blood cholesterol and blood sugar levels. Garlic contains the active component allicin which also lowers

> **Did You Know?**
> Fenugreek seeds help to lower blood cholesterol and blood sugar levels

blood pressure and prevents clogging of arteries. Besides, a substance called quercetin present in onions helps reduce the morbidity and mortality from coronary heart disease. Highly coloured onions have more quercetin, but much quercetin is lost when the papery skin is discarded. Fresh and dried ginger are greatly valued as a digestive, and their analgesic properties help to reduce the painful swelling and stiffness associated with arthritis.

Cumin seeds are a good digestive. The Tamil word for digestion is "jeeranum" which is probably what gave the spice its name.

Turmeric has been recently found to reduce the risk of cancer and heart disease in much the same manner as vitamin E (See Vitamin E). Substances called curcumin and turmerin in turmeric are antioxidants, and they obviate the damaging effects of chemicals called free radicals that are produced by cell metabolism and other external pollutants. Besides, turmeric has a blood cholesterol lowering effect and anti-inflammatory properties. Turmeric is also known to promote wound healing.

The word "perungkayam" is Tamil for asafoetida and literally translates "big wound". Legend has it that a bull with a large wound on its neck sought relief by rubbing it against a shrub. Some days later, the wound healed. On investigating the plant, it was found that the resin with curative properties that exuded from it was asafoetida. Asafoetida is added to foods like pulses (dhals), peas and beans to reduce flatulence, and is also useful in the treatment of worms.

1.19.3 Water

Water is as essential as the other nutrients mentioned. A conscious intake of 10 to 12 glasses of water per day is recommended. Other fluids that may be consumed will only add to the benefits of sufficient water in the diet (See Water discussed earlier).

1.19.4 Alcohol

Alcohol provides energy, approximately 7 kcal per g. But, the alcohol content of spirits varies. At the lower end of the scale, mild beer has a value of 3 g of alcohol in 100 ml, rising to 6.5 g in strong beer. Red and white wine contain 10 g of alcohol per 100 ml, though port and sherry approach 16 g for the same volume. Spirits of 70 per cent proof such as brandy, gin and whisky contain the highest at 31 g for every 100 ml. However, they are usually diluted before consumption, and hence the alcoholic content is generally reduced by a third at least.

Except for providing calories, spirits provide minimal nutrition. Beer, if consumed in large quantities, contributes some carbohydrate, calcium, phosphorus, potassium and niacin.

> **Did You Know?**
> Distilled liquors have no nutrients

Drinking in moderation is no hazard. Formerly, it was recommended that men consume 21 units and women, 14 units a week. One unit equals 8 g of alcohol. (One small glass of wine or sherry, one single measure of distilled spirits/aperitifs or 300 ml of mild–medium beer can each be described as one unit.) This view has changed somewhat, and today it is believed that two to six drinks (or units) are ideal for men, and one to three drinks (or units) weekly are considered safe for women. Consumed in these amounts, alcohol might protect against heart disease by increasing the serum levels of high-density lipoprotein (HDL), the "good" lipoprotein (See Cholesterol). Averaging two or more drinks a day significantly increases the risk of cancer of the throat, stomach, urinary tract and brain.

While whisky (warmed with lemon) helps to ward off coughs and colds among non-smokers, by far the most beneficial alcoholic beverage is wine, especially red wine. It contains a substance found in red grapes called quercetin which by itself has little protective value, but when activated by a fermentative process, either by bacteria in the gut or by yeast in wine-making, helps to combat heart attacks and strokes. If red wine is used regularly, quercetin could also help in the fight against cancer. Red wine also contains an antioxidant called procyanidin which prevents a build-up of fatty deposits in arterial walls. Another non-alcoholic compound in wine is resveratrol which is a natural chemical that destroys fungi in grapes. It controls fat and cholesterol levels in the blood. Sunlight destroys this chemical, so wine should be stored in tinted bottles away from light.

Chronic alcoholism, on the other hand, will lead to a number of serious health problems and nutritional deficiencies (See effects under individual vitamins, minerals and electrolytes). A woman trying to get pregnant, and one who is already, should avoid alcohol altogether, especially during the crucial first 12 weeks of the pregnancy.

1.19.5 Food Intake

Though this book does not specify the amounts of foods from each group that should make up the daily diet, it is enough to say that some foods from every group must be selected every day. Needless to say, the bulk of the Indian diet is drawn from the first group of the Basic 5—cereal grains and their products.

One easy means of balancing a meal is to make sure that it is as naturally colourful as possible. The white of rice and curds if combined with the green of spinach and the orange of carrots and the yellow of pulses (dhals) can only be nutritionally beneficial. Moreover, a highly colourful meal is bound to increase the appetite and ensure a higher intake.

Every non-dieting adult should aspire to consume, on an average, a 2,000 kcal diet every day (See Calories for individual energy requirements). Of this, 50 to 60 per cent of the calories should come from carbohydrates, 10 to 15 per cent from protein, and 20 to 30 per cent from fat. In real terms, this would be 250 to 300 g carbohydrate, 50 to 75 g protein, and 44 to 67 g fat (including invisible fat), even though the recommended daily allowances for these nutrients are less than the aforementioned amounts. Most importantly, the fat component should comprise ten per cent saturated fats, and, 90 per cent monounsaturated fatty acids and polyunsaturated fatty acids (See Fats).

1.20 PROCESSED FOODS

In India, though an expanding processed food industry puts on shop shelves a vast array of products, the cost in relation to most incomes is exorbitant. Much of the food that appears on the table does not come from a packet or can, so without knowing it, we are probably eating right, and do not have to worry about getting all the nutrients we need.

However, it must be stressed that packaged foods are not bad or unhealthy. Much of the nutrients are retained in commercial food processing. The losses of vitamin C and the B vitamins are probably the greatest. Many contain added vitamins and minerals. Though beneficial, the balance of nutrients will not be the same as in natural foods. Prolonged storage of preserved foods leads to further losses. This can be slowed down by storing them away from direct sunlight and in a cool place.

Various means are employed to increase shelf-life. Pasteurization of milk is one means of improving the keeping quality of milk which also destroys disease-producing organisms. Milk that is treated by the ultra-high temperature (UHT) process will remain unspoiled for many months without refrigeration if the carton is not opened. In India, it is usually given a shelf-life of about three months, given the tropical climate.

Food additives are chemicals added to preserved foods to prevent spoilage. Contrary to popular belief, they are not harmful, since manufacturers are careful to keep within the limits specified by regulation. Artificial colours and flavours, and, sugar and salt, are also additives.

Unfortunately in India, home preservation takes the form of pickles which are, in most cases, nothing more than high-salt, high-fat concoctions. Fruit murrabas like petta (from pumpkin or gourds) are examples of preservation with sugar in Indian cookery.

Section 2

How to Use This Book

All Indians must know that they eat right, probably without knowing it. It is truly amazing how foods are combined without forethought to provide the best utilization of nutrients. Except perhaps for our fondness for fried foods (even sweets are fried), Indian cuisine is probably one of the most healthful in the world. Otherwise, Indians who are largely vegetarian would be poorly nourished, given that nutrients like proteins and iron are better utilized in the human body if they come from animal foods. But foods from vegetable sources are combined so judiciously that each makes up for the deficiencies of the other. For instance, the cereal-pulse combinations of iddli, khichidi or just plain rice and dhal offset the discrepancies of essential amino acids (the building blocks of protein) present in each group individually (See Proteins).

Though this book deals with the healthy aspects of food, it does not advocate a drastic switch to a whole new way of cooking. Only those foods that are commonly found in any Indian kitchen have been employed in the recipes. The exotic has been kept out to encourage more people to cook this way.

However, given that the Indian intake of fat is rather high, particularly among the middle and affluent classes, a conscious effort has been made to keep fat within acceptable limits. This means that all the recipes in the book are fat controlled. As a first step, all recipes requiring deep-frying have been deliberately omitted.

To support this action, consider the following reasons:

(1) Despite the many assurances from manufacturers, no oil is better than the rest when it comes to frying. The consistency of the food (whether dry or wet) is a decisive factor in determining the amount of fat absorbed. Wet batters used in the making of vadais and bhajjis absorb greater quantities of fat than do dry foods. Subsequent drainage and blotting with paper will remove only a fraction of the fat absorbed. Even more untrue is the notion that the food that weighs less after frying contains less fat. What is true, though, is that water has evaporated from the food making it lighter.

(2) The addition of baking powder to improve the appearance of fried foods further increases fat absorption.

(3)   Heating fats is a tricky business. If the fat is not hot enough, too much of it is absorbed by the food. On the other hand, when a fat is heated to its smoking temperature, chemical changes begin to take place which have many health risks. Prolonged heating at high temperatures (at the smoking point or higher) over long periods of time leads to its degradation. A substance called acrolein is formed which can cause irritation of the gastrointestinal lining. Fat that has decomposed to acrolein is easily recognized as it will appear dark and viscous and is almost always rancid too. Usually, this does not take place in normal home cooking. But when the same fat is recycled many times for deep-frying, then the fat begins to decompose. By rule of thumb, do not hold fats at their smoking temperatures for more than 15 minutes at a time. This will ensure that the fat is hot enough to allow the least absorption, and is also safe to consume. Also, avoid repeated use of the same oil or fat.

While deep-frying has been excluded from the book, Indian recipes requiring shallow-frying have been selected, because oil from shallow-frying is rarely left over.

Still on the subject of reducing fat intake, all the milk used in the recipes is skimmed. People living in cities and towns tend to buy milk from the Milk Board, which is usually skimmed or toned (the fat content is maintained between 3 and 8 per cent). Most others get their milk from private vendors where whole milk is the norm. To reduce the fat content of milk once it is purchased, after boiling, cool the milk and place it in the refrigerator. Skim off the cream that gathers on the surface. Repeated a couple of times effectively reduces the fat in milk.

Though reduced fat intake has been advocated, it will come as a surprise that coconut is used in many of the recipes. Especially in combination with fish, coconut which contains saturated fat, has defied scientific explanation as to why it does not increase the risk of heart disease. One explanation is that fish and seafood have a protective effect because of the high levels of Omega-3 fatty acids found in them. Most of the recipes employing coconut will, therefore, appear in this combination.

Liberty has also been taken with the use of groundnut, a concentrated source of fat, because of its many other benefits.

Further attempts to reduce fat involve cookware and cooking practice. Always use heavy-bottomed iron or aluminium pans for cooking. Woks or kadais are a good example. They distribute heat evenly and less oil is required to prevent food from sticking to the pan.

Did You Know?
All nuts and oilseeds comprise natural, invisible fat that equals half their weight

Set aside pans for exclusive use in the kitchen. This might be a little expensive initially, but in time, when the cooking oil bills run low, this expense will be more than compensated for. At least three such pans should be available in any kitchen. A tawa for shallow-frying foods like dosai, another tawa for chappatis and parathas, and a frying pan for eggs and the like. They should not be washed after every use, merely wiped, covered properly (to prevent the fat from going rancid and to keep out insects) and stored. Before use, they should be wiped again. Ultimately, only a few drops of oil will be required to cook the same type of food.

However, these pans will have to be washed from time to time, and a pattern should be established. After a week or ten days of continuous use, wash them in hot, soapy water and rinse clean. Once dry, they will have to be seasoned or "proved". This is done by placing them over the fire and allowing them to heat through, which evaporates all the water that may be present, especially in the pores of the metal. Then a few drops of oil are smeared over the surface and allowed to come to the temperature when the oil begins to smoke. At this point, the pans may be removed from the fire, cooled and stored. They are now ready for use again.

With the advent of non-stick cookware, the face of fat-filled cooking has changed considerably. Very little fat is needed to cook in these pans. However, care should be taken to ensure that the surface is not damaged nor scratched as it could be potentially harmful. *Only wooden spoons and ladles should be used to stir food in non-stick vessels to protect their coating. Also, they cannot be cleaned by harsh scouring with powders, steel wool or brushes.*

With cooking practice, a number of seemingly insignificant ways can reduce fat intake. First, always heat the pan *before* adding oil. A hot pan requires less oil to achieve the same desired effect. Second, never pour oil into a pan. Measure it before you start cooking. This may appear tedious, but there is an easy way out. Keep a teaspoon in the oil crucible. Every time you are tempted to pour out the oil, the spoon will get in the way and you will be forced to use it. Moreover, it gives a good measure of the amount of fat being used. Avoid the use of solid fats. Solid fats are not only unhealthy, but their intake can be ascertained only by weighing them. And, this is not practical in daily cooking routines.

Third, always keep oil in the kitchen in small containers. The urge to pour oil results from storing it in large cans or jars. Since the amount that is poured out from the large container is less than what is left behind, the eye is unable to determine when the safe limit for fat intake has been exceeded.

This book has a number of other features that promote eating healthily.

Among them:

(i)   The preferred method of cooking is pressure-cooking, or autoclaving as it is known in scientific language. Most nutrients are saved if cooking time is reduced. Pressure-cooking also destroys most bacteria and their spores especially *Clostridium* which survive ordinary cooking temperatures, and the cysts and eggs of worms (See Food-borne Illness and Parasitic Infestations). Further, pressure-cooking allows foods that require the same cooking time to be cooked together. Rice, dhal and vegetables can all be cooked at one go. The saving on fuel is also enormous as food is cooked in one-third the time.

Pressure-cooked vegetables will, however, suffer some discoloration as the organic acids present in them cannot escape, effectively causing the pigment chlorophyll in particular to lose its bright green colour.

Mutton, beef, pork and chicken available in Western countries are frequently softer in texture than what is sold in India. Pressure-cooking times indicated in the book will have to be reduced by a *third* in those recipes employing them.

Unfortunately, most people use the pressure-cooker wrongly. They start cooking with the weight on the lid. This is incorrect, as the precise pressure-cooking temperature of 121.5 degrees Celsius/250.7 degrees Fahrenheit (at 15 pounds pressure) is never reached. To arrive at this temperature, it is important that all the air in the cooker is replaced by steam. This can only be done if the correct method is followed.

First, fit the gasket in the groove of the lid, pour sufficient water in the body of the cooker, and put it on the fire. Allow a steady jet of steam to flow through the vent pipe, then place the weight over the vent. To start counting cooking time, wait for a continuous hiss which indicates that the right temperature and pressure have been reached within the cooker. Then lower the flame to "simmer" or "low" until the end of cooking time.

Never force the weight off the lid. If there is steam within the cooker, it indicates that the pressure has not dissipated fully. Allow to cool naturally or under a running tap or in a bowl of cold (not iced) water. Always remove the weight before taking off the lid.

The gasket is also an important feature of the pressure-cooker. It should seal the cooker completely. This can be done by pulling it gently to stretch like a rubber band before fitting it in the lid. Any leakage of steam will increase cooking time because of lowered pressure within the cooker. If the leakage persists, then the gasket needs to be replaced. The life of the gasket can be extended if a little care is taken. After every use, remove it from the lid, wash and hang it up to dry until it is required again.

(ii) All the recipes in this book were prepared on an ordinary gas range. Even the tandoor mentioned is one that fits conveniently over an open gas flame. (The tandoori recipes may be prepared over an open spit too.) All the vessels too are those that may be found in any kitchen anywhere in the world. However, those familiar with Indian cooking might notice that the cooking times appear a little in excess. This is because the cooking was done at an elevation of approximately 1,800 metres (6,000 feet) above sea level. In the plains, these very same recipes will be ready in a much shorter time.

(iii)   A number of foods are used in Indian cooking as a garnish (coriander leaves, tomatoes and green chillies, for example) or for tempering, the practice of heating small amounts of mustard seeds, cumin seeds, black gram dhal, curry leaves, chillies and the like in a little oil before they are added to the dish. Very often they are carefully picked out, and their nutritional benefit denied us. In this book, these ingredients have been finely chopped, puréed or ground, so that their flavours are nicely blended and the bonus of extra nutrients is also retained. The use of the mixer/liquidizer ensures that this is swiftly and efficiently done. Further, purées have not been strained before adding them to curries. The "waste" is, in fact, valuable fibre.

(iv)   Though the recipes indicate the entire process, ways to save time are also suggested. It is convenient to roast, powder and store spices and condiments, separately or in combination, in advance. No doubt, freshly ground ingredients have a flavour all of their own, but when one is rushed, powdered condiments are as good an alternative as any.

Similarly, fresh root ginger and garlic may be ground to a paste with a little vinegar and stored in the refrigerator. Keep them tightly covered or all the other foods will absorb their strong flavours. If ginger-garlic paste is required, take an equal quantity of each *by weight* and grind them together. Do not wash them in water. Use only vinegar even to clean them.

(v)   All the ingredients used in the recipes have been weighed, with values given in the metric and imperial systems. However, since Indians cook largely by volume or by "eye measure", wherever possible, every attempt has been made to accommodate this feature as well. Moreover, it is hoped that this dual presentation will make everyone aware of the nutritive contributions of Indian foods for a given weight, at least for the major nutrients like proteins, carbohydrates and fats, besides, kilocalories. These values can be easily cross-referenced with the text under the heading Food Selection—Sources of Nutrients, and in particular, Basic 5.

(vi)   In keeping with the health aspect of this book, for every recipe, the nutritive contribution per serving has been given, rounded off to the nearest whole number. These values are based on the metric weights of measure. They may be checked against the Recommended Dietary Allowances (RDA) for Indians, proposed by the Indian Council of Medical Research, given in the text for all the major nutrients. Only the values for adults are given, not adolescents and children. The increased requirements during pregnancy and lactation in women are also shown. Though the ingredient list will indicate the amounts of foods to be purchased or prepared, the calculations are based on the actual food consumed. Adjustments have been made for wastage. For example, the difference between unshelled and shelled peas. However, calculations have not been given for accompaniments.

(vii)   A word about servings. In dietary parlance, a serving indicates a measure of food that provides the *same number of calories,* and when taken from the same food group, similar nutrients (See Basic 5). However, servings in this book refer to yield, i.e., the number of people who may partake of the dish once it is prepared. The calculations are, therefore, based on total yield divided by the number of servings to get the nutrients per serving.

(viii)   Serving suggestions and tips to conserve nutrients have been given, wherever relevant.

(ix)   The nutritional benefits of each recipe have been discussed. Detailed explanations and elaborations on the subject can be found in the section Nutrients and Nutrition.

(x)   Although the recipes may be considered regionally representative, some liberty has been taken in the choice of ingredients. This action has been deliberate, to either avail of a substitute that is more readily available, or to improve the nutritive value by modifying the original recipe. Hence, sambhar podi has found its way into dhansak, instead of the traditional dhansak masala powder. An example of the latter is rasam, a version prepared with onions in this book beacuse it is healthier, but which is normally never the case.

NB: Either the Prestige or Hawkins pressure-cooker was used in preparing the recipes.

Section 3

Recipes

Recipe Index

3.2 Rice
Breads

3.1 Weights and Measures

The average Indian rarely uses the balance or a measure of volume standard for cooking unlike in the West. While most Indians cook by visually gauging the right measure, this book attempts to satisfy both systems. This is not to suggest that the recipes have been overly compromised. In view of the fact that nutritive values are given for every recipe, each ingredient has been meticulously weighed or measured.

To avoid constant referring back to this page, the measures for every recipe are given both by weight in the metric and imperial systems, and by volume.

The pattern followed is given below:

	Volume Measures	
	Metric	*Imperial*
1 teaspoon (tsp)	5 ml	1/6 fl oz
1 tablespoon (tbsp)	15 ml	1/2 fl oz
2 tablespoons	30 ml	1 fl oz
1/2 standard cup	125 ml	4 fl oz
1 standard cup	250 ml	8 fl oz (16 tbsp)
	300 ml	1/2 pint
	600 ml	1 pint

All measurements by volume are level

Weight Measures	
Metric	*Imperial*
30 g	1 oz
100 g	3 oz
250 g	8 oz
500 g	17 oz (1.1 lb)
750 g	25 oz (1 1/2 lb)
1 kg	35 oz (2.2 lb or 2 1/5 lb)

Note

For convenience, the figures of the imperial system have been rounded off to the nearest whole number. However, the recipes will show fractions, necessary for accuracy in computing nutritive values.

For greatest ease in cooking, use volume measures. If, however, either the metric or imperial system is preferred, use either one. Do not interchange while cooking.

3.2.1 Mutton Biriyani (Spicy Meat and Rice Mix)

Preparation Time : 25 min
Soaking Time   : 30 min
Cooking Time   : 35 min

Serves 8

Ingredients

1 kg/2.2 lb uncooked raw rice, cleaned and washed
1/2 tsp red chilli powder
1 tsp turmeric powder
Salt to taste
1 kg/2.2 lb mutton, cleaned, washed and cubed
2 tbsp/30 ml/1 fl oz refined oil
1 tbsp/15 g/ 1/2 oz ghee
6 medium/500 g/1.1 lb Bombay onions, thinly sliced
8 medium/500 g/1.1 lb ripe tomatoes, quartered
About 24/120 g/4 oz sambhar onions, ground
6 whole pods/60 g/2 oz garlic, ground
4" or 10 cm piece/30 g/1 oz fresh ginger, ground
1 1/2 bundles/45 g/1 1/2 oz mint leaves, ground
2 1/2 bundles/75 g/2 1/2 oz coriander leaves, ground
6 medium/15 g/ 1/2 oz green chillies, ground
2 tbsp/10 g/ 1/3 oz poppy seeds, ground with a little water
6 cups/1 1/2 litres/2 1/2 pints soup stock/hot water
1 1/2 cups/375 ml/12 1/2 fl oz curds (from skimmed milk)
*1 tbsp/15 g/ 1/2 oz mixed spices, roasted without oil and powdered
6 bay leaves

(1) Soak the rice in sufficient water to cover for 30 minutes. Place in a colander lined with cloth to drain.

(2) Place the red chilli powder, turmeric powder, salt and mutton in a pressure-cooker container. Mix well. Do not add extra water to the meat. Pour sufficient water in the body of the pressure-cooker. Lower the container into the pressure-cooker. Close the cooker. Bring to maximum pressure over high heat, then lower the flame and pressure-cook for 10 minutes. Remove from the fire and allow to cool naturally.

(3) In the body of a pressure-cooker of minimum 10-litre capacity, heat the oil and ghee together. When the fat begins to smoke, add the sliced onions and

soften until pink. Add the tomatoes and cook until mushy.

(4) Add the ground ingredients one by one, first the onions, garlic and ginger, followed by the mint and coriander leaves, green chillies and poppy seeds.

(5) Cook the mixture for about 5 minutes, then add the drained rice and stir well.

(6) Measure the soup stock that has been drawn out of the cooked meat and set aside. Make up the balance of 6 cups with hot water.

(7) When the rice begins to stick, add the cooked meat, curds, soup stock and hot water. Stir continuously.

(8) Check the seasoning. Add the powdered spices and bay leaves.

(9) Mix well and close the cooker immediately. Allow to come to maximum pressure, then lower the heat and pressure-cook for 5 minutes. Next place a heated tawa under the pressure-cooker, and cook for another 5 minutes with the heat turned down low.

(10) Turn off the fire and allow the pressure inside the cooker to dissipate. Open and stir the contents quickly with a long-handled fork.

(11) Serve with tamatar piyaz ka raita or devil's chutney.

*Suggested Spice Mix	
30 black peppercorns	1" or 2.5 cm stick cinnamon
8 small, green cardamoms, seeds only	1/4 tsp cumin seeds
	6 cloves

Per Serving			
Kilocalories	787	Vitamin C	42 mg
Protein	33 g	Vitamin A (as carotene)	4,403 mcg
Fat	22 g	Vitamin A (as retinol)	21 mcg
Carbohydrate	115 g	Fibre	2 g
Calcium	351 mg	Cholesterol	116 mg
Phosphorus	503 mg		
Iron	6 mg	1,000 mcg = 1 mg	

Cooking Notes

Using basmati or parboiled rice for this recipe needs extra care. To pressure-cook basmati rice, the fire should be turned off as soon as maximum pressure is reached. Parboiled rice takes about 10 minutes longer than the time indicated. These can be used if the biriyani is prepared traditionally by heaping live coals on the lid of the vessel (dum) or in a slow oven.

Ghee is used here only as a flavouring. It may be substituted with refined oil.

Use 1 bundle fennel leaves, if available, and reduce 1/2 bundle each of mint and coriander leaves.

Chicken Biriyani is prepared in the same way, except that in Step 2, the cleaned and jointed chicken is pressure-cooked for 2 minutes after maximum pressure is reached.

Biriyani is associated with the Muslims of the country. While an aura of mystery surrounds the special flavours they are able to create, simpler versions like the recipe given here, have brought the biriyani into virtually every home.

Health Hint

Hot biriyani is believed to dispel some of the misery that accompanies a common cold.

3.2.2 Bhugal Chawal (Sindhi Onion Pulao)

Preparation Time	:	30 min
Soaking Time	:	30 min
Cooking Time	:	45 min

Serves 4

Ingredients

2 cups/480 g/1 lb uncooked raw rice, cleaned and washed
About 24/120 g/4 oz sambhar onions, peeled
2 medium/5 g/ 1/6 oz green chillies
2 whole pods/20 g/ 2/3 oz garlic
1 tsp cumin seeds
5 cloves
5 small, green cardamoms, seeds only
2" or 5 cm stick cinnamon
1 tbsp/5 g/ 1/6 oz poppy seeds
1 handful/30 g/1 oz shelled groundnuts
2 tbsp/30 ml/1 fl oz refined oil
4 large/480 g/1 lb Bombay onions, thinly sliced
3 1/2 cups/900 ml/1 1/2 pints hot water
1 tbsp/15 g/ 1/2 oz powdered jaggery
Salt to taste
1/2 bundle/15 g/ 1/2 oz coriander leaves, finely chopped

(1) *Soak the rice in sufficient water to cover for 30 minutes. Place in a colander lined with cloth to drain.*

(2)　Grind the sambhar onions, green chillies and garlic together to a coarse paste.

(3)　Roast the cumin seeds, cloves, cardamom seeds, cinnamon and poppy seeds together, without oil, until the poppy seeds begin to change colour. Powder.

(4)　Roast the groundnuts, without oil, until they begin to crackle. Remove the papery skin and set aside.

(5)　In the body of a pressure-cooker of minimum 7 1/2-litre capacity, heat the oil until it begins to smoke. Add the sliced onions and fry until quite brown. Then add the ground paste and fry for 1 minute.

(6)　Add the rice and keep stirring until it begins to stick. Pour in the hot water. Add the jaggery, salt and powdered spices.

(7)　Close the cooker immediately. Bring to maximum pressure over high heat, then lower the flame and pressure-cook for 5 minutes. Next place a heated tawa under the pressure-cooker and cook for a further 5 minutes over low heat.

(8)　Remove from the fire and allow the pressure inside the cooker to dissipate. Open and stir quickly with a fork.

(9)　Serve garnished with the chopped coriander leaves and roasted groundnuts.

Per Serving			
Kilocalories	631	Iron	3 mg
Protein	13 g	Vitamin C	21 mg
Fat	12 g	Vitamin A (as carotene)	597 mcg
Carbohydrate	119 g	Fibre	2 g
Calcium	118 mg		
Phosphorus	324 mg	1,000 mcg = 1 mg	

Health Wise

Use soup stock from vegetables, meat, fish or chicken, or even whey, to cook the rice instead of hot water. It will add flavour and nudge the vitamin and mineral tally upwards.

Onions and garlic are Nature's antibiotics. Onions reduce blood sugar levels and are, therefore, of special importance for diabetics. Rheumatism and gout often call for greater consumption of onions as do upper respiratory tract infections. Raw onions in particular raise the levels of "good" cholesterol or HDL, prevent heart attacks and reduce blood pressure. They also remove dietary fat from the blood.

Garlic lowers blood cholesterol levels, thereby preventing the accumulation of fatty deposits or plaques (of which a major component is cholesterol) in the walls of arteries that could lead to atherosclerosis or narrowing of the arteries.

This, in turn, helps to reduce high blood pressure or hypertension as the arteries are clear and blood flows freely through them, relieving any stress on the heart. Moreover, garlic acts as a blood thinner, reducing the stickiness of blood which discourages clot formation. For these reasons, garlic is recommended for those prone to heart attacks and strokes.

Garlic also helps to inhibit the growth of cancer cells. Besides, people with respiratory ailments like asthma and bronchitis are particularly helped by a high intake of garlic. Apparently, garlic thins mucus and reduces its production, thereby relieving congestion.

Notes of Interest

Browning onions can be hurried up a bit if they are sliced, crushed to separate the layers and then placed in the sun or in a warm place. The drier the onions, the sooner they will brown. For those who live in the countryside, here is a little tip. Snakes have a particular loathing for garlic. Burn the papery skin of garlic and sprinkle the ashes near all the doors of the house. Snakes will not attempt to gain entry.

3.2.3 Puliodarai (Tamarind Rice)

Preparation Time	:	25 min
Soaking Time	:	10 min
Cooking Time	:	50 min

Serves 6

Ingredients

3 cups/720 g/1 1/2 lb uncooked raw rice, cleaned and washed
5 cups/1 1/4 litres/2 pints hot water
1 handful/30 g/1 oz shelled groundnuts
An orange-sized ball/60 g/2 oz tamarind
1 1/2 cups/375 ml/12 1/2 fl oz hot water
6 tbsp/90 g/3 oz powdered jaggery
1/2 cup/125 ml/4 fl oz hot water
1 1/2 tsp/7.5 g/ 1/4 oz fenugreek seeds
1 tsp cumin seeds
4 tbsp/60 g/2 oz bengal gram dhal
2 tbsp/30 ml/1 fl oz oil (preferably gingelly)
1 tsp mustard seeds

6 whole dried red chillies
1 tbsp/15 g/ 1/2 oz black gram dhal (without husk)
1" or 2.5 cm piece/8 g/ 1/4 oz fresh ginger, finely chopped
A large sprig of curry leaves, finely chopped
1/2 tsp turmeric powder
1/4 tsp red chilli powder
1/4 tsp asafoetida powder
Salt to taste

(1) Soak the rice in sufficient water to cover for 10 minutes. Place in a colander lined with cloth to drain.

(2) Place the rice and 5 cups hot water in the body of a pressure-cooker. Close the cooker. Bring to maximum pressure over high heat, then lower the flame and pressure-cook for 5 minutes. Remove from the fire. When the pressure inside the cooker dissipates, open and fluff up the rice with a fork. Set aside to cool.

(3) Roast the groundnuts, without oil, until they begin to crackle. Remove the papery skin and set aside.

(4) Soak the tamarind in 1/2 cup hot water for 10 minutes. Squeeze to extract pulp. Repeat twice more, adding 1/2 cup hot water each time to the same tamarind.

(5) Dissolve the jaggery in another 1/2 cup hot water over a moderate flame. Strain and set aside.

(6) Roast the fenugreek seeds and cumin seeds together, without oil, until the cumin seeds begin to change colour. Powder.

(7) Roast the bengal gram dhal, without oil, until beginning to turn red. Powder coarsely.

(8) Mix the tamarind extract, jaggery syrup, and, powdered fenugreek seeds, cumin seeds and bengal gram dhal together. Set aside.

(9) Heat a wide pan, then add the oil. Add the mustard seeds and whole dried red chillies torn in two. When the mustard seeds begin to splutter, add the black gram dhal and fry until golden. Add the chopped ginger, curry leaves, and, turmeric, red chilli and asafoetida powders. Stir for 1 minute, then add the tamarind-jaggery mixture. Add salt. Cook until the sauce thickens and the oil rises to the surface.

(10) Keep the tamarind sauce simmering over a low flame, and add the cooked rice, a little at a time. Stir until each grain of rice is well coated. Mix thoroughly after all the rice has been added. Add more salt if necessary.

(11) Garnish with the roasted groundnuts and serve with mint chutney, coriander chutney or fried (devilled) meat.

Per Serving			
Kilocalories	625	Iron	4 mg
Protein	13 g	Vitamin C	0.5 mg
Fat	8 g	Vitamin A (as carotene)	197 mcg
Carbohydrate	125 g	Fibre	1 g
Calcium	64 mg		
Phosphorus	276 mg	1,000 mcg = 1 mg,	

Helpful Hints

Tamarind rice may be made with parboiled rice as well. Allow 2 1/2 cups hot water per cup of rice. Parboiled rice has the additional benefit of greater yield and more B vitamins.

Leftover plain, white rice (cooked) may be easily and conveniently transformed into tamarind rice.

Puliodarai is prepared mainly in South Indian Brahmin homes. Since it can be served without a runny gravy like dhal curry, it is popular in everyday cooking as well as for picnic fare. Puliodarai does not spoil easily, so it can be taken on long trips of up to a day without refrigeration.

Sour Struck

Many are stuck with the notion that if a food is sour in its natural state, it automatically contains loads of vitamin C. Nothing could be further from the truth. Tamarind is a good example of this misconception, as it provides only 3 mg of vitamin C per 100 g of pulp. Others with low vitamin C content and a good deal of sourness are raw mango, woodapple, curds, apple, cherry, grape, loquat, peach, pear and plum, and tree tomato.

3.2.4 Plain Fried Rice

Preparation Time	:	20 min
Soaking Time	:	30 min
Cooking Time	:	35 min

Serves 4

Ingredients

2 cups/480 g/1 lb uncooked raw rice, cleaned and washed
30 black peppercorns

1 tsp cumin seeds
5 cloves
5 small, green cardamoms, seeds only
2" or 5 cm stick cinnamon
1 tbsp/15 ml/ 1/2 fl oz refined oil
2 medium/180 g/6 oz Bombay onions, thinly sliced
3 1/2 cups/900 ml/1 1/2 pints hot water
1 tbsp/15 g/ 1/2 oz powdered jaggery
Salt to taste

(1) *Soak the rice in sufficient water to cover for 30 minutes. Place in a colander lined with cloth to drain.*

(2) *Roast the peppercorns, cumin seeds, cloves, cardamom seeds and cinnamon together, without oil, until a nice aroma arises. Powder.*

(3) *In the body of a pressure-cooker of minimum 7 1/2-litre capacity, heat the oil until it begins to smoke. Add the onions and fry until quite brown. Remove 2 tbsp of the fried onions and reserve for garnishing.*

(4) *Add the rice and fry until it begins to stick. Pour in the hot water. Add the jaggery, salt and powdered spices. Cover immediately.*

(5) *Bring to maximum pressure over high heat, then lower the flame and pressure-cook for 5 minutes. Next place a heated tawa under the pressure-cooker, and cook for a further 5 minutes over low heat. Remove from the fire.*

(6) *Allow the pressure inside the cooker to dissipate, then open and fluff up the rice with a fork. Serve garnished with the browned onions kept in reserve.*

Plain fried rice can be easily converted to Vegetable Fried Rice by adding 1 cup diced carrots, peas and sprigs of cauliflower to the rice before pressure-cooking. Increase the amount of hot water by another 1/2 cup (125 ml/4 fl oz).

Per Serving			
Kilocalories	485	Iron	1 mg
Protein	9 g	Vitamin C	5 mg
Fat	4 g	Vitamin A	Nil
Carbohydrate	102 g	Fibre	0.5 g
Calcium	36 mg		
Phosphorus	216 mg	1,000 mcg = 1 mg	

Top Tip

To make this dish more attractive (and nutritious), garnish with nuts and raisins. These will have to be fried in the hot oil and removed before the onions are added. Just before serving, sprinkle them over the rice with the reserved, browned onions.

Health Hint

Onions prevent heart disease by thinning blood, which lowers the likelihood of the formation of clots. Even onions browned crisp retain the factor that inhibits platelet aggregation.

3.2.5 Peas Pulao

Preparation Time	:	25 min
Soaking Time	:	30 min
Cooking Time	:	20 min

Serves 4

Ingredients

2 cups/480 g/1 lb uncooked raw rice, cleaned and washed
2 whole pods/20 g/ 2/3 oz garlic
2" or 5 cm piece/15 g/ 1/2 oz fresh ginger
2 medium/5 g/ 1/6 oz green chillies, deseeded
1" or 2.5 cm stick cinnamon
5 cloves
3 1/2 cups/900 ml/1 1/2 pints hot water
1 tbsp/15 ml/ 1/2 fl oz refined oil
Salt to taste
1 tbsp/15 ml/ 1/2 fl oz refined oil
2 medium/180 g/6 oz Bombay onions, thinly sliced
1/2 cup/125 ml/4 fl oz hot water
3/4 cup or 4 handfuls/120 g/4 oz shelled peas (from 250 g/8 oz unshelled peas)

(1) Soak the rice in sufficient water to cover for 30 minutes. Place in a colander lined with cloth to drain.

(2) Grind the garlic, ginger and green chillies together to a paste.

(3) Powder the cinnamon and cloves together. Set aside.

(4) Place the rice, 3 1/2 cups hot water, 1 tbsp refined oil and 1 tsp salt in the body of a pressure-cooker of minimum 7 1/2-litre capacity. Close the cooker. Bring to maximum pressure over high heat, then lower the flame and pressure-cook for 5 minutes. Remove from the fire. When the pressure inside the cooker dissipates, open and fluff up the rice with a fork. Allow to cool.

(5) In the meantime, heat a pan, then add the remaining 1 tbsp refined oil. Add the onions and fry until soft. Stir in the ground paste and powdered spices. Fry

for a minute or two. Pour in 1/2 cup hot water. Add the peas and a little salt. Simmer for 5 minutes.

(6) When all the water is absorbed and the oil begins to separate out, add the cooked rice and stir with a fork. Mix well. Serve hot with mutton kheema or chicken curry.

Per Serving			
Kilocalories	542	Iron	2 mg
Protein	11 g	Vitamin C	10 mg
Fat	8 g	Vitamin A (as carotene)	57 mcg
Carbohydrate	106 g	Fibre	2 g
Calcium	42 mg		
Phosphorus	275 mg	1,000 mcg = 1 mg	

Pea Talk

Peas are an excellent source of soluble fibre. This category of fibre does not exhibit any fibrous characteristics, but is responsible for two very important functions—keeping blood cholesterol and blood glucose levels within acceptable limits. Peas, especially dried, also contain the fat soluble vitamin E and the water soluble B vitamins of thiamine, pyridoxine, folic acid, pantothenic acid and biotin. Of the minerals, peas supply iron, zinc, magnesium, sulphur, manganese, copper, molybdenum and selenium, besides the electrolytes sodium and potassium.

3.2.6 Plain Boiled Rice (Drainage Method)

Preparation Time	:	6 min
Soaking Time	:	10 min
Cooking Time	:	45 min
Drainage Time	:	10 min

Serves 8

Ingredients

3 1/2 cups/850 g/1 3/4 lb uncooked parboiled rice, cleaned and washed
26 cups/6 1/2 litres/10.83 pints water

(1) Soak the rice in sufficient water to cover for 10 minutes. Drain.

(2) In the meantime, pour the water into a deep and wide pan, and place it on

the fire. Bring to the boil.

(3) *Add the rice to the boiling water. Regulate the heat to get a steady, rolling boil. The rice is cooked when a single grain pressed between thumb and forefinger squashes completely.*

(4) *Remove and pour into a colander. Allow to drain for at least 10 minutes before serving.*

(5) *Collect the rice water in a vessel—about 2 litres (3 1/3 pints). Makes excellent Rice Water Soup.*

Per Serving			
Kilocalories	368	Fibre	Trace
Protein	7 g	B Vitamins	
Fat	Less than 0.5 g	Vitamin B_1	Trace
Carbohydrate	84 g	Vitamin B_2	Trace
Calcium	10 mg	Vitamin B_3	4 mg
Phosphorus	152 mg	Vitamin B_6	Trace
Iron	1 mg	Folic Acid	12 mcg
Vitamin C	Nil		
Vitamin A	Nil	1,000 mcg = 1 mg	

Plain Talk

Cooking rice by the drainage method leads to a loss of B vitamins, minerals and electrolytes, some of which may be retained if parboiled rice is used. The process of parboiling ensures that the nutrients are trapped in the grain and are not lost when the rice water is discarded. Raw rice does not have this benefit. Therefore, this method of cooking rice is not recommended.

However, if it must be done, it is possible to recover some of the nutrients by utilizing the rice water to make Rice Water Soup.

Rice Water Soup
Heat 1 tsp refined oil and add 1/2 tsp mustard seeds. When the mustard seeds begin to splutter, add 1 Bombay onion and 1 green chilli, both finely chopped. Fry the onion until soft. Add the rice water, a squeeze of lime and salt. Garnish with chopped coriander leaves and serve. About 8 glasses of soup can be made from 2 litres of rice water.

Dos And Don'ts

Do not add salt or oil to rice when it is cooking. It only adds, unnecessarily, sodium and fat to the diet, and calories. Sufficient water for cooking will ensure that the grains remain fluffy and separate.

Also, do not use poor quality rice. It absorbs more water, takes longer to cook and gives a very soggy product. A good indicator of the quality is the price.

The more expensive, the more likely raw or parboiled rice will serve you well. Older rice is also superior.

> By rule of thumb, parboiled rice should yield four-and-a-half times the raw weight when cooked, and raw rice, three times.

Non-dietary Uses for Rice Water

Rice water makes an excellent shampoo. Though it will not froth like soap does, it will leave your hair absolutely smooth and glossy. Wash off with water, just as you would after using regular shampoo. Particularly if you live in a hot and dusty place or even after a long journey, washing with rice water can be the kindest treatment you can give your hair.

Additionally, rice water is an excellent source of starch for adding stiffness to fabrics. Dilute the rice water with water in the ratio 2:1 and immerse the clothes in it. Squeeze out and dry. The same water can be used twice after which more rice water will have to be added to get the same quality of starching.

3.2.7 Plain Boiled Rice (Absorption Method)

Preparation Time	:	6 min
Soaking Time	:	10 min
Cooking Time	:	25 min

Serves 6

Ingredients

3 1/2 cups/850 g/1 3/4 lb uncooked raw rice, cleaned and washed
6 1/4 cups/1.6 litres/2 2/3 pints water

(1) Soak the rice in sufficient water to cover for 10 minutes. Place in a colander lined with cloth to drain.

(2) Bring the water to the boil in the body of a pressure-cooker. Add the rice. Close the cooker. Bring to maximum pressure over high heat, then lower the flame and pressure-cook for 5 minutes.

(3) Allow the pressure inside the cooker to dissipate, then open and fluff up the rice with a fork. Serve hot.

Per Serving			
Kilocalories	489	Fibre	Trace
Protein	10 g	B Vitamins	
Fat	1 g	Vitamin B_1	Negligible
Carbohydrate	111 g	Vitamin B_2	Negligible
Calcium	14 mg	Vitamin B_3	3 mg
Phosphorus	227 mg	Vitamin B_6	Nil
Iron	1 mg	Folic Acid	11 mcg
Vitamin C	Nil		
Vitamin A	Nil	1,000 mcg = 1 mg	

All About Rice

The absorption method is the recommended method for cooking rice. As the rice water is not discarded, all the nutrients are retained.

However, raw rice suffers a loss of vitamins through milling, a benefit that is retained when rice is first parboiled. Parboiled rice may also be cooked this way except that the volume of water has to be increased by two-and-a-half times, not almost doubled as in raw rice.

Rice increases blood glucose levels. In contrast, wheat has a reducing effect, similar to high-fibre foods. Diabetics need to take a closer look at the composition of their diets.

3.2.8 Chappati/Phulka/Roti (Unleavened Indian Bread)

Preparation Time	:	20 min
Resting Time	:	1 hour
Cooking Time	:	35 min

Makes 24

Ingredients

Salt to taste
Warm water
3 1/3 cups/600 g/1 1/4 lb wholemeal wheat flour
Flour for dredging

(1) *Dissolve the salt in the warm water. Add it gradually to the flour until the dough is soft and pliable. Knead thoroughly for at least 5 minutes.*

(2) Cover with a damp cloth and set aside for 1 hour.

(3) Divide the dough into 24 portions and roll up into balls. Flatten, dredge with flour, and roll each out to circles as thinly as possible.

(4) Heat a tawa and place a chappati on it. When the surface begins to blister, turn it over and cook for about 15 seconds.

(5) Remove the tawa and place the chappati directly over the gas flame. Wait until it puffs up, then turn it over using a pair of tongs. Remove almost immediately. Replace the tawa over the fire and continue cooking the remaining chappatis.

(6) Serve with plain dhal curry or any preparation with a gravy.

Per Chappati			
Kilocalories	85	Iron	1 mg
Protein	3 g	Vitamin C	Nil
Fat	Trace	Vitamin A (as carotene)	7 mcg
Carbohydrate	17 g	Fibre	0.5 g
Calcium	12 mg		
Phosphorus	89 mg	1,000 mcg = 1 mg	

Food Wise

To get a softer chappati, make the dough with buttermilk, curds, whey, milk or even starch drained from cooked rice. Not only will the chappati be more delicious, but its nutritive value will also be improved.

Persons with elevated blood sugar levels should be encouraged to increase their intake of wheat products which have a regulatory effect. Chappatis help in sugar control as it is now known that increasing the chew count (the number of times a mouthful of food has to be chewed before it is swallowed) raises blood sugar levels more slowly. Chappatis are also ideal for weight reduction.

Do not sieve wholemeal wheat flour. It removes the bran and germ which have enormous nutritional benefits. Bran receives nutritive distinction because it is an outstanding source of dietary fibre.

Wheat germ contains the vitamins E and B (thiamine, riboflavin, niacin, pyridoxine, folic acid, pantothenic acid and biotin), the minerals zinc, phosphorus, magnesium, copper, iron, manganese, selenium, chromium and molybdenum, and, the electrolytes sodium and potassium. The protein of wheat germ is of a very high quality—almost as good as most animal proteins which are better utilized in the human body.

3.2.9 Naan (Leavened Indian Bread)

Preparation Time : 20 min
Leavening Time : 12 hours or Overnight
Cooking Time : 45 min

Makes 14

Ingredients

- 1 tbsp/8 g/ 1/4 oz yeast
2 tsp/10 g/ 1/3 oz sugar
1/2 cup/125 ml/4 fl oz warm water
4 cups/750 g/1 lb 9 oz refined wheat flour
1 medium/45 g/1 1/2 oz egg, lightly beaten
1 1/2 cups/375 ml/12 1/2 fl oz curds (from skimmed milk)
3/4 tsp salt
1/2 tsp poppy seeds
1/4 tsp onion seeds
Raw onion rings
Wedges of lime

(1) *Dissolve the yeast and sugar in the warm water and set aside for 5 minutes.*

(2) *Place the flour in a bowl. Make a well in the centre, and add the egg, curds, yeast and sugar mixture, and salt. Draw the flour into the mixture and mix well. Knead thoroughly (for 10 minutes at least), adding more warm water if necessary to get a soft and pliable dough. Cover with a damp cloth and leave in a warm place for 12 hours or overnight.*

(3) *Divide the dough into 14 portions. Roll up, then roll out or stretch to get a thick elongated pyramid, about 7" (18 cm) long and 5" (12 cm) broad at the base.*

(4) *Heat a tawa which has a handle. Moisten one side of a naan with water and stick it onto the hot tawa. On the other side of the naan (the exposed top), press a few poppy seeds and onion seeds into the wet dough.*

(5) *Place the tawa over a gas flame and cook until the surface of the naan begins to bubble. Invert the tawa and hold it directly over the flame (the naan will not fall off). Move the tawa up and down to expose the whole naan to the naked flame. When brown spots begin to appear, insert a spatula under the naan and loosen it from the tawa. Prepare the remaining naans.*

(6) *Serve with tandoori chicken, raw onion rings and wedges of lime.*

Per Naan			
Kilocalories	205	Vitamin C	Trace
Protein	7 g	Vitamin A (as carotene)	33 mcg
Fat	1 g	Vitamin A (as retinol)	12 mcg
Carbohydrate	42 g	Fibre	Trace
Calcium	47 mg	Cholesterol	17 mg
Phosphorus	108 mg		
Iron	2 mg	1,000 mcg = 1 mg	

Nutritionally Speaking

Most recipes for naan will indicate the use of bicarbonate of soda in addition to yeast. Its use can be wholly avoided as the final product does not depend on its inclusion. Many valuable B vitamins, normally destroyed by soda-bicarbonate, are saved as a consequence.

Yeast has the benefit of providing magnesium, copper, phosphorus and chromium, and most of the B complex vitamins. Additionally, it contains phytase, an enzyme which releases phosphorus from its bound form, phytate.

3.2.10 Aloo Paratha (Shallow-fried Bread with Potato Filling)

Preparation Time   : 30 min
Resting Time   : 1 hour
Cooking Time   : 1 hour

Makes 12

Ingredients
___

4 medium/360 g/12 oz potatoes
Salt to taste
1 whole pod/10 g/ 1/3 oz garlic
1" or 2.5 cm piece/8 g/ 1/4 oz fresh ginger
1 medium/90 g/3 oz Bombay onion, finely chopped
2 medium/5 g/ 1/6 oz green chillies, deseeded and finely chopped
1/2 bundle/15 g/ 1/2 oz coriander leaves, finely chopped
1 tsp cumin seeds, crushed
3 1/3 cups/600 g/1 1/4 lb wholemeal wheat flour
Salt
Warm water
Flour for dredging
4 tbsp/60 ml/2 fl oz refined oil
___

(1) *Scrub the potatoes. Place them in a pressure-cooker container. Pour sufficient water in the body of the pressure-cooker. Pressure-cook for 7 minutes. Peel, add a little salt and mash until smooth.*

(2) *Grind the garlic and ginger together to a paste. Add the ground and chopped ingredients, and cumin seeds to the mashed potatoes. Mix well. Divide into 12 portions.*

(3) *Make a soft dough with the flour, salt and sufficient warm water. Set aside for 1 hour.*

(4) *Divide the dough into 12 portions and form into balls. Dredge with flour and roll each out to circles of about 6" (15 cm) in diameter. Place a portion of the potato mixture in the centre and work the dough to enclose it. Roll out once again to make quite a thick paratha.*

(5) *Heat a tawa until very hot. Lower the heat. Dot the tawa with 1/2 tsp oil and place a paratha on it. Smear another 1/2 tsp oil on top of the paratha. Allow to cook for 2 minutes. Turn it over and cook for a further 2 minutes. Prepare the remaining parathas.*

(6) *Serve hot or cold with curds and mint chutney.*

Per Paratha			
Kilocalories	251	Iron	3 mg
Protein	7 g	Vitamin C	8 mg
Fat	6 g	Vitamin A (as carotene)	220 mcg
Carbohydrate	43 g	Fibre	1 g
Calcium	33 mg		
Phosphorus	198 mg	1,000 mcg = 1 mg	

About the Paratha

For school children, this is an ideal packed lunch. Stuff with mutton kheema for a meaty filling.

Plain Parathas may be made without any stuffing. Use the same amount of flour. However, when rolling out the dough, smear each circle with 1/2 tsp refined oil, fold into four, and roll out once again. Cook on a hot tawa as indicated above.

Traditionally, parathas are served with lashings of home-made (desi) ghee. Though the calorie and fat content of ghee is the same as vegetable oils, it is best avoided as it is a saturated fat and contains cholesterol, both of which are a major cause of heart disease.

3.3 Curries

3.3.1 Methi ki Dhal (Fenugreek Leaves in Split Lentil Curry)

Preparation Time	:	7 min
Soaking Time	:	2 hours
Cooking Time	:	15 min

Serves 4

Ingredients

1 cup/240 g/8 oz split lentils, cleaned and washed
1 1/2 cups/375 ml/12 1/2 fl oz water
3 bundles/240 g/8 oz fenugreek leaves, washed, cleaned and coarsely chopped
About 12/60 g/2 oz sambhar onions, peeled
3 whole pods/30 g/1 oz garlic, crushed
1/2 tsp turmeric powder
1/2 tsp red chilli powder
Pinch of asafoetida powder
Salt to taste
2 tsp/10 ml/ 1/3 fl oz oil
1/2 tsp mustard seeds
1/4 tsp cumin seeds, crushed
A large sprig of curry leaves, finely chopped
1 tbsp/15 g/ 1/2 oz powdered jaggery
1 cup/250 ml/8 fl oz hot water

---

(1) Soak the lentils in 1 1/2 cups water for 2 hours.

(2) Place the lentils, soaking water, fenugreek leaves, sambhar onions, garlic, turmeric powder, red chilli powder, asafoetida powder and salt in the body of a pressure-cooker. Close the cooker. Bring to maximum pressure over high heat, then lower the flame and pressure-cook for 2 minutes. Remove from the fire and allow the pressure inside the cooker to dissipate.

(3) Heat a pan, then add the oil. Add the mustard seeds and cumin seeds. When the mustard seeds begin to splutter, add the curry leaves and cooked lentils.

(4) Dissolve the jaggery in 1 cup hot water over a low flame. Strain and add to the cooked dhal.

(5) Bring to the boil, then reduce the heat and simmer for 5 minutes.

(6) Serve hot with chappatis or rice.

Per Serving			
Kilocalories	293	Iron	6 mg
Protein	19 g	Vitamin C	33 mg
Fat	4 g	Vitamin A (as carotene)	7,507 mcg
Carbohydrate	47 g	Fibre	1 g
Calcium	300 mg		
Phosphorus	241 mg	1,000 mcg = 1 mg	

Believe in Turmeric

The bright yellow colour of turmeric is indispensable to bringing life to many Indian delicacies. However, caution must be exercised in the purchase of ready-made turmeric powder as often the colour is enhanced by the addition of a poisonous chemical, lead chromate. Buying reputed brands and from well-known stores with a name to uphold will ensure that the product is not adulterated.

Many wrongly believe that the English word for turmeric is saffron. Saffron is a spice, turmeric is a condiment. Saffron is used primarily in sweets and pulaos and is probably the most expensive spice in the world.

Turmeric has also been known to have curative properties and this attribute is exploited in a number of home remedies. More recently, turmeric has aroused scientific interest as a possible factor in reducing the risk of cancer and heart disease because of the antioxidants it contains. It also has anti-inflammatory and blood cholesterol lowering properties. The fact that most Indians have fine skin despite the tropical sun could be attributed to turmeric which is always used in Indian cooking.

Turmeric powder dusted in the path of ants making a beeline for the larder or spice cupboard disorients them and keeps them away. This is safer than using DDT.

3.3.2 Rasam (Pepper Water)

Preparation Time	:	8 min
Soaking Time	:	10 min
Cooking Time	:	15 min

Serves 4

Ingredients

A lime-sized ball/30 g/1 oz tamarind

1 cup/250 ml/8 fl oz hot water

About 12/60 g/2 oz sambhar onions, peeled

1 1/2 whole pods/15 g/ 1/2 oz garlic

40 black peppercorns

1/2 tsp cumin seeds

A sprig of curry leaves

2 tsp/10 ml/ 1/3 fl oz oil

1/2 tsp mustard seeds

2 whole dried red chillies

1 medium /60 g/2 oz ripe tomato, diced

1/2 tsp turmeric powder

1/4 tsp red chilli powder

2 cups/500 ml/16 fl oz water

Salt to taste

2 tsp/10 g/ 1/3 oz powdered jaggery

(1) *Soak the tamarind in 1/2 cup hot water for 10 minutes. Squeeze to extract pulp. Add another 1/2 cup hot water to the same tamarind, and extract pulp a second time.*

(2) *Grind the sambhar onions, garlic, peppercorns, cumin seeds and curry leaves together to a coarse paste.*

(3) *Heat a pan, then add the oil. Add the mustard seeds and red chillies torn in two. When the mustard seeds begin to splutter, add the tomato and cook until soft. Add the ground paste, turmeric powder, red chilli powder and 2 cups water. Bring to the boil.*

(4) *Add the salt, jaggery and tamarind extract. Simmer for 3 minutes. Serve with plain, hot rice.*

Per Serving			
Kilocalories	71	Iron	2 mg
Protein	1 g	Vitamin C	5 mg
Fat	3 g	Vitamin A (as carotene)	511 mcg
Carbohydrate	11 g	Fibre	1 g
Calcium	31 mg		
Phosphorus	33 mg	1,000 mcg = 1 mg	

Good Health

Rasam, a thin, soupy curry eaten with rice, is the second course after sambhar and rice in a typical South Indian meal because its digestive properties are highly regarded. Rasam also relieves the heaviness and stuffiness that accompany a common cold or influenza.

Cooking Hint

It is possible to vary the colour of rasam by using dark-coloured tamarind for a dark product and a lighter-coloured tamarind to obtain a paler rasam.

3.3.3 Plain Dhal Curry

Preparation Time	:	5 min
Soaking Time	:	2 hours
Cooking Time	:	15 min

Serves 6

Ingredients

1 cup/240 g/8 oz red gram dhal, cleaned and washed
2 1/2 cups/625 ml/1 pint water
1/2 tsp turmeric powder
1/4 tsp red chilli powder
Pinch of asafoetida powder
Salt to taste
2 tsp/10 ml/ 1/3 fl oz oil
1/2 tsp cumin seeds, crushed
1/2 tsp mustard seeds
A sprig of curry leaves, finely chopped
1/2 cup/125 ml/4 fl oz hot water

(1) Soak the dhal in 2 1/2 cups water for 2 hours.

(2) Place the dhal, soaking water, turmeric powder, red chilli powder, asafoetida powder and salt in the body of a pressure-cooker. Close the cooker. Bring to maximum pressure over high heat, then lower the flame and pressure-cook for 2 minutes. Remove from the fire and allow the pressure inside the cooker to dissipate.

(3) Heat a pan, then add the oil. Add the cumin seeds and mustard seeds. When the mustard seeds begin to splutter, add the curry leaves, cooked dhal and hot water. Taste for salt. Simmer for 5 minutes.

(4) Serve with rice or chappatis.

Per Serving			
Kilocalories	149	Iron	1 mg
Protein	9 g	Vitamin C	Nil
Fat	2 g	Vitamin A (as carotene)	88 mcg
Carbohydrate	23 g	Fibre	1 g
Calcium	31 mg		
Phosphorus	122 mg	1,000 mcg = 1 mg	

Leftover Musings

Any leftover dhal curry can be added to rasam to give Parupoo (Dhal) Rasam. Simply stir it into the prepared rasam and simmer for 5 minutes before serving.

Mineral Matters

Calcium and phosphorus if taken in the ratio 1:1 are best utilized in the human body. Phosphorus is, however, usually found in greater quantities in foods. Fortunately, most Indian meals include dhal (high in phosphorus) and curds (high in calcium), so the optimum level is normally attained with no conscious effort.

3.3.4 Kadhi (Curds and Gram Flour Curry)

Preparation Time : 15 min
Cooking Time : 20 min

Serves 6

Ingredients

1 1/2 cups/375 ml/12 1/2 fl oz curds (from skimmed milk)
1/2 cup/125 ml/4 fl oz cold water
Salt to taste
1/2 cup/60 g/2 oz bengal gram flour
3 cups/750 ml/1 1/4 pints cold water
2 tsp/10 ml/ 1/3 fl oz oil
1/2 tsp mustard seeds
2 whole dried red chillies
1 whole pod/10 g/ 1/3 oz garlic, finely chopped
A sprig of curry leaves, finely chopped
1/2 tsp cumin seeds, coarsely powdered
1/2 tsp fenugreek seeds, coarsely powdered
1/2 tsp turmeric powder
Pinch of asafoetida powder

(1) Dilute the curds with 1/2 cup cold water and beat until smooth. Add salt. Set aside.

(2) Mix the gram flour first with 1/2 cup cold water to make a smooth paste. Then add the remaining 2 1/2 cups cold water to dilute.

(3) Heat a heavy pan, then add the oil. Add the mustard seeds. When the mustard seeds begin to splutter, add the red chillies torn in two, garlic, curry leaves, powdered cumin seeds, powdered fenugreek seeds, turmeric powder and asafoetida powder. Fry for 1 minute, then gradually stir in the gram flour mixture and diluted curds. Stirring continuously, bring to the boil over moderate heat. Maintain a rolling boil for 5 minutes once the curry thickens. Serve hot with rice.

Per Serving			
Kilocalories	73	Iron	1 mg
Protein	4 g	Vitamin C	1 mg
Fat	2 g	Vitamin A (as carotene)	48 mcg
Carbohydrate	9 g	Fibre	Trace
Calcium	83 mg	Cholesterol	1 mg
Phosphorus	95 mg	1,000 mcg = 1 mg	

Down with Fat

Traditionally, kadhi, a North Indian dish, is garnished with pakoras or deep-fried bengal gram flour fritters that are floated in the curry. In view of the attempt being made in this book to reduce fat and keep it to the very minimum, this aspect of the recipe has been omitted.

The fat content of bengal gram is relatively higher than the other pulses (dhals) and legumes with the exception of soya bean.

3.3.5 Sambhar (South Indian Dhal) Curry

Preparation Time	:	20 min
Soaking Time	:	2 hours
Cooking Time	:	30 min

Serves 6

Ingredients

1 cup/240 g/8 oz red gram dhal, cleaned and washed
2 1/2 cups/625 ml/1 pint water

1 tsp turmeric powder
1/4 tsp red chilli powder
Salt to taste
20 black peppercorns
1 tsp cumin seeds
A sprig of curry leaves
1 tsp fenugreek seeds
1/4 tsp asafoetida powder
A lime-sized ball/30 g/1 oz tamarind
1 cup/250 ml/8 fl oz hot water
2 medium/120 g/4 oz ripe tomatoes
About 20/120 g/4 oz broad beans
2 medium/100 g/3 1/3 oz round brinjals
About 12/60 g/2 oz sambhar onions
2 tsp/10 ml/ 1/3 fl oz oil
1/2 tsp mustard seeds
2 whole dried red chillies
1 tsp black gram dhal (without husk)
2 tsp coriander powder
Salt to taste
1 1/2 cups/375 ml/12 1/2 fl oz water
1 tbsp/15 g/ 1/2 oz powdered jaggery

(1) Soak the dhal in 2 1/2 cups water for 2 hours. Place the dhal, soaking water, turmeric powder, red chilli powder and salt in the body of a pressure-cooker. Close the cooker. Bring to maximum pressure over high heat, then lower the flame and pressure-cook for 5 minutes. Remove from the fire and allow the pressure inside the cooker to dissipate.

(2) Grind the peppercorns, cumin seeds and curry leaves together to a paste, adding a little water.

(3) Roast the fenugreek seeds, without oil, until they begin to change colour. Powder and mix with the asafoetida powder.

(4) Soak the tamarind in 1/2 cup hot water for 10 minutes. Squeeze to extract pulp. Add another 1/2 cup hot water to the same tamarind and extract pulp a second time.

(5) Quarter the tomatoes, then cut across in half again. String the broad beans and cut them into 1" (2.5 cm) pieces. Quarter the brinjals, retaining the stalk (prepare the brinjals just before cooking as they will discolour if exposed to air for too long). Peel the sambhar onions and set aside.

(6) Heat a pan, then add the oil. Add the mustard seeds and red chillies torn in two. When the mustard seeds begin to splutter, add the black gram dhal and fry until golden. Add the ground masala, coriander powder, prepared

vegetables, salt and 1 1/2 cups water. Bring to the boil. Lower the heat and simmer until the vegetables are cooked.

(7) *Add the tamarind extract, jaggery and cooked dhal. Simmer for 5 minutes until well blended. Sprinkle with the powdered fenugreek and asafoetida. Bring to the boil and draw off the heat. Serve with plain, white rice or iddlis or dosais.*

Per Serving			
Kilocalories	203	Iron	3 mg
Protein	11 g	Vitamin C	10 mg
Fat	3 g	Vitamin A (as carotene)	720 mcg
Carbohydrate	34 g	Fibre	2 g
Calcium	76 mg		
Phosphorus	167 mg	1,000 mcg = 1 mg	

Matters of Interest

Nutritionists recommend that the day's calorie needs be met by carbohydrates and proteins. Sambhar is a perfect example of how carbohydrates and proteins are the major contributors of energy (kcal), not fat.

Any other vegetable may be used in the sambhar. Those that are particularly suitable are drumstick and ladies fingers.

Drumstick is an excellent source of vitamin C and sulphur. It also provides potassium, phosphorus and vitamin A (as carotene). Some people just do not know what to do with this vegetable. To get at the marrow inside, pull the tough, fibrous outer skin apart and scrape the meat off, either with your teeth or with a fork and spoon.

Ladies fingers are a very good source of soluble fibre.

As elsewhere in this book, a distinction has been made between onions— Bombay and sambhar. Sambhar onions are used more in South Indian cooking and are rarely, if ever, employed in cuisine from other parts of India.

The distinction is, however, more than just a matter of size. Sambhar or small onions are considered marginally more nutritious than Bombay or big onions. They contain more protein, carbohydrate, phosphorus and iron but less calcium. Bombay onions contain more vitamin C but no vitamin A (as carotene) which is found in sambhar onions. Both types have more or less equal amounts of the B complex vitamins, though Bombay onions are a better source for folic acid. Bombay and sambhar onions have the same amounts of fibre.

Sambhar onions are also believed to have more flavour. They are certainly more pungent. In cooking, one may be substituted for the other, especially if they are to be ground to a paste or crushed. By rule of thumb, 1 medium Bombay onion would adequately substitute 12 sambhar onions—a handful.

Sambhar can be made from sambhar podi (Recipe No: 3.11.9) as well. Omit black peppercorns, cumin seeds and coriander powder from the recipe, and substitute with 2 tsp (10 g/ 1/3 oz) sambhar podi. Finely chop the curry leaves and add them along with the mustard seeds and red chillies. Proceed as instructed earlier.

3.3.6 Potato Curry

Preparation Time   :   5 min
Cooking Time   :   25 min

Serves 6

Ingredients

4 medium/360 g/12 oz potatoes
2 tsp/10 ml/ 1/3 fl oz oil
1 medium/90 g/3 oz Bombay onion, thinly sliced
2 medium/120 g/4 oz ripe tomatoes, diced
1/2 tsp turmeric powder
1/4 tsp red chilli powder
1 tsp/5 g/ 1/6 oz sugar
Salt to taste
3 cups/750 ml/1 1/4 pints water
1/2 tsp cumin seeds, crushed

(1) Scrub the potatoes. Place them in a pressure-cooker together with sufficient water. Close the cooker. Bring to maximum pressure over high heat, then lower the flame and pressure-cook for 5 minutes. Remove from the fire. Allow the pressure inside the cooker to dissipate, then peel and mash the potatoes coarsely with a fork.

(2) Heat a pan, then add the oil. Add the sliced onion. Cook until the onion is soft and glassy. Add the tomatoes and fry until soft and mushy. Add the turmeric powder, red chilli powder, sugar, salt and water. Bring to the boil.

(3) Stir in the potatoes and simmer for 8 minutes. Sprinkle with the crushed cumin seeds. Serve hot with chappatis.

Per Serving			
Kilocalories	88	Iron	0.5 mg
Protein	1 g	Vitamin C	17 mg
Fat	2 g	Vitamin A (as carotene)	616 mcg
Carbohydrate	17 g	Fibre	0.5 g
Calcium	23 mg		
Phosphorus	36 mg	1,000 mcg = 1 mg	

Heaven Sent

This curry is a life-saver when guests drop in unexpectedly.

To make it more flavoursome, add chopped coriander leaves and fresh capsicum just before serving. This will also improve its nutritive value, as will substituting whey (obtained from making paneer) for water.

3.3.7 Kaachia Mohru (Spicy Buttermilk Digestive Curry)

Preparation Time   :   15 min
Cooking Time   :   25 min

Serves 6

Ingredients

About 12/60 g/2 oz sambhar onions, peeled
1 whole pod/10 g/ 1/3 oz garlic
1/2" or 1 cm piece/4 g/ 1/8 oz fresh ginger
1 tsp cumin seeds
1/2 tsp turmeric powder
1/4 tsp red chilli powder
1/2 tsp fenugreek seeds
Pinch of asafoetida powder
2 cups/500 ml/16 fl oz curds (from skimmed milk)
1 cup/250 ml/8 fl oz cold water
2 tsp/10 ml/ 1/3 fl oz oil
1 tsp mustard seeds
A sprig of curry leaves, finely chopped
1 whole dried red chilli
Salt to taste

(1) Grind the sambhar onions, garlic, ginger and cumin seeds together to a smooth paste. Add the turmeric powder and red chilli powder. Mix well.

(2) Roast the fenugreek seeds lightly, without oil, until they begin to change colour. Powder coarsely, then mix with the asafoetida powder.

(3) Whisk the curds lightly, and gradually beat in the cold water. Stir in the ground paste. Set aside.

(4) Heat a heavy pan, then add the oil. Add the mustard seeds. When the mustard seeds begin to crackle, add the curry leaves and red chilli torn in two. Fry for 1 minute. Remove from the fire and stir in the prepared curds mixture. Add salt. Return to the fire and bring to the boil over low heat. Simmer for 5 minutes. Sprinkle with the fenugreek mixture and remove from the fire. Serve hot with plain, white rice.

Per Serving			
Kilocalories	48	Iron	Less than 0.5 mg
Protein	2 g	Vitamin C	1 mg
Fat	2 g	Vitamin A (as carotene)	37 mcg
Carbohydrate	6 g	Fibre	Trace
Calcium	106 mg	Cholesterol	2 mg
Phosphorus	87 mg	1,000 mcg = 1 mg	

Sound Food Sense

The people of Kerala value this curry because it is considered to be light on the stomach. Much of Indian cooking relies heavily on the use of spices and condiments because of their digestive and carminative properties.

Always use "live" curds if bought from a store. Their properties are more beneficial than pasteurized yoghurt.

3.3.8 Dhansak (Spicy Meat and Vegetables in Dhal Curry)

Preparation Time	:	25 min
Soaking Time	:	4 hours
Cooking Time	:	40 min

Serves 6

Ingredients

1/2 cup/120 g/4 oz red gram dhal, cleaned and washed
1/4 cup/60 g/2 oz split lentils, cleaned and washed

1/4 cup/60 g/2 oz split lentils, cleaned and washed
1/4 cup/60 g/2 oz whole green gram, cleaned and washed
2 1/2 cups/625 ml/1 pint water
1 (3" x 3" or 7.5 cm x 7.5 cm) piece/125 g/4 oz white pumpkin
1 (3" x 3" or 7.5 cm x 7.5 cm) piece/125 g/4 oz red pumpkin
3 medium/270 g/9 oz Bombay onions
1 medium/50 g/1 2/3 oz brinjal
2" or 5 cm piece/15 g/ 1/2 oz fresh ginger
1 whole pod/10 g/ 1/3 oz garlic
1/2 tsp cumin seeds
20 black peppercorns
1/2" or 1 cm stick cinnamon
5 cloves
1 tbsp/15 g/ 1/2 oz powdered jaggery
1 1/2 cups/375 ml/12 1/2 fl oz water
500 g/1.1 lb mutton, cleaned, washed and cubed
1/2 big bundle/90 g/3 oz fenugreek leaves, washed, cleaned and coarsely chopped
1/2 bundle/15 g/ 1/2 oz coriander leaves, coarsely chopped
1/2 tbsp/5 g/ 1/6 oz coriander powder
1 tsp turmeric powder
1/2 tsp red chilli powder
Salt to taste
2 tsp/10 ml/ 1/3 fl oz oil
2 medium/120 g/4 oz ripe tomatoes, diced
1 tbsp/15 g/ 1/2 oz sambhar podi (Recipe No: 3.11.9)
2 bay leaves

---

(1)   Soak the red gram dhal, split lentils and whole green gram together in 2 1/2 cups water for 4 hours.

(2)   Peel the white and red pumpkin and cut into big chunks. Quarter 1 Bombay onion and chop the remaining 2 onions finely. Quarter the brinjal.

(3)   Grind the ginger and garlic together to a paste.

(4)   Roast the cumin seeds, peppercorns, cinnamon and cloves together, without oil, until the cumin seeds begin to change colour. Powder.

(5)   Dissolve the jaggery in 1 1/2 cups water over a low flame. Strain and set aside.

(6)   Place the soaked pulses, soaking water, white and red pumpkin, quartered onion, quartered brinjal, mutton, chopped fenugreek leaves and coriander leaves in the body of a pressure-cooker together with the coriander powder, turmeric powder, red chilli powder and a little salt. Close the cooker. Bring to maximum pressure over high heat, then lower the flame and pressure-cook for 15 minutes. Remove from the fire and allow the pressure inside the cooker to dissipate. Pick out the meat from the mixture. Mash the dhal until smooth.

(7)   Heat a wide pan, then add the oil. Add the chopped onions. Allow to brown, then add the ground paste. Fry for a minute or two. Add the tomatoes and cook until soft and mushy. Add the roasted spice powder, sambhar podi and bay leaves. Fry until a nice aroma arises. Add the mashed dhal. Bring to the boil. Stir in the jaggery syrup. Add the cooked meat. Simmer for 5 minutes.

(8)   Serve with plain fried rice and cachumber.

Per Serving			
Kilocalories	362	Vitamin C	21 mg
Protein	26 g	Vitamin A (as carotene)	2,622 mcg
Fat	13 g	Vitamin A (as retinol)	7 mcg
Carbohydrate	36 g	Fibre	3 g
Calcium	246 mg	Cholesterol	75 mg
Phosphorus	304 mg		
Iron	5 mg	1,000 mcg = 1 mg	

Notes of Interest

Dhansak dhal is the creation of a small, migrant community from Persia which made India their home—the Parsees. Sunday lunch in Parsee homes is a dhansak affair. It tastes better if made the previous day.

Dhansak can be made with chicken as well or only with vegetables. Equal quantities of chicken or vegetables should be substituted for the mutton. Reduce the pressure-cooking time to 5 minutes.

Soak the pulses overnight for a softer, smoother finish. It saves time too because very little mashing is needed after cooking.

Usually green gram dhal (split) is used. It has been deliberately substituted with whole green gram because it improves the nutritive quality of dhansak. With the benefit of more fibre (as much as five times more), calcium, iron and vitamin A (as carotene), this switch is more than amply justified. And the final product is just as pleasing to the eye and palate.

3.4 Pulses
Legumes

3.4.1 Vaalase Birdha (Curried Green Gram Sprouts)

Preparation Time	:	20 min
Soaking Time	:	12 hours *or* Overnight
Sprouting Time	:	24 hours minimum
Cooking Time	:	45 min

Serves 6

Ingredients

1 cup/240 g/8 oz whole green gram, cleaned and washed
4 garlic cloves
1/2" or 1 cm piece/4 g/ 1/8 oz fresh ginger
1 tbsp/15 ml/ 1/2 fl oz oil
1/4 tsp cumin seeds
4 medium/360 g/12 oz Bombay onions, finely chopped
2 medium/5 g/ 1/6 oz green chillies, slit lengthways
A sprig of curry leaves, finely chopped
1 cup/250 ml/8 fl oz hot water
About 4 medium/250 g/8 oz ripe tomatoes, diced
1/2 tsp coriander powder
1/2 tsp turmeric powder
Salt to taste
1 tbsp/15 ml/ 1/2 fl oz lime juice
1/2 bundle/15 g/ 1/2 oz coriander leaves, finely chopped

(1) *Soak the green gram in generous amounts of water for 12 hours, preferably overnight.*

(2) *Drain and wrap the soaked gram in a damp cloth. Hang up in a warm place for 24 hours or until sprouts appear. Keep the cloth moist at all times.*

(3) *Grind the garlic and ginger together to a paste.*

(4) *Heat the oil in the body of a pressure-cooker. Add the cumin seeds and fry until golden. Add the chopped onions and cook until soft and fairly brown. Stir in the ground paste, green chillies and curry leaves. Fry for 1 minute.*

(5) *Add the sprouted green gram and stir for 1 minute. Pour in 1 cup hot water. Bring to the boil. Add the tomatoes, coriander powder, turmeric powder and salt. Close the cooker. Bring to maximum pressure over high heat, then lower the flame and pressure-cook for 3 minutes. Remove from the fire and allow the pressure inside the cooker to dissipate.*

(6)   Open the cooker. Stir in the lime juice and chopped coriander leaves. Serve hot with plain, white rice or chappatis.

Per Serving			
Kilocalories	198	Iron	3 mg
Protein	11 g	Vitamin C	27 mg
Fat	3 g	Vitamin A (as carotene)	1,723 mcg
Carbohydrate	31 g	Fibre	3 g
Calcium	106 mg		
Phosphorus	172 mg	1,000 mcg = 1 mg	

Sound Indian Food Sense

As many parts of India are arid, food crops are seldom cultivated by irrigation. Fresh fruits and vegetables are, therefore, grown primarily in the monsoon months. For the rest of the year, dried pulses and food grains are the staples, and both are devoid of vitamin C. Good old Indian wisdom saved the situation with the idea of sprouting grams, which allowed significant amounts of vitamin C to be available throughout the year. Three-day-old sprouts have almost double the vitamin C content of pulses allowed to germinate only for 24 hours.

A mixture of sprouts may further enhance the nutritive value of this dish, popular among the Maharashtrians of the west coast.

3.4.2   Chhole (Yellow Chickpeas in Gravy)

Preparation Time : 7 min
Soaking Time : Overnight
Cooking Time : 25 min

Serves 4

Ingredients

1 cup/240 g/8 oz dried whole bengal gram (kabuli variety), cleaned and washed
2 1/2 cups/625 ml/1 pint water
1/4 tsp red chilli powder
Salt to taste
2" or 5 cm piece/15 g/ 1/2 oz fresh ginger, finely chopped
2 medium/180 g/6 oz Bombay onions, finely chopped
2 tsp/10 ml/ 1/3 fl oz oil
2 medium/5 g/ 1/6 oz green chillies, finely chopped

1 tsp cumin seeds, crushed

1/4 tsp garam masala (Recipe No: 3.11.6)

1/2 bundle/15 g/ 1/2 oz coriander leaves, finely chopped

(1) *Soak the bengal gram in 2 1/2 cups water overnight.*

(2) *The next day, place the gram, soaking water, red chilli powder, salt, ginger and half the chopped onions in the body of a pressure-cooker. Close the cooker. Bring to maximum pressure over high heat, then lower the flame and pressure-cook for 10 minutes. Remove from the fire and allow the pressure inside the cooker to dissipate.*

(3) *Heat a pan, then add the oil. Fry the remaining onions until soft and fairly brown. Add the green chillies, cooked gram and any gravy left over from pressure-cooking. Simmer for 5 minutes. Sprinkle with the crushed cumin seeds, garam masala and chopped coriander leaves.*

(4) *Serve hot with imli ki chutney as a snack.*

Per Serving			
Kilocalories	266	Fibre	3 g
Protein	11 g	*B Vitamins*	
Fat	6 g	Vitamin B_1	0.22 mg
Carbohydrate	42 g	Vitamin B_2	0.10 mg
Calcium	150 mg	Vitamin B_3	2 mg
Phosphorus	216 mg	Vitamin B_6	Nil
Iron	3 mg	Folic Acid	115 mcg
Vitamin C	13 mg		
Vitamin A (as carotene)	708 mcg	1,000 mcg = 1 mg	

Nutrition Loss

Common to the people of the Punjab, traditionally 1/2 tsp bicarbonate of soda is added to chhole to soften the bengal gram and to reduce cooking time. All the B vitamins present, which are many, are destroyed by this practice, as is much of the vitamin C.

A few tea leaves tied in a piece of muslin or a tea bag is also added during cooking to give chhole a deep maroon colour. Nutritionally speaking, this again is unhealthy, because it adds tannins which reduce the availability of vitamin B_1 and iron. Browning onions will have the same effect, and spares these nutrients.

3.4.3 Saabut Masoor (Whole Lentils in Gravy)

Preparation Time   :   20 min
Soaking Time   :   2 hours
Cooking Time   :   35 min

Serves 6

Ingredients

1 cup/240 g/8 oz whole lentils, cleaned and washed
2 1/2 cups/625 ml/1 pint water
1 whole pod/10 g/ 1/3 oz garlic, finely chopped
1" or 2.5 cm piece/8 g/ 1/4 oz fresh ginger, finely chopped
2 medium/5 g/ 1/6 oz green chillies, deseeded and finely chopped
1/2 tsp turmeric powder
Salt to taste
2 tsp/10 ml/ 1/3 fl oz oil
1 medium/90 g/3 oz Bombay onion, finely chopped
1/2 tsp cumin seeds, powdered
Pinch of asafoetida powder
1 tsp coriander powder
2 medium/120 g/4 oz ripe tomatoes, diced
1/2 tsp garam masala (Recipe No: 3.11.6)
1 cup/250 ml/8 fl oz curds, lightly beaten (from skimmed milk)
1/2 bundle/15 g/ 1/2 oz coriander leaves, finely chopped

(1) Soak the lentils in 2 1/2 cups water for 2 hours. Place the gram, soaking water, chopped garlic, ginger, green chillies, turmeric powder and salt in the body of a pressure-cooker. Close the cooker. Bring to maximum pressure over high heat, then lower the flame and pressure-cook for 5 minutes. Remove from the fire and allow the pressure inside the cooker to dissipate. Crush a few lentils with a fork.

(2) Heat a pan, then add the oil. Fry the onion until golden. Stir in the powdered cumin seeds, asafoetida powder and coriander powder. Fry for 1 minute. Add the tomatoes and cook until soft. Add the cooked lentils and any gravy left over from pressure-cooking. Simmer for 5 minutes. Sprinkle with the garam masala.

(3) Lower the heat and pour in the curds in a steady stream, stirring all the time. Bring to the boil and then turn off the heat.

(4) Garnish with the chopped coriander leaves. Serve hot with chappatis.

Per Serving			
Kilocalories	182	Iron	4 mg
Protein	12 g	Vitamin C	12 mg
Fat	2 g	Vitamin A (as carotene)	1,111 mcg
Carbohydrate	29 g	Fibre	2 g
Calcium	104 mg	Cholesterol	1 mg
Phosphorus	177 mg	1,000 mcg = 1 mg	

Fibre Fact

Saabut masoor is typical of the cuisine of northern India, particularly of Punjab.

All whole pulses (grams) have significantly higher levels of fibre than the split ones (dhals) that are derived from them. Sometimes, the fibre content of whole pulses may be as much as four times more.

Interestingly, cooking *increases* the fibre content of pulses and legumes. Cooking cereals like rice does not bring about a similar change.

3.4.4 Rajmah (Dried French Beans in Gravy)

Preparation Time	:	10 min
Soaking Time	:	Overnight
Cooking Time	:	30 min

Serves 4

Ingredients

1 cup/240 g/8 oz dried French beans, cleaned and washed

2 1/2 cups/625 ml/1 pint water

1/2 tsp turmeric powder

Salt to taste

2 tsp/10 ml/ 1/3 fl oz oil

2 medium/180 g/6 oz Bombay onions, finely chopped

2 whole pods/20 g/ 2/3 oz garlic, finely chopped

2" or 5 cm piece/15 g/ 1/2 oz fresh ginger, finely chopped

1 tsp cumin seeds, powdered

20 black peppercorns, powdered

2 tsp coriander powder

2 medium/120 g/4 oz ripe tomatoes, diced

1/4 tsp garam masala (Recipe No: 3.11.6)

1/2 bundle/15 g/ 1/2 oz coriander leaves, finely chopped

(1) Soak the dried French beans in 2 1/2 cups water overnight.

(2) The next day, place the French beans, soaking water, turmeric powder and salt in the body of a pressure-cooker. Close the cooker. Bring to maximum pressure over high heat, then lower the flame and pressure-cook for 10 minutes. Remove from the fire and allow the pressure inside the cooker to dissipate. Crush a few beans with a fork.

(3) Heat a pan, then add the oil. Fry the onions until brown. Add the chopped garlic and ginger, and fry until golden. Add the powdered cumin seeds, powdered peppercorns and coriander powder. Fry for 1 minute, then stir in the tomatoes. Soften the tomatoes before adding the cooked beans and any gravy left over from pressure-cooking.

(4) Simmer for 5 minutes. (If too thick, add a little hot water.) Sprinkle with the garam masala and chopped coriander leaves.

(5) Serve hot with chappatis.

Per Serving			
Kilocalories	275	Iron	4 mg
Protein	15 g	Vitamin C	19 mg
Fat	4 g	Vitamin A (as carotene)	1,484 mcg
Carbohydrate	45 g	Fibre	4 g
Calcium	212 mg		
Phosphorus	302 mg	1,000 mcg = 1 mg	

Bean Blessing

Rajmah is almost synonymous with Punjabi cooking.

Legumes contain 5 to 10 per cent more amylose (a component of starch, the other being amylopectin) than cereals. Amylose is digested significantly slower than amylopectin and is, therefore, responsible for reducing blood glucose levels—an indication that diabetics should eat more pulses, beans and legumes.

Indian Intelligence

Traditional garnishes are typical of Indian cooking. In the north, it is usually fresh coriander leaves. In the south, freshly grated coconut is preferred. The tempering routine, another Indian culinary feature, helps to release fat-soluble carotene from coriander leaves. The fat in coconut achieves the same purpose in foods rich in the fat-soluble vitamins, namely, A, D, E and K. The vitamin C in coriander leaves makes the iron from pulses, and, dried peas and beans readily available for absorption.

3.4.5 Sundal (Savoury Brown Chickpeas)

Preparation Time	:	5 min
Soaking Time	:	12 hours *or* Overnight
Cooking Time	:	20 min

Serves 4

Ingredients

1 cup/210 g/7 oz dried whole bengal gram (brown), cleaned and washed

2 cups/500 ml/16 fl oz water

Salt to taste

2 tsp/10 ml/ 1/3 fl oz oil

1/2 tsp mustard seeds

1 tsp black gram dhal (without husk)

2 whole dried red chillies

A sprig of curry leaves, finely chopped

Pinch of asafoetida powder

(1) *Soak the bengal gram in 2 cups water for 12 hours or overnight.*

(2) *Place the bengal gram, soaking water and a little salt in the body of a pressure-cooker. Close the cooker. Bring to maximum pressure over high heat, then lower the flame and pressure-cook for 5 minutes. Remove from the fire and allow the pressure inside the cooker to dissipate.*

(3) *Heat a pan, then add the oil. Add the mustard seeds. When the mustard seeds begin to splutter, add the black gram dhal and fry until golden. Add the red chillies torn in two and chopped curry leaves. Stir for 1 minute. Add the cooked bengal gram and any gravy left over from pressure-cooking. Sprinkle with the asafoetida powder. Simmer until all the moisture is absorbed.*

(4) *Serve with imli ki chutney.*

Per Serving			
Kilocalories	216	Iron	3 mg
Protein	9 g	Vitamin C	2 mg
Fat	5 g	Vitamin A (as carotene)	152 mcg
Carbohydrate	33 g	Fibre	2 g
Calcium	110 mg		
Phosphorus	169 mg	1,000 mcg = 1 mg	

Cooking Notes

Sundal is the Tamil equivalent of chhole, and it is traditionally prepared from brown chickpeas (although any pulse or dried peas are used today), while chhole employs yellow chickpeas (kabuli channa). A good teatime or mid-morning snack, sundal may be made with other dried legumes and pulses. This recipe is especially good for dried peas and cow-peas.

Health Notes

A regular intake of all varieties of rehydrated and uncooked whole bengal gram (kabuli/brown) helps to prevent and dissolve kidney stones (renal calculi).

All grams cause wind, so asafoetida (often in combination with cumin seeds) is used in Indian cooking to reduce the unpleasant effects of abdominal discomfort and flatulence. It is also a good digestive and has healing properties. Asafoetida is also believed to be useful in the treatment of worm (intestinal) infestation.

The Indian Tempering Tradition

It is customary in much of India to complete the preparation of a dish by tempering, which involves adding small amounts of ingredients like mustard seeds, black gram dhal, dried red chillies, cumin seeds, curry leaves, asafoetida or the like that have been heated in a little oil.

Apart from the distinctive flavour it imparts, tempering has many healthful aspects to it. First, essential fatty acids have to be supplied by the diet because the body cannot synthesize them. Fats used in tempering, particularly the vegetable oils, contain these fatty acids, as do ingredients like mustard seeds, cumin seeds and black gram dhal.

Besides, the vitamins A, D, E and K, found in foods like green leafy vegetables, carrots and cauliflower, are soluble in fat, and can only be released and utilized if some fat is also available at the same time. Tempering meets this requirement too. The carotene in curry leaves is also automatically transferred by this process. Many vegetable oils used in tempering are, additionally, rich in vitamin E.

Further, while pungency is associated with mustard, few are aware that this results only when mustard seeds are ground with water or vinegar. In hot oil, mustard seeds taste unquestionably nutty.

3.5 Vegetables

3.5.1 Aloo Mattar (Potato and Peas in Thick Sauce)

Preparation Time : 12 min
Cooking Time : 25 min

Serves 6

Ingredients

1 whole pod/10 g/ 1/3 oz garlic
2" or 5 cm piece/15 g/ 1/2 oz fresh ginger
2 medium/5 g/ 1/6 oz green chillies
4 large/500 g/1.1 lb potatoes
2 tsp/10 ml/ 1/3 fl oz oil
2 medium/180 g/6 oz Bombay onions, finely chopped
2 medium/120 g/4 oz ripe tomatoes, diced
1 cup/250 ml/8 fl oz water
1/2 tsp turmeric powder
1 tsp/5 g/ 1/6 oz sugar
Salt to taste
1 1/2 cups or 8 handfuls/240 g/8 oz shelled peas (from 500 g/1.1 lb unshelled peas)
1/2 bundle/15 g/ 1/2 oz coriander leaves, finely chopped

(1) Grind the garlic, ginger and green chillies together to a paste.

(2) Scrub the potatoes. Place them in a pressure-cooker together with sufficient water. Close the cooker. Bring to maximum pressure over high heat, then lower the flame and pressure-cook for 5 minutes. Remove from the fire. Allow the pressure inside the cooker to dissipate, then chop the potatoes coarsely.

(3) Heat a pan, then add the oil. Add the onions and fry until soft. Add the tomatoes. Cook for 2 minutes. Add the ground paste and stir for 1 minute.

(4) Pour in the water. Add the turmeric powder, sugar and salt. Bring to the boil. Add the peas and lower the heat.

(5) When the peas are tender, add the potatoes. Stir well and simmer for 5 minutes.

(6) Garnish with the chopped coriander leaves. Serve hot with chappatis.

Per Serving			
Kilocalories	161	Iron	2 mg
Protein	5 g	Vitamin C	31 mg
Fat	2 g	Vitamin A (as carotene)	1,052 mcg
Carbohydrate	31 g	Fibre	2 g
Calcium	46 mg		
Phosphorus	117 mg	1,000 mcg = 1 mg	

Food Wise

On an average, 500 g/1.1 lb unshelled peas yield about 240 g/8 oz shelled peas. This might appear a colossal waste, but it is possible to put the pods to some use as well.

Boil the pea pods in sufficient water to cover them completely for about 15 minutes. Add this Vegetable Stock to curries and gravies or simply cook rice in it. Many vitamins and minerals will end up inside you instead of in the garbage bin.

Shelled peas can be easily sprouted to increase their vitamin C content. Place them in a polythene bag or plastic box and seal completely. Leave them undisturbed in the refrigerator (not freezer). Sprouts should appear in a week.

Always cook potatoes in their jackets. The vitamins are retained even if the potatoes are peeled later.

Aloo mattar is traditional fare in North India.

3.5.2 Beans Poriyal (South Indian Stir-fried Beans)

Preparation Time : 12 min
Cooking Time : 12 min

Serves 4

Ingredients

500 g/1.1 lb fresh beans
2 tsp/10 ml/ 1/3 fl oz oil
1/2 tsp mustard seeds
1 medium/90 g/3 oz Bombay onion, finely chopped
A sprig of curry leaves, finely chopped
2 medium/5 g/ 1/6 oz green chillies, deseeded and finely chopped
1/2 tsp turmeric powder
1 tbsp/15 ml/ 1/2 fl oz hot water
Salt to taste

(1) Wash and string the beans. Cut them into 1/2" (1 cm) pieces.

(2) Heat a pan, then add the oil. Add the mustard seeds. When the mustard seeds begin to splutter, add the chopped onion, curry leaves and green chillies. Cook until the onion is soft. Stir in the beans and cook for 1 minute. Add the turmeric powder, hot water and salt. Cook uncovered over high heat, stirring occasionally, until the beans are tender and all the moisture is absorbed.

(3)   Serve with hot rice and sambhar.

Per Serving			
Kilocalories	232	Iron	3 mg
Protein	10 g	Vitamin C	38 mg
Fat	4 g	Vitamin A (as carotene)	125 mcg
Carbohydrate	40 g	Fibre	3 g
Calcium	76 mg		
Phosphorus	212 mg	1,000 mcg = 1 mg	

Notes on Nutrition

This is the basic recipe for cooking a "dry" vegetable in Tamil Nadu.

In the traditional recipe, 2 tbsp/15 g/ 1/2 oz freshly grated coconut will be added to the poriyal just before it is removed from the fire. Its inclusion may be considered optional because of the high saturated fat content in coconut. However, adding fat-laden coconut to vegetables with a high level of fat-soluble carotene like carrots and greens is beneficial because it helps to release the carotene in them, making it readily available for absorption.

Among the fresh vegetables, all beans have a marginally higher protein content with the exception of green leafy vegetables.

3.5.3 Bakla ki Bhaaji (Spice-flavoured Broad Beans)

Preparation Time   :   12 min
Cooking Time   :   25 min

Serves 4

Ingredients

250 g/8 oz broad beans
A marble-sized ball of tamarind
1/2 tsp cumin seeds
1/2 tsp fenugreek seeds
1/2 tsp mustard seeds
2 tsp/10 ml/ 1/3 fl oz oil (preferably gingelly or mustard)
1 medium/90 g/3 oz Bombay onion, finely chopped
1/2 tsp turmeric powder
1/4 tsp red chilli powder
1/2 tsp sugar

Salt to taste
1/2 cup/125 ml/4 fl oz hot water

(1) Wash and string the beans. Cut them into 1" (2.5 cm) pieces.

(2) Grind the tamarind, cumin seeds, fenugreek seeds and mustard seeds together to a paste, adding a little water.

(3) Heat a pan, then add the oil. Add the onion and fry until transparent. Stir in the beans and fry until they are well coated with oil and are beginning to soften—about 8 minutes. Add the ground paste, turmeric powder, red chilli powder, sugar, salt and hot water. Cook uncovered over high heat, stirring occasionally, until all the moisture is absorbed.

(4) Serve with rice or chappatis and plain dhal curry.

Per Serving			
Kilocalories	70	Iron	1 mg
Protein	3 g	Vitamin C	10 mg
Fat	3 g	Vitamin A (as carotene)	6 mcg
Carbohydrate	9 g	Fibre	2 g
Calcium	44 mg		
Phosphorus	53 mg	1,000 mcg = 1 mg	

Did You Know?

Beans, and broad beans in particular, contain more protein than any other fresh vegetable, except those of the green leafy variety. However, raw or partially cooked broad beans could cause a form of anaemia called favism in persons with a rare genetically inherited condition called G6PD deficiency.

3.5.4 Stuffed Brinjal

Preparation Time	:	15 min
Cooking Time	:	25 min

Serves 6

Ingredients

1 medium/90 g/3 oz Bombay onion, coarsely chopped
1 whole pod/10 g/ 1/3 oz garlic
1/2" or 1 cm piece/4 g/ 1/8 oz fresh ginger
1/2 tsp cumin seeds

1/4 tsp fenugreek seeds
A marble-sized ball of tamarind
1/4 tsp sugar
1/2 tsp turmeric powder
1/2 tsp coriander powder
1/4 tsp red chilli powder
Salt to taste
6 medium/300 g/10 oz round brinjals
1 tbsp/15 ml/ 1/2 fl oz oil
3 tbsp/45 ml/1 1/2 fl oz hot water

(1) *Grind the onion, garlic, ginger, cumin seeds, fenugreek seeds, tamarind and sugar together to a paste. Mix in the turmeric powder, coriander powder, red chilli powder and a little salt.*

(2) *Wash the brinjals and slit lengthways into four, retaining the stalk. Stuff them with the ground paste and set aside.*

(3) *Heat a heavy, round-bottomed kadai, then add the oil. Lower the heat and place the brinjals gently in the hot oil. Cook until the outside is well fried, turning occasionally. Add the hot water and any leftover paste. Simmer, covered, turning the brinjals once until they are tender and all the water is absorbed.*

(4) *Serve with rice or chappatis.*

Per Serving			
Kilocalories	48	Iron	0.5 mg
Protein	1 g	Vitamin C	8 mg
Fat	3 g	Vitamin A (as carotene)	38 mcg
Carbohydrate	5 g	Fibre	1 g
Calcium	18 mg		
Phosphorus	38 mg	1,000 mcg = 1 mg	

Health Tip

In India, stuffed brinjals are usually basted in generous amounts of oil until they are cooked. No water is added. In this recipe, to reduce the amount of oil, a little water has been included.

Safety in the Kitchen

Never leave oil or fat unguarded on the stove. It could lead to a dangerous fat fire. Try to keep your cool if you see a pan of oil in flames and follow these steps. Turn off the heat at once. Switch off all the fans in the kitchen and close all the doors and windows. Place a large lid over the pan to cover it completely or sprinkle with salt or bicarbonate of soda. If neither is available, remove some soil from a flowerpot and put out the flame. Never try to douse a fat fire with water which will only encourage burning or flour which could cause an explosion.

3.5.5 Potato Masala (Spicy Potato Mash)

Preparation Time : 5 min
Cooking Time : 25 min

Serves 6

Ingredients

5 medium/450 g/15 oz potatoes
2 tsp/10 ml/ 1/3 fl oz oil
1/2 tsp mustard seeds
2 medium/180 g/6 oz Bombay onions, thinly sliced
2 medium/5 g/ 1/6 oz green chillies, finely chopped
1/4 tsp cumin seeds, coarsely crushed
A sprig of curry leaves, finely chopped
1 cup/250 ml/8 fl oz water
1/2 tsp turmeric powder
1/4 tsp red chilli powder
Salt to taste

(1) Scrub the potatoes. Place them in a pressure-cooker together with sufficient water. Close the cooker. Bring to maximum pressure over high heat, then lower the flame and pressure-cook for 5 minutes. Remove from the fire. Allow the pressure inside the cooker to dissipate, then peel and mash the potatoes coarsely with a fork.

(2) Heat a pan, then add the oil. Add the mustard seeds. When the mustard seeds begin to splutter, add the onions, green chillies, cumin seeds and curry leaves. Fry until the onions turn pink and soft.

(3) Add the water, turmeric powder, red chilli powder and salt. Bring to the boil, then add the mashed potatoes. Lower the heat and continue stirring until the mixture is well blended and begins to lump together.

(4) Remove from the fire and serve with rice or chappatis. Also use as a filling for masala dosais.

Per Serving			
Kilocalories	103	Iron	1 mg
Protein	2 g	Vitamin C	17 mg
Fat	2 g	Vitamin A (as carotene)	73 mcg
Carbohydrate	20 g	Fibre	0.5 g
Calcium	23 mg		
Phosphorus	46 mg	1,000 mcg = 1 mg	

Potato Paradox

The potato is not a nutritional outcast. One medium potato (90 g/3 oz) provides 87 kcal which is less than 98 kcal, the energy yield of 2 slices (40 g/1 1/3 oz) of white bread. However, because it lends itself to every possible culinary manipulation, the *form* in which it is eaten assumes great significance. All too often, potatoes are incorporated with fat—French fries, potato wafers, creamed potatoes—which naturally provide kilocalories in abundance. These variations are best avoided.

Almost every preparation of potatoes in Indian cooking, including this recipe from Tamil Nadu, is extremely healthy except perhaps deep-fried batata vadas and bondas. Besides providing many useful calories through carbohydrates, potatoes are also a reliable source of vitamin C. One medium potato has as much vitamin C as 1 medium ripe tomato, since 100 g of potatoes give 17 mg of vitamin C. Cooking potatoes in their jackets helps to retain this vitamin better. Vitamin C is destroyed by heating. This can be prevented by creating an acidic medium which has a protective effect by the addition of tamarind, lime juice, mango powder, kokum, raw mango, tomatoes, curds or vinegar.

Potatoes also contain vitamin B_1, vitamin B_3, vitamin B_6 and pantothenic acid of the B complex group, so necessary for optimum cardiovascular, gastrointestinal, skin and neurological functioning.

Potatoes also contain iodine which is essential for the formation of the hormones produced by the thyroid gland. Magnesium, sulphur and molybdenum are the other minerals found in potatoes, besides the electrolyte potassium.

3.5.6 Indian Vegetable Stew

Preparation Time : 20 min
Cooking Time : 30 min

Serves 6

Ingredients

2 large/250 g/8 oz potatoes
1 medium/500 g/1.1 lb cauliflower
4 medium/180 g/6 oz carrots
About 8/90 g/3 oz fresh beans
About 12/60 g/2 oz sambhar onions, peeled
2" or 5 cm piece/15 g/ 1/2 oz fresh ginger
2 medium/5 g/ 1/6 oz green chillies
5 small, green cardamoms
5 cloves
1" or 2.5 cm stick cinnamon
2 medium/180 g/6 oz Bombay onions, thinly sliced
2 handfuls/60 g/2 oz shelled peas
1/4 tsp turmeric powder
Salt to taste
2 cups/500 ml/16 fl oz hot water
1 cup/250 ml/8 fl oz skimmed milk
1 tbsp/15 g/ 1/2 oz refined wheat flour
1/2 cup/125 ml/4 fl oz cold water
1/2 bundle/15 g/ 1/2 oz coriander leaves, finely chopped

(1) Scrub the potatoes. Place them in a pressure-cooker together with sufficient water. Close the cooker. Bring to maximum pressure over high heat, then lower the flame and pressure-cook for 5 minutes. Remove from the fire. Allow the pressure inside the cooker to dissipate, then peel and cut the potatoes into large cubes. Set aside.

(2) Remove the leaves of the cauliflower, wash and break into florets.

(3) Wash the carrots and peel. Slice them across to get little circles.

(4) Wash and string the beans. Cut them into 1" (2.5 cm) pieces.

(5) Grind the sambhar onions, ginger and green chillies together to a coarse paste.

(6) Remove the seeds from the cardamom pods. Powder them together with the cloves and cinnamon. Set aside.

(7)   Place the cauliflower, carrots, beans, ground paste, sliced onions, peas, turmeric powder and salt in a wide pan together with 2 cups hot water. Bring to the boil. Lower the heat and simmer until the vegetables are tender. Add the cooked potatoes.

(8)   Pour in the skimmed milk and sprinkle with the powdered spices.

(9)   Mix the refined flour with 1/2 cup cold water until smooth. Pour the mixture in a steady stream into the stew and bring to the boil. Allow to thicken. Add more salt if necessary.

(10) Garnish with the chopped coriander leaves and serve with iddlis or white bread.

Per Serving			
Kilocalories	131	Iron	2 mg
Protein	6 g	Vitamin C	55 mg
Fat	0.5 g	Vitamin A (as carotene)	3,107 mcg
Carbohydrate	26 g	Fibre	2 g
Calcium	132 mg	Cholesterol	1 mg
Phosphorus	293 mg	1,000 mcg = 1 mg	

What's (Indian) Stewing?

Traditionally, coconut milk is used instead of cow's milk in this recipe from the Kanyakumari district of Tamil Nadu. The vegetables are cooked in the second and third extract of coconut milk (not in hot water) and the first thick milk, also known as coconut cream, is added just before the stew is drawn off the fire. For health reasons, coconut milk, which is comprised largely of saturated fatty acids, has been replaced with skimmed cow's milk.

Vegetable stew is the perfect food for children and those recovering from illness or surgery as it is low in fat and packed with vitamins and minerals so necessary for growth and repair. It may be noted that no fat is added to this dish, not even in the manner of the customary Indian tempering.

Carrots are particularly rich in carotene, phosphorus, sodium and potassium. Cauliflower is abundant in vitamin K, vitamin C, pantothenic acid, the B vitamin which protects against certain pollutants especially the pesticide DDT, other B vitamins like vitamin B_6 and folic acid, the mineral sulphur, and the electrolyte potassium. Since potatoes are likely to be available throughout the year, they should be considered a constant source of many vitamins and minerals.

To improve the protein content, cooked meat or chicken may be added. It also presents a delightful Mixed Stew. Stir it in before thickening the stew.

3.5.7 Zimikand Bhartha (Mashed Yam)

Preparation Time   :   15 min
Cooking Time   :   25 min

Serves 6

Ingredients

500 g/1.1 lb elephant yam
2 medium/5 g/ 1/6 oz green chillies, deseeded
1" or 2.5 cm piece/8 g/ 1/4 oz fresh ginger
4 tsp/20 ml/ 2/3 fl oz oil
1 medium/90 g/3 oz Bombay onion, finely chopped
1/2 tsp turmeric powder
Salt to taste
1 tsp/5 ml/ 1/6 fl oz lime juice
1/2 bundle/15 g/ 1/2 oz coriander leaves, finely chopped

(1)   Remove the outer skin of the yam, chop coarsely and wash in salted water. Place the yam in a pressure-cooker container. Do not add extra water to the yam. Pour sufficient water in the body of the pressure-cooker. Lower the container into the pressure-cooker. Close the cooker. Bring to maximum pressure over high heat, then lower the flame and pressure-cook for 7 minutes. Remove from the fire. Allow the pressure inside the cooker to dissipate.

(2)   Grind the green chillies and ginger together to a paste.

(3)   Heat a pan, then add the oil. When the oil is very hot, add the onion and fry until soft and glassy. Add the ground paste and turmeric powder. Fry for 2 minutes. Add the cooked yam and stir until well mixed. Add salt.

(4)   Sprinkle with the lime juice and coriander leaves. Serve hot with chappatis.

Per Serving			
Kilocalories	100	Iron	1 mg
Protein	1 g	Vitamin C	7 mg
Fat	4 g	Vitamin A (as carotene)	591 mcg
Carbohydrate	16 g	Fibre	1 g
Calcium	50 mg		
Phosphorus	36 mg	1,000 mcg = 1 mg	

Health Notes

This recipe is a variation of the well-known Baingan Bhartha (roasted, mashed brinjals) of North India. No spices have been used since elephant yam and onions are known to be beneficial in the treatment of haemorrhoids (piles). Yam also helps to relieve chest conditions such as excessive phlegm and asthma.

3.5.8 Mattar Paneer (Peas and Cottage Cheese in Gravy)

Preparation Time	:	15 min
Cooking Time	:	30 min

Serves 6

Ingredients

250 g/8 oz Indian cottage cheese (Recipe No: 3.11.3)
2 medium/5 g/ 1/6 oz green chillies, deseeded
1 whole pod/10 g/ 1/3 oz garlic
1" or 2.5 cm piece/8 g/ 1/4 oz fresh ginger
1 tbsp/15 ml/ 1/2 fl oz oil
1 medium/90 g/3 oz Bombay onion, finely chopped
2 medium/120 g/4 oz ripe tomatoes, diced
1 1/2 cups/375 ml/12 1/2 fl oz water
1 1/2 cups or 8 handfuls /240 g/8 oz shelled peas (from 500 g/1.1 lb unshelled peas)
1 tsp turmeric powder
Pinch of red chilli powder
1/2 tsp sugar
Salt to taste
1 tsp garam masala (Recipe No: 3.11.6)
1/2 bundle/15 g/ 1/2 oz coriander leaves, finely chopped

(1) *Cut the cottage cheese into 1/2" (1 cm) squares of 1" (2.5 cm) thickness.*

(2) *Grind the green chillies, garlic and ginger together to a paste.*

(3) *Heat a pan, then add the oil. When it begins to smoke, add the cottage cheese cubes and fry until golden. Drain from the oil and set aside.*

(4) *To the same oil, add the chopped onion and fry until just brown. Stir in the ground paste and fry for a minute or two. Add the tomatoes and cook until soft and mushy. Pour in the water. Add the peas, turmeric powder, red chilli powder, sugar and salt. Bring to the boil. Lower the heat and simmer until the peas are tender.*

(5) *Add the fried cottage cheese cubes. Simmer for 5 minutes. Sprinkle with the garam masala and coriander leaves. Serve hot with chappatis or rice.*

Per Serving			
Kilocalories	191	Vitamin C	17 mg
Protein	11 g	Vitamin A (as carotene)	1,035 mcg
Fat	12 g	Vitamin A (as retinol)	46 mcg
Carbohydrate	11 g	Fibre	2 g
Calcium	123 mg	Cholesterol	39 mg
Phosphorus	135 mg		
Iron	1 mg	1,000 mcg = 1 mg	

Slimmer's Alternative

A great favourite in North India, it will be possible to use only 2 tsp/10 ml/ 1/3 fl oz oil for this dish if home-made cottage cheese is substituted for the bought one. Use chenna, the soft, crumbly cheese that is obtained from separating the curd or milk solids from the whey before it is pressed and flattened into paneer (Recipe No: 3.11.3). Stir it into the gravy after the peas are cooked without frying. Simmer for 5 minutes before serving.

Use skimmed milk to make paneer. The fat and cholesterol content with be cut drastically. However, vitamin A as retinol, being fat soluble, will be lost too.

Substituting whey for water will ensure that all the nutrients in milk are consumed besides giving this dish a delicate, piquant flavour.

Commercially prepared cottage cheese was used for this recipe.

3.5.9 Muttaikose-Muttai Pugath (Indian Stir-fried Cabbage with Egg)

Preparation Time	:	10 min
Cooking Time	:	15 min

Serves 6

Ingredients

2 medium/90 g/3 oz eggs
Salt to taste
Pinch of red chilli powder
2 tsp/10 ml/ 1/3 fl oz oil

1/2 tsp mustard seeds
1 medium/90 g/3 oz Bombay onion, finely chopped
A sprig of curry leaves, finely chopped
2 medium/5 g/ 1/6 oz green chillies, deseeded and finely chopped
1 small or 1/2 medium/500 g/1.1 lb cabbage, washed and shredded
1/4 tsp turmeric powder
Salt
2 tbsp/30 ml/1 fl oz hot water
1 1/2 tsp/7.5 ml/ 1/4 fl oz lime juice

(1) *Whisk the eggs lightly, adding a little salt and the red chilli powder.*

(2) *Heat a kadai, then add the oil. Add the mustard seeds. When the mustard seeds begin to splutter, add the chopped onion, curry leaves and green chillies. Cook until the onion is soft. Stir in the cabbage and continue to fry for about 3 minutes. Add the turmeric powder, some salt and the hot water. Cook uncovered until the cabbage is tender.*

(3) *Heap the cabbage around the sides of the kadai, making a well in the centre. Pour in the beaten egg. Over low heat, stir only the egg until it just begins to set. Gradually draw the cabbage into the egg by stirring in ever-widening circles.*

(4) *When all the cabbage has been mixed with the egg, stir for a minute or two longer, then sprinkle with the lime juice. Serve with hot rice or chappatis.*

Per Serving			
Kilocalories	72	Vitamin C	107 mg
Protein	4 g	Vitamin A (as carotene)	245 mcg
Fat	4 g	Vitamin A (as retinol)	54 mcg
Carbohydrate	6 g	Fibre	1 g
Calcium	51 mg	Cholesterol	75 mg
Phosphorus	78 mg		
Iron	1 mg	1,000 mcg = 1 mg	

Other Uses

Although pugath is typical of the cuisine of Tamil Nadu, this particular variation can be used for stuffing parathas or even as a filling for deep-fried savouries like samosas.

Nutritionally Speaking

Always wash vegetables before cutting them, never after. This practice helps retain the water soluble vitamins like vitamin C (of which cabbage is a very good source) and the B complex vitamins.

3.5.10 Aloo aur Palak ki Bhaaji
(Spice-flavoured Potato and Spinach)

Preparation Time	:	20 min
Cooking Time	:	30 min

Serves 4

Ingredients

2 large/250 g/8 oz potatoes
2 bundles/100 g/3 1/3 oz spinach
1 tsp cumin seeds
20 black peppercorns
2 tsp/10 ml/ 1/3 fl oz oil
1 medium/90 g/3 oz Bombay onion, finely chopped
1 whole pod/10 g/ 1/3 oz garlic, finely chopped
1" or 2.5 cm piece/8 g/ 1/4 oz fresh ginger, finely chopped
1/2 tsp coriander powder
1/2 cup/125 ml/4 fl oz hot water
1/2 tsp turmeric powder
Salt to taste
1 1/2 cups/375 ml/12 1/2 fl oz hot water
1 1/2 tsp/7.5 ml/ 1/4 fl oz lime juice
1/4 tsp garam masala (Recipe No: 3.11.6)

(1) Scrub the potatoes. Place them in a pressure-cooker together with sufficient water. Close the cooker. Bring to maximum pressure over high heat, then lower the flame and pressure-cook for 5 minutes. Remove from the fire. Allow the pressure inside the cooker to dissipate, then peel and mash 1 potato until smooth with a fork. Cube the other. Set aside.

(2) Wash the spinach and strip the leaves from the stalks. Retain the tender terminal shoot. Shred coarsely by hand (if a knife is used, select one with a stainless steel blade only).

(3) Powder the cumin seeds and peppercorns together.

(4) Heat a pan, then add the oil. When the oil begins to smoke, add the chopped onion and garlic. Fry until the onion browns. Add the ginger and stir for 1 minute. Add the powdered spices and coriander powder. Fry for 1 minute.

(5) Add the spinach and stir until limp. Pour in 1/2 cup hot water. Add the turmeric powder and salt. Cook uncovered for 5 minutes. Draw off the heat and mash

the spinach thoroughly. (If a blender/mixer is used, cool the spinach, then blend for 15 seconds at the lowest speed. Open the jar, stir the contents, and blend once more for 15 seconds or until smooth.)

(6) *Return the spinach to the fire, and stir in the cooked potatoes, 1 1/2 cups hot water and more salt if necessary. Bring to the boil, then lower the heat and simmer for 5 minutes or until the gravy is just thick.*

(7) *Sprinkle with the lime juice and garam masala. Serve hot with chappatis or rice.*

Per Serving			
Kilocalories	107	Iron	1 mg
Protein	2 g	Vitamin C	22 mg
Fat	3 g	Vitamin A (as carotene)	2,376 mcg
Carbohydrate	19 g	Fibre	1 g
Calcium	38 mg		
Phosphorus	51 mg	1,000 mcg = 1 mg	

Some Effects of Common Cooking Practices

To prevent discoloration of green vegetables, cook them uncovered so that the naturally present, volatile organic acids can escape.

The addition of acids (tamarind, lime and lemon juice, vinegar) during cooking also renders the green pigment, chlorophyll, a dull, greenish-brown.

Alkalis have the opposite effect—they heighten the colour of the vegetables to which they are added. The practice of adding baking soda (an alkaline substance) to retain the colours of vegetables is, however, nutritionally unsound. It destroys all the B vitamins present with the exception of vitamin B_3, and, possibly, folic acid.

Leafy Protein?

Incredible, but it's true. Green leaves do contain protein. Much research has been done to investigate the possibility of recommending proteins derived from green leafy vegetables (which have the highest among fresh vegetables) as a good means of meeting the daily protein requirement of Indians who are largely vegetarian. So far, however, the results drawn are not comparable with animal proteins which are better utilized in the human body. So until proved otherwise, vegetarians will have to bank on cereals, pulses, legumes, nuts, oilseeds and milk for their protein needs.

Indian Food Sense

Getting iron from vegetable sources is never very satisfactory, though one of the factors that assist in increasing the availability of iron from vegetable foods is vitamin C. Combining iron-rich spinach with potatoes which contain a fair amount of vitamin C in aloo aur palak ki bhaaji reflects the soundness of food combinations in Indian cooking in recipes like this staple from North India.

3.5.11 Curried Mushroom

Preparation Time   :   20 min
Cooking Time   :   25 min

Serves 4

Ingredients

1 tbsp/5 g/ 1/6 oz poppy seeds
1/2" or 1 cm piece/4 g/ 1/8 oz fresh ginger
1/2 tsp cumin seeds
25 black peppercorns
1" or 2.5 cm stick cinnamon
2 tsp/10 ml/ 1/3 fl oz oil
About 24/120 g/4 oz sambhar onions, finely chopped
1/4 tsp turmeric powder
Pinch of red chilli powder
2 medium/120 g/4 oz ripe tomatoes, diced
200 g/7 oz button (or closed/open cup) mushrooms, washed and quartered
Salt to taste
1/2 cup/125 ml/4 fl oz hot water

(1) *Grind the poppy seeds, ginger, cumin seeds, peppercorns and cinnamon together to a paste, adding a little water.*

(2) *Heat a pan, then add the oil. When the oil begins to smoke, add the onions. Fry until the onions are just brown. Add the ground paste, turmeric powder and red chilli powder. Stir for 1 minute. Add the tomatoes and cook until they are soft and mushy. Add the mushrooms and stir for about 2 minutes. When all the ingredients are well blended, add the salt. Pour in the hot water. Simmer until most of the water is absorbed and the gravy is thick.*

(3) *Serve hot with rice or chappatis.*

Per Serving			
Kilocalories	73	Iron	2 mg
Protein	3 g	Vitamin C	9 mg
Fat	3 g	Vitamin A (as carotene)	908 mcg
Carbohydrate	8 g	Fibre	1 g
Calcium	49 mg		
Phosphorus	85 mg	1,000 mcg = 1 mg	

Health Viewpoint

Mushrooms contain no cholesterol, and have negligible amounts of fat. They are ideal as a slimmer's food. They are an excellent source of copper and the B vitamin pantothenic acid. Other B vitamins present in them are vitamin B_1, vitamin B_2, vitamin B_3, vitamin B_6 and folic acid. Mushrooms contain ergosterol, which is converted to vitamin D when exposed to ultraviolet rays such as those in sunlight. Mushrooms also provide fair amounts of protein (one of the highest among vegetables), phosphorus and zinc. Their potassium content is on par with most fruits. They are low in sodium and have a high fibre content.

> Persons susceptible to gout should restrict their intake of mushrooms.

Poppy seeds contain large amounts of calcium, chromium, phosphorus, iron and zinc. But it is of little dietary significance, because its use in cooking is limited. Moreover, the availability of these minerals is in doubt because of the presence of various naturally occurring nutrient inhibitors that interfere with absorption.

Poppy seeds are, additionally, an excellent remedy to ease the pain and discomfort of non-infectious stomach ailments like colic.

3.6 Seafood
Meat
Poultry

3.6.1 Fish Fry

Preparation Time   :   3 min
Marination Time   :   15 min
Cooking Time   :   24 min

Serves 4

Ingredients

1/2 tsp turmeric powder
1/4 tsp red chilli powder
1/2 tsp salt
4 large slices/600 g/1 1/4 lb seer fish, cleaned and washed
2 tbsp/30 ml/1 fl oz oil

(1) *Make a paste with the turmeric powder, red chilli powder and salt by adding a little water.*

(2) *Smear the paste evenly over the fish slices. Set aside for 15 minutes.*

(3) *Heat a frying pan, then add 2 tsp oil. When the oil begins to smoke, reduce the heat and place 2 slices of fish in it. Cook for 6 minutes on one side, then turn over. Dot with another teaspoon of oil and cook for a further 6 minutes. Remove and drain on absorbent paper.*

(4) *Fry the remaining slices of fish. Serve with hot rice and plain dhal curry.*

Per Serving			
Kilocalories	257	Iron	8 mg
Protein	34 g	Vitamin C	Nil
Fat	14 g	Vitamin A	Nil
Carbohydrate	Nil	Fibre	Nil
Calcium	107 mg	Cholesterol value not available	
Phosphorus	858 mg	1,000 mcg = 1 mg	

Cooking Tips

Heating the pan *before* adding oil reduces the amount of oil necessary to prevent the food from sticking.

Keep the heat low when cooking fish. This will cook the fish evenly, and will prevent the odour of fish frying from filling the whole house.

Any large fish may be substituted for seer.

3.6.2 Goan Prawn Curry

Preparation Time   :   50 min
Soaking Time   :   10 min
Cooking Time   :   35 min

Serves 6

Ingredients

500 g/1.1 lb unshelled prawns
Salt to taste
A lime-sized ball/30 g/1 oz tamarind
1 cup/250 ml/8 fl oz hot water
10 fresh Kashmiri chillies
1/2 medium shell/90 g/3 oz freshly grated coconut
3 whole pods/30 g/1 oz garlic
1/2 tsp cumin seeds
1/4 tsp mustard seeds
15 black peppercorns
2 tsp/10 ml/ 1/3 fl oz oil
1 medium/90 g/3 oz Bombay onion, finely chopped
2 cups/500 ml/16 fl oz hot water
2 tsp coriander powder
2 medium/5 g/ 1/6 oz green chillies, slit lengthways

(1) Shell and devein the prawns. Mix in a little salt and set aside.

(2) Soak the tamarind in 1/2 cup hot water for 10 minutes. Squeeze to extract pulp. To the same tamarind, add another 1/2 cup hot water and extract pulp a second time.

(3) Deseed the Kashmiri chillies. Grind the Kashmiri chillies, grated coconut, garlic, cumin seeds, mustard seeds and peppercorns together to a smooth paste, adding a little water.

(4) Heat a pan, then add the oil. Add the chopped onion and cook until transparent. Add the ground paste, and fry for 3 minutes over moderate heat. Pour in the 2 cups hot water and tamarind extract. Add the coriander powder and green chillies. Bring to the boil. Lower the heat and simmer for 5 minutes. Add the prawns. Taste for salt and adjust the seasoning. Cook over low heat for 10 minutes.

(5) Serve hot with plain, white rice.

Per Serving			
Kilocalories	159	Iron	4 mg
Protein	11 g	Vitamin C	4 mg
Fat	9 g	Vitamin A (as carotene)	34 mcg
Carbohydrate	9 g	Fibre	1 g
Calcium	188 mg	Cholesterol	75 mg
Phosphorus	209 mg	1,000 mcg = 1 mg	

Cooking Notes

The yield from 500 g/1.1 lb unshelled prawns is 300 g/10 oz of edible meat.

Kashmiri chillies will give the curry a fiery red colour, but not the pungency to match it. So, do not hestitate to use them, especially with the seeds removed. Soak the chillies in sufficient water to cover for 30 minutes before grinding. The curry will look richer—and redder. Use 1 tsp Kashmiri chilli powder if the fresh chillies are not available.

If neither fresh Kashmiri chillies nor the powder is available, substitute with whole dried red chillies but use half the number mentioned in the recipe. The colour will be missing though.

Goan Fish Curry is also cooked this way. Common to the west coast of India, fish and seafood are typically combined with coconut. Chillies and various souring agents like tamarind or raw mango are also responsible for the distinct flavours of this region.

Nutrition Talk

Seafood and coconut together are not half as detrimental to one's health as coconut consumed outside this combination. Even though prawns contain relatively high amounts of cholesterol, they are less likely to adversely affect blood cholesterol levels. Further, prawns are extremely low in fat, providing only 1 g per 100 g of the edible portion. (The fat in this recipe comes primarily from coconut—42 per cent of fresh coconut flesh is fat.)

3.6.3 Masala Crab

Preparation Time	:	20 min
Cooking Time	:	25 min

Serves 6

Ingredients

About 6/2 kg/4 1/4 lb crabs
1/2 tsp turmeric powder
1/2 tsp red chilli powder
Salt to taste
About 12/60 g/2 oz sambhar onions, peeled
2 whole pods/20 g/ 2/3 oz garlic
2" or 5 cm piece/15 g/ 1/2 oz fresh ginger
20 black peppercorns
1/2 tsp cumin seeds
Pinch of fenugreek seeds
A sprig of curry leaves
2 tbsp/30 ml/1 fl oz oil
2 medium/180 g/6 oz Bombay onions, finely chopped

(1) *Clean and wash the crabs. Cut across in half. Sprinkle the turmeric powder, red chilli powder and salt over the crabs. Mix well. Set aside.*

(2) *Grind the sambhar onions, garlic, ginger, peppercorns, cumin seeds, fenugreek seeds and curry leaves together to a paste, adding a little water.*

(3) *Heat a kadai, then add the oil. Add the chopped onions and fry until brown. Stir in the ground paste and cook for about 2 minutes. Add the crabs and stir continuously until well coated with the paste. Cover and cook (without adding any extra water) over low heat until all the water is absorbed and the oil begins to separate out.*

(4) *Serve with plain, white rice and rasam.*

Per Serving			
Kilocalories	138	Iron	24 mg
Protein	11 g	Vitamin C	4 mg
Fat	6 g	Vitamin A (as carotene)	902 mcg
Carbohydrate	10 g	Fibre	Trace
Calcium	1,539 mg	Cholesterol	89 mg
Phosphorus	199 mg	1,000 mcg = 1 mg	

A Crabby Matter

Crab is a good source of carotene, the precursor of vitamin A, many B vitamins especially vitamin B_{12}, vitamin B_3 and pantothenic acid, and, the minerals of calcium, iron, zinc and cobalt. Excellent though crab is for its low-fat protein, it contains some cholesterol.

When purchasing crab, a good measure of caution should be exercised. It is safer to buy deep-sea crabs, as those caught closer to the shore or from the backwaters are more likely to concentrate the wastes of civilization in their bodies, and are, therefore, a potential health hazard.

Two kilograms of crab yield a little over 600 g of edible meat. Crab meat is influenced by the lunar cycle. Unless you are careful, you could end up buying mere shells around full moon.

3.6.4 Meen Kolumbu (South Indian Fish Curry)

Preparation Time	:	20 min
Soaking Time	:	10 min
Cooking Time	:	20 min

Serves 6

Ingredients

1 large/1 kg/2.2 lb black pomfret
About 24/120 g/4 oz sambhar onions, peeled
1 1/2 whole pods/15 g/ 1/2 oz garlic
A large sprig/15 g/ 1/2 oz curry leaves
1 tsp cumin seeds
40 black peppercorns
1/2 medium shell/90 g/3 oz freshly grated coconut
A lime-sized ball/30 g/1 oz tamarind
1 cup/250 ml/8 fl oz hot water
2 tsp coriander powder
2 tsp turmeric powder
1 tsp red chilli powder
Salt to taste
2 cups/500 ml/16 fl oz water

(1) *Clean and wash the fish. Cut across into 3/4" (2 cm) thick slices (get it done at the fishmonger's—quicker and cleaner).*

(2) Grind the onions, garlic, curry leaves, cumin seeds and peppercorns together to a smooth paste, adding a little water. Grind the coconut separately until very smooth, adding the drained coconut water or plain water.

(3) Soak the tamarind in 1/2 cup hot water for 10 minutes. Squeeze to extract pulp. Add another 1/2 cup hot water to the same tamarind and extract pulp a second time.

(4) Place the ground paste, coconut paste, tamarind extract, coriander powder, turmeric powder, red chilli powder, salt and 2 cups water in a wide, (preferably) earthen vessel. Stir to blend, then immerse the fish slices in the mixture. Bring to the boil over high heat. Lower the heat and simmer for 10 minutes or until the fish is done. When the curry is cooking, do not use a spoon to stir it. Instead pick up the vessel and swirl the contents around every now and again.

(5) Serve hot with plain, white rice.

Per Serving			
Kilocalories	250	Iron	5 mg
Protein	29 g	Vitamin C	1 mg
Fat	10 g	Vitamin A (as carotene)	542 mcg
Carbohydrate	11 g	Fibre	2 g
Calcium	428 mg	Cholesterol value not available	
Phosphorus	475 mg	1,000 mcg = 1 mg	

Fish Facts

Cocount and fish in combination is a favourite in many regional cuisines like this recipe from the western coast of Tamil Nadu. The inherent wisdom of Indian cooking is evident because when combined with fish, coconut which is made up largely of saturated fat, is believed not to predispose to heart disease. Omega-3 fatty acids in fish, especially oily fish, appear to provide a protective effect.

In India, there exists a general conviction that fish and seafood should be avoided in the months of May, June, July and August. Two reasons are given. First, during these months, more refuse is carried to the sea by the monsoon waters, and sewage dumped in it or in inland bodies of water, is likely to get churned up. Second, it is believed that fish and seafood spawn at this time of the year and avoiding their intake ensures continuation of the species. If you wish to abide by this injunction, these months are rather easy to remember. They are the only four that do not have an "r" in them.

The Benefits of Traditional Cookware

It is customary to cook this curry in an earthen vessel, probably because of the special flavour it imparts. However, it has an interesting health angle to it. Since tamarind is always used, the acid could dissolve a greater amount of metal from vessels of aluminium, brass or copper than is generally considered safe, especially if the curry is cooked and stored in the same vessel for any length of time. Earthen vessels are non-reactive, and are, hence, a healthier option.

3.6.5 Mutton Tikki (Spiced Minced Mutton Cutlet)

Preparation Time	:	10 min
Resting Time	:	10 min
Cooking Time	:	1 hour 15 min

Makes 30

Ingredients

1 kg/2.2 lb minced mutton
1/2 tsp turmeric powder
1/4 tsp red chilli powder
Salt to taste
4 medium/360 g/12 oz potatoes
2 tsp/10 ml/ 1/3 fl oz refined oil
2 medium/180 g/6 oz Bombay onions, coarsely chopped
1 whole pod/10 g/ 1/3 oz garlic, coarsely chopped
2" or 5 cm piece/15 g/ 1/2 oz fresh ginger, coarsely chopped
2 medium/5 g/ 1/6 oz green chillies, coarsely chopped
1/2 tsp cumin seeds, powdered
A few coriander leaves, coarsely chopped
A few mint leaves, coarsely chopped
4 tbsp/60 ml/2 fl oz refined oil

(1) Wash the minced mutton using very little water and tip into a wide sieve to drain. Remove and place the mutton in a pressure-cooker container. Stir in the turmeric powder, red chilli powder and salt. Mix well. Do not add extra water to the mutton. Pour sufficient water in the body of the pressure-cooker. Lower the container into the pressure-cooker. Close the cooker. Bring to maximum pressure over high heat, then lower the flame and pressure-cook for 15 minutes. Remove from the fire and allow the pressure inside the cooker to dissipate.

(2) Scrub the potatoes. Place them in another pressure-cooker together with sufficient water. Close the cooker. Bring to maximum pressure over high heat, then lower the flame and pressure-cook for 10 minutes. Remove from the

fire. Allow the pressure inside the cooker to dissipate, then peel and mash the potatoes coarsely.

(3)   *Heat a kadai, then add 2 tsp oil. Add the onions and fry until glassy. Add the garlic, ginger and green chillies, and stir for 2 minutes. Add the cooked minced mutton and any stock that is drawn from it during pressure-cooking. Simmer uncovered until all the water is absorbed and the mixture is completely dry — about 15 minutes. Stir in the cooked potatoes. Sprinkle with the powdered cumin seeds, coriander leaves and mint leaves.*

(4)   *Put the meat-potato mixture through a mincer to get a fine paste. Add more salt if necessary.*

(5)   *Divide the mixture into 30 portions. Moisten both hands with water and flatten each portion into a round tikki (cutlet), 2" (5 cm) in diameter and 1/2" (1 cm) thick. Allow to dry for 10 minutes, preferably in the refrigerator.*

(6)   *Heat a frying pan, then add 2 tsp oil. Lower the heat and place 10 tikkis in the hot oil. When brown on one side, flip over and brown the reverse, adding another 2 tsp oil. Remove and drain on paper. Prepare the remaining 20 tikkis, frying them in two batches of 10 each.*

(7)   *Serve as a snack with coriander chutney or mint chutney, or with plain dhal curry and rice. Tikkis are also ideal for school lunches and picnics when placed in a hamburger bun.*

Per Tikki			
Kilocalories	92	Vitamin C	3 mg
Protein	6 g	Vitamin A (as carotene)	19 mcg
Fat	6 g	Vitamin A (as retinol)	3 mcg
Carbohydrate	4 g	Fibre	Trace
Calcium	47 mg	Cholesterol	28 mg
Phosphorus	52 mg		
Iron	1 mg	1,000 mcg = 1 mg	

Notes of Interest

By rule of thumb, 15 per cent of the kilogram will be lost to bone/gristle in meat. To make these tikkis, be sure to get the butcher to mince the mutton first. This greatly shortens the time spent in the kitchen.

If one does not mind a coarser texture, then it is not necessary to mince the meat again after cooking. Instead, mash the potatoes until very smooth and add 1 well-beaten egg to the mixture before it is divided up. The addition of egg will, however, increase the cholesterol content of each tikki by a further 8 mg. To avoid this, 2 egg whites will bind just as well and they contain no cholesterol as it is concentrated only in the yolk.

If a mixer/blender is used to do the second mincing, cool the cooked minced mutton and place in the jar. Blend at the lowest speed for 1 minute. Open the jar, stir the contents and blend again at the same speed for 2 minutes or until smooth. The grinding stone may also be used to get a smooth texture.

It is very important that the mincer/mixer/blender/grinding stone is cleaned with hot soapy water immediately after use as otherwise it will provide the perfect medium for bacteria to grow, especially those responsible for food poisoning. The mincer particularly should be cleaned with a brush (a toothbrush is eminently suitable) to get at all the difficult-to-reach crannies that are ideal breeding grounds for bacteria. Rinse and dry thoroughly before storage.

3.6.6 Pork Vindaloo (Pork Curry with Vinegar)

Preparation Time	:	25 min
Cooking Time	:	40 min

Serves 6

Ingredients

500 g/1.1 lb pork
2 whole pods/20 g/ 2/3 oz garlic
2" or 5 cm piece/15 g/ 1/2 oz fresh ginger
About 12/60 g/2 oz sambhar onions, peeled
1/2 cup/125 ml/4 fl oz vinegar
2 tsp. cumin seeds
1 tsp black peppercorns
1/2 tsp mustard seeds
1 tbsp/15 ml/ 1/2 fl oz oil
2 medium/180 g/6 oz Bombay onions, thinly sliced
2 tsp coriander powder
1 tsp red chilli powder
1 tsp turmeric powder
1/2 cup/125 ml/4 fl oz hot water
Salt to taste
1/2 bundle/15 g/ 1/2 oz coriander leaves, finely chopped

(1) Wash the pork, cube and squeeze out as much water as possible. Set aside.

(2) Grind the garlic, ginger and sambhar onions coarsely and separately, using a little vinegar if needed.

(3) Grind the cumin seeds, peppercorns and mustard seeds together to a paste, adding a little vinegar.

(4) Heat the oil in the body of a pressure-cooker. Add the garlic paste and fry for 1 minute. Add the ground ginger and sambhar onions. Fry until the paste begins to stick. Add the sliced onions and stir until they appear limp. (The mixture will be very dry at this stage but do not be tempted to add more oil. Fat will be drawn from the pork during cooking.) Put in the pork, coriander powder, red chilli powder, turmeric powder and spices ground in vinegar. Keep stirring until the pork loses its pinkish tinge. Pour in the remaining vinegar and hot water. Add salt. Close the cooker. Bring to maximum pressure over high heat, then lower the flame and pressure-cook for 10 minutes. Remove from the fire and allow the pressure inside the cooker to dissipate.

(5) Open the cooker and allow the vindaloo to simmer for 5 minutes. Sprinkle with the chopped coriander leaves. Serve with chappatis, naan or plain, white rice.

Vindaloo tastes best with iddlis and white bread. It improves on keeping, so make it a day in advance.

Per Serving			
Kilocalories	130	Vitamin C	9 mg
Protein	14 g	Vitamin A (as carotene)	389 mcg
Fat	6 g	Fibre	1 g
Carbohydrate	6 g	Cholesterol	59 mg
Calcium	52 mg	(cholesterol content of lean pork)	
Phosphorus	173 mg		
Iron	2 mg	1,000 mcg = 1 mg	

Pork in Perspective

Vindaloo made this way will have to be eaten the same day or kept refrigerated if any is left over. However, there exists a version (Pickled Vindaloo) that will remain unspoilt, unrefrigerated, for about 2 days, even in the hot plains of India.

Pickled Vindaloo

Wash the pork in vinegar, not water. Omit the onions and water completely. Instead, increase the amount of vinegar to 1 cup (250 ml/8 fl oz). Proceed as indicated in the recipe. Just before serving (each time), soften 2 thinly sliced Bombay onions (180 g/6 oz) in a little oil, add 2 diced ripe tomatoes (120 g/4 oz) (if liked) and stir in the vindaloo. Allow to simmer for 5 minutes before serving.

It must be noted that for a good vindaloo the fat has to be retained for a truly authentic flavour. Using vinegar helps to sharpen the flavour, and reduce the amount of salt. Goa and Mangalore on the west coast represent the regions in India where pork vindaloo is most popular.

Pork is an excellent source of vitamin B_1, necessary for the optimum functioning of the cardiovascular, nervous and gastrointestinal systems, and vitamin B_6. Vitamin B_3, pantothenic acid and vitamin B_{12} are the other B vitamins found in pork. Zinc, phosphorus, iron and sulphur are also found in abundance in pork. However, the fat in pork contains a high level of saturated fatty acids and cholesterol which makes it a less desirable alternative to other flesh foods like fish and poultry.

3.6.7 Mutton Curry

Preparation Time   :   20 min
Cooking Time   :   50 min

Serves 6

Ingredients

500 g/1.1 lb mutton
1/2 tsp turmeric powder
Salt to taste
About 24/120 g/4 oz sambhar onions, peeled
2 whole pods/20 g/ 2/3 oz garlic
2" or 5 cm piece/15 g/ 1/2 oz fresh ginger
4 medium/10 g/ 1/3 oz green chillies
1/2 tsp cumin seeds
4 cloves
4 small, green cardamoms, seeds only
1" or 2.5 cm stick cinnamon
2 tsp/10 ml/ 1/3 fl oz oil
2 medium/180 g/6 oz Bombay onions, thinly sliced
2 medium/180 g/6 oz potatoes, scrubbed and quartered
2 medium/120 g/4 oz ripe tomatoes, quartered
5 small/120 g/4 oz carrots, diced
1 1/2 cups/375 ml/12 1/2 fl oz hot water

(1) *Clean and wash the mutton. Cut into big chunks. Add the turmeric powder and salt. Mix well and set aside.*

(2) *Grind the sambhar onions, garlic, ginger and green chillies together to a coarse paste.*

(3) *Powder the cumin seeds, cloves, cardamom seeds and cinnamon together.*

(4) *In the body of a pressure-cooker of minimum 7 1/2-litre capacity, heat the oil and fry the sliced onions until soft. Add the ground paste and stir for 1 minute. Put in the potatoes, tomatoes and carrots. When the tomatoes begin to soften, add the mutton and fry for 10 minutes. Pour in the hot water. Add the powdered spices and more salt if necessary. Close the cooker. Bring to maximum pressure over high heat, then lower the flame and pressure-cook for 10 minutes. Remove from the fire and allow the pressure inside the cooker to dissipate. Open and stir well.*

(5) *Serve hot with rice, iddlis or chappatis.*

Per Serving			
Kilocalories	237	Vitamin C	17 mg
Protein	16 g	Vitamin A (as carotene)	2,422 mcg
Fat	12 g	Vitamin A (as retinol)	7 mcg
Carbohydrate	17 g	Fibre	1 g
Calcium	165 mg	Cholesterol	75 mg
Phosphorus	275 mg		
Iron	3 mg	1,000 mcg = 1 mg	

Cholesterol in Meat

It is rather well known that removing the skin of poultry markedly lowers the cholesterol present. In meats, however, removing or trimming the fat does not drastically reduce their cholesterol content as both the lean and fat contain about the same levels of cholesterol.

The mutton used in this recipe was not trimmed. A daily intake of 300 to 500 mg of cholesterol does not seem to alter the normal serum cholesterol levels of 120 to 200 mg per 100 ml in adult human beings.

3.6.8 Devilled Beef

Preparation Time	:	25 min
Cooking Time	:	45 min

Serves 6

Ingredients

2" or 5 cm piece/15 g/ 1/2 oz fresh ginger
1 whole pod/10 g/ 1/3 oz garlic
A sprig of curry leaves

1 kg/2.2 lb beef (undercut), cut into strips
1/2 tsp turmeric powder
1/4 tsp red chilli powder
Salt to taste
2 tbsp/30 ml/1 fl oz oil
2 medium/180 g/6 oz Bombay onions, thinly sliced
3 whole dried red chillies, pounded
4 tbsp/60 ml/2 fl oz vinegar
20 black peppercorns, powdered

(1) Grind the ginger, garlic and curry leaves together to a paste.

(2) Wash and pound the meat to flatten. Place the meat, ground paste, turmeric powder, red chilli powder and salt in a pressure-cooker container. Mix well. Do not add extra water to the meat. Pour sufficient water in the body of the pressure-cooker. Lower the container into the pressure-cooker. Close the cooker. Bring to maximum pressure over high heat, then lower the flame and pressure-cook for 20 minutes. Remove from the fire and allow the pressure inside the cooker to dissipate.

(3) Heat the oil until smoking in a heavy iron kadai. Add the sliced onions and pounded chillies. Fry until the onions are quite brown. Add the cooked meat and any stock that is drawn from it during pressure-cooking. Stir in the vinegar. Simmer uncovered until dry.

(4) Add the powdered peppercorns. Stir continuously until the oil begins to separate out. Serve hot with white rice and plain dhal curry or puliodarai.

Per Serving			
Kilocalories	226	Vitamin C	7 mg
Protein	33 g	Vitamin A (as carotene)	36 mcg
Fat	9 g	Vitamin A (as retinol)	26 mcg
Carbohydrate	4 g	Fibre	Trace
Calcium	31 mg	Cholesterol	128 mg
Phosphorus	291 mg		
Iron	1 mg	1,000 mcg = 1 mg	

Food Facts

This recipe has been included because it is impossible to ignore the culinary contributions of a minority that is fast dwindling in India, the Anglo-Indian community.

Get the meat cut into strips by the butcher—easier and quicker.

It is important that the oil is very hot before the onions are added. Only then will the meat be nice and dry when finished.

The vitamin A present in this dish is in the form of carotene, the precursor of vitamin A, and as retinol, the vitamin itself. Retinol is especially beneficial as no conversion is necessary before the vitamin is utilized by the human body, and it is the form usually present in animal foods.

Vinegar added to foods cooked in an iron vessel has two important benefits. First, it makes the iron salts present in the food more readily available for absorption in the human gut. Second, being acidic, it liberates iron from the vessel, thereby increasing the iron content of the dish.

However, the iron per serving indicated in this recipe is the value obtained from food sources only and does not include the contribution of the iron dissociated from the vessel.

3.6.9 Mutton Kheema (Spicy Minced Mutton)

Preparation Time : 20 min
Cooking Time : 45 min

Serves 6

Ingredients

2 large/250 g/8 oz potatoes
500 g/1.1 lb minced mutton
1/2 tsp turmeric powder
1/4 tsp red chilli powder
Salt to taste
About 12/60 g/2 oz sambhar onions, peeled
2 whole pods/20 g/ 2/3 oz garlic
2" or 5 cm piece/15 g/ 1/2 oz fresh ginger
1 tsp cumin seeds
2 tsp/10 ml/ 1/3 fl oz oil
2 medium/180 g/6 oz Bombay onions, finely chopped
2 medium/120 g/4 oz ripe tomatoes, diced
1 tsp garam masala (Recipe No: 3.11.6)
30 black peppercorns, powdered
1/2 bundle/15 g/ 1/2 oz coriander leaves, finely chopped

(1) *Scrub the potatoes. Place them in a pressure-cooker together with sufficient water. Close the cooker. Bring to maximum pressure over high heat, then lower the flame and pressure-cook for 10 minutes. Remove from the fire. Allow the pressure inside the cooker to dissipate, then peel and dice the potatoes.*

(2) Wash the minced mutton using very little water and tip into a wide sieve to drain. Remove and place the mutton in a pressure-cooker container. Mix the turmeric powder, red chilli powder and salt into the mutton. Do not add extra water to the mutton. Pour sufficient water in the body of the pressure-cooker. Lower the container into the pressure-cooker. Close the cooker. Bring to maximum pressure over high heat, then lower the flame and pressure-cook for 15 minutes. Remove from the fire and allow the pressure inside the cooker to dissipate.

(3) Grind the sambhar onions, garlic, ginger and cumin seeds together to a paste.

(4) Heat a heavy kadai, then add the oil. Add the chopped onions and fry until just brown. Add the ground paste and fry for 2 minutes. Stir in the tomatoes and cook until soft and mushy. Add the cooked minced mutton and any stock that is drawn from it during pressure-cooking. Lower the heat and sprinkle with the garam masala. Add the potatoes. Taste for salt and adjust the seasoning. Simmer uncovered until the moisture is absorbed, but do not allow the minced mutton to get too dry. Drizzle with the powdered peppercorns. Mix well.

(5) Garnish with the chopped coriander leaves and serve with chappatis or rice. Can also be used as a stuffing for parathas.

Per Serving			
Kilocalories	236	Vitamin C	20 mg
Protein	16 g	Vitamin A (as carotene)	994 mcg
Fat	12 g	Vitamin A (as retinol)	7 mcg
Carbohydrate	17 g	Fibre	1 g
Calcium	157 mg	Cholesterol	75 mg
Phosphorus	170 mg		
Iron	3 mg	1,000 mcg = 1 mg	

Cooking Hints ·

Substitute 240 g/8 oz shelled peas (from 500 g/1.1 lb unshelled peas) for the potatoes to get an equally delicious kheema.

Pans and tableware used for non-vegetarian foods (egg, meat, fish, poultry) should be first cleaned with cold water and soap then rinsed with hot water. Rub with either lime/lemon peel or spent tamarind before the last rinse. Both are equally effective in removing odours that might linger, nearly impossible to eliminate with only hot water and soap.

3.6.10 Kheema per Eda (Eggs on Spicy Minced Mutton)

Preparation Time   :   15 min
Cooking Time   :   45 min

Serves 6

Ingredients

500 g/1.1 lb minced mutton
1/2 tsp turmeric powder
1/4 tsp red chilli powder
Salt to taste
2 whole pods/20 g/ 2/3 oz garlic
1" or 2.5 cm piece/8 g/ 1/4 oz fresh ginger
1 tsp cumin seeds
2 tsp/10 ml/ 1/3 fl oz oil
2 medium/180 g/6 oz Bombay onions, finely chopped
2 large/240 g/8 oz ripe tomatoes, diced
1 tbsp/15 g/ 1/2 oz powdered jaggery
1 tbsp/15 ml/ 1/2 fl oz vinegar
1/2 bundle/15 g/ 1/2 oz coriander leaves, finely chopped
2 medium/90 g/3 oz eggs
1/4 tsp salt
2 tsp/10 ml/ 1/3 fl oz oil

(1) Wash the minced mutton using very little water and tip into a wide sieve to drain. Remove and place the mutton in a pressure-cooker container. Mix the turmeric powder, red chilli powder and salt into the mutton. Do not add extra water to the mutton. Pour sufficient water in the body of the pressure-cooker. Lower the container into the pressure-cooker. Close the cooker. Bring to maximum pressure over high heat, then lower the flame and pressure-cook for 15 minutes. Remove from the fire and allow the pressure inside the cooker to dissipate.

(2) Grind the garlic, ginger and cumin seeds together to a paste.

(3) Heat a kadai, then add 2 tsp oil. Add the onions and fry until brown. Add the ground paste and fry for 1 minute. Add the tomatoes and cook until soft and mushy. Stir in the cooked minced mutton, any stock that is drawn from it during pressure-cooking, the jaggery, vinegar and more salt if necessary. Simmer uncovered until all the moisture is absorbed and the mixture is barely dry. Sprinkle with the coriander leaves and remove from the fire.

(4) *In the meantime, separate the eggs and beat the egg whites until stiff, adding 1/4 tsp salt. Whisk the yolks lightly and fold into the whites until well blended.*

(5) *Place a well-seasoned frying pan on the fire. Add 1 tsp oil. When the oil begins to smoke, spread the minced mutton evenly over the whole surface. Pour the beaten egg over the mutton. Dribble another teaspoon of oil along the sides of the pan. Cook covered for about 5 minutes over low heat or until the egg sets.*

(6) *Cut into wedges and serve, egg side up, with rice or bread.*

Per Serving			
Kilocalories	241	Vitamin C	18 mg
Protein	17 g	Vitamin A (as carotene)	1,670 mcg
Fat	16 g	Vitamin A (as retinol)	61 mcg
Carbohydrate	9 g	Fibre	1 g
Calcium	163 mg	Cholesterol	150 mg
Phosphorus	182 mg		
Iron	3 mg	1,000 mcg = 1 mg	

Notes on Nutrition

From the figures per serving indicated, it will be noticed that carbohydrates are the least of the three major nutrients, namely, proteins, fats and carbohydrates, and consequently, provide the lowest number of calories.

In planning meals intelligently, there must always be a conscious effort to increase the carbohydrate and protein levels of the diet rather than that of fat. This is because 1 g of fat provides 9 kcal of energy in the body as against 4 kcal each per gram of protein and carbohydrate. Moreover, the body utilizes energy from proteins and carbohydrates more readily and takes a somewhat "lazy" attitude towards fat, tending to store rather than burn it.

Another aspect of animal fats is cholesterol. Egg provides 225 to 300 mg of cholesterol per yolk. Egg white has no cholesterol. What must be understood is that the human body itself manufactures its own cholesterol which is independent of dietary sources.

The Parsees are fond of eggs, and have eggs on everything. Kheema per eda is among the more popular egg recipes.

3.6.11 Chicken Curry

Preparation Time   :   25 min
Cooking Time   :   35 min

Serves 6

Ingredients

1 large/1 1/2 kg/3 lb 2 oz chicken
1 tsp turmeric powder
1/2 tsp red chilli powder
Salt to taste
9 tbsp/45 g/1 1/2 oz freshly grated coconut
About 12/60 g/2 oz sambhar onions, chopped
3 whole pods/30 g/1 oz garlic, chopped
2" or 5 cm piece/15 g/ 1/2 oz fresh ginger, chopped
1/4 tsp cumin seeds
20 black peppercorns
A sprig of curry leaves
3 cloves
1/2" or 1 cm stick cinnamon
1 tbsp/15 ml/ 1/2 fl oz oil
2 medium/180 g/6 oz Bombay onions, thinly sliced
2 tbsp/20 g/ 2/3 oz coriander powder
1 cup/250 ml/8 fl oz hot water

(1)   Wash and joint the chicken. Place the chicken in a pressure-cooker container.
       Add the turmeric powder, red chilli powder and 2 tsp salt. Mix well. Do not
       add extra water to the chicken. Pour sufficient water in the body of the pressure-
       cooker. Lower the container into the pressure-cooker. Close the cooker. Bring
       to maximum pressure over high heat, then lower the flame and pressure-
       cook for 7 minutes. Remove from the fire.

(2)   Roast the grated coconut, sambhar onions, garlic, ginger, cumin seeds,
       peppercorns and curry leaves together, without oil, until the coconut emits a
       nice aroma—about 6 minutes. Grind to a smooth paste, adding a little water.

(3)   Roast the cloves and cinnamon together, without oil, until the cinnamon turns
       crisp. Powder.

(4)   Heat a wide pan, then add the oil. When it begins to smoke, add the sliced
       onions and fry until pink and transparent. Add the ground paste and coriander
       powder. Stir for 2 minutes. Add the cooked chicken, reserving the stock. Fry

for 2 minutes. Add the chicken stock, hot water and powdered spices.

(5)　*Taste for salt and adjust the seasoning. Simmer for 5 minutes. Remove from the fire. Serve hot with rice or chappatis and tamatar piyaz ka raita.*

Per Serving			
Kilocalories	346	Iron	5 mg
Protein	61 g	Vitamin C	4 mg
Fat	8 g	Vitamin A (as carotene)	69 mcg
Carbohydrate	8 g	Fibre	2 g
Calcium	101 mg	Cholesterol	196 mg
Phosphorus	633 mg	1,000 mcg = 1 mg	

Notes of Interest

The North Indian shuns the use of coconut, and onions and tomatoes are substituted as gravy thickeners. This recipe too may be suitably modified to accommodate this far more beneficial and nutritious alternative.

Take 300 g/10 oz each of Bombay onions (about 4 medium) and ripe tomatoes (about 5 medium). Chop them finely. Heat the oil and soften the onions first and then the tomatoes. Add the ground paste (without the coconut). Proceed as indicated in the recipe. Substitute coriander leaves for curry leaves.

Much of the fat in chicken is found in the skin and just below it. To reduce calories, fat and cholesterol, remove the skin and cook the chicken without it. The skin was retained in this recipe. Chicken has no carbohydrate and no fibre.

3.6.12 Tandoori Chicken

Preparation Time　　:　　20 min
Marination Time　　　:　　12 hours *or* Overnight
Cooking Time　　　　:　　30 min

Serves 6

Ingredients

　　1 tender/1.2 kg/2 1/2 lb broiler chicken
　　3 whole pods/30 g/1 oz garlic
　　2" or 5 cm piece/15 g/ 1/2 oz fresh ginger
　　1 medium/90 g/3 oz Bombay onion, coarsely chopped
　　2 medium/5 g/ 1/6 oz green chillies

1/2 bundle/15 g/ 1/2 oz coriander leaves
1 tsp garam masala (Recipe No: 3.11.6)
1/4 tsp red chilli powder
Pinch of chicken (tandoori) red colour
2 tbsp/30 ml/1 fl oz lime juice
Salt to taste
1 cup/250 ml/8 fl oz curds, lightly beaten (from skimmed milk)
1 tbsp/15 ml/ 1/2 fl oz oil
Wedges of lime
Raw onion rings

(1) *Wash and joint the chicken.*

(2) *Grind the garlic, ginger, Bombay onion, green chillies and coriander leaves together to a paste.*

(3) *Add the ground paste, garam masala, red chilli powder, chicken red colour, lime juice and salt to the beaten curds. Mix well. Taste for salt and adjust the seasoning. Immerse the chicken pieces in the marinade placed in a stainless steel or glass bowl. Leave undisturbed for 12 hours or overnight, well covered, in the refrigerator.*

(4) *Heat a gas tandoor (or grill) until very hot—about 10 minutes. Lower the heat. Lightly grease the grid and place the chicken pieces on it. Cover and cook for 8 minutes. Baste with oil, then turn the chicken pieces over. Baste the reverse side with oil, cover and cook for a further 8 minutes.*

(5) *Serve with naan, wedges of lime and raw onion rings.*

Per Serving			
Kilocalories	254	Iron	4 mg
Protein	49 g	Vitamin C	10 mg
Fat	4 g	Vitamin A (as carotene)	401 mcg
Carbohydrate	6 g	Fibre	0.5 g
Calcium	120 mg	Cholesterol	154 mg
Phosphorus	508 mg	1,000 mcg = 1 mg	

Cooking Tips

Only tender broiler chicken cooks best by this method. Any other meat will first have to be tenderized with ground, raw papaya or similar tenderizer before it is marinated.

This marinade may also be used to make Tandoori Fish. Follow the same method.

Tandoori chicken/fish may be prepared over an open barbecue spit as well.

Health Hints

Consumption of tandoori foods should be kept to the minimum because the burning and charring which give so much flavour also create substances that are carcinogenic. Moreover, when fat from fatty meats or the oil used in basting drips onto glowing embers or heating elements, unhealthy chemical compounds are produced which mingle with the rising smoke and coat the food. Barbecuing also generates the same hazardous substances. So, indulging in tandoori or barbecued foods on a regular basis could be detrimental to our health. Partially cooking foods before exposing them to direct heat, and subjecting only lean meats to tandoori cooking and barbecuing, lowers the likelihood of the formation of many of these harmful compounds.

Important in Indian tandoori cooking are the ingredients used and the traditional accompaniments. Many of them are high in vitamin C, vitamin A and fibre which play a crucial role in offsetting the damaging effects of the compounds developed by charring. Curds, garlic, onions, ginger, cumin seeds and turmeric are also highly regarded as protective agents.

3.6.13 Chicken in Curd

Preparation Time	:	30 min
Marination Time	:	8 hours *or* Overnight
Cooking Time	:	35 min

Serves 6

Ingredients

1 large/1 1/2 kg/3 lb 2 oz broiler chicken
3 whole pods/30 g/1 oz garlic
2" or 5 cm piece/15 g/ 1/2 oz fresh ginger
1 tbsp/10 g/ 1/3 oz coriander powder
1 tsp garam masala (Recipe No: 3.11.6)
1 tsp turmeric powder
1/2 tsp red chilli powder
Pinch of saffron powder
Salt to taste
1 cup/250 ml/8 fl oz curds, lightly beaten (from skimmed milk)
1 tbsp/15 ml/ 1/2 fl oz refined oil
3 medium/270 g/9 oz Bombay onions, finely chopped

1/2 cup/125 ml/4 fl oz hot water
1/2 bundle/15 g/ 1/2 oz coriander leaves, finely chopped

(1) *Wash and joint the chicken.*

(2) *Grind the garlic and ginger together to a paste.*

(3) *Add the ground paste, coriander powder, garam masala, turmeric powder, red chilli powder, saffron powder and a little salt to the beaten curds. Mix to blend. Taste for salt and adjust the seasoning. Immerse the chicken pieces in the marinade placed in a stainless steel or glass bowl. Leave, well covered, in the refrigerator for 8 hours or overnight.*

(4) *Heat the oil in the body of a pressure-cooker. When it begins to smoke, add the onions and fry until brown. Put in the chicken with the marinade. Stir for 1 or 2 minutes. Add the hot water and more salt if necessary. Close the cooker. Bring to maximum pressure over high heat, then lower the flame and pressure-cook for 7 minutes. Turn off the heat and allow the pressure inside the cooker to dissipate.*

(5) *Open the cooker and simmer for 5 minutes. Garnish with the chopped coriander leaves. Serve with rice or chappatis.*

Per Serving			
Kilocalories	325	Iron	5 mg
Protein	62 g	Vitamin C	10 mg
Fat	5 g	Vitamin A (as carotene)	396 mcg
Carbohydrate	10 g	Fibre	1 g
Calcium	152 mg	Cholesterol	196 mg
Phosphorus	651 mg	1,000 mcg = 1 mg	

Protein Packed

This delicacy, extremely high in protein, is an excellent means of meeting the day's protein requirement and more. It is especially good for teenage boys and girls with a daily protein need of 78 g and 63 g, respectively.

Indian Cooking Wisdom

Curds does not only flavour or tenderize meat. Meat and other flesh foods that are marinated in curds before cooking have fewer micro-organisms. This is because lactic acid (found in curds) when heated (as in cooking) is an effective antiseptic.

Ginger promotes the digestion of proteins, conclusively proving the soundness of adding ginger, often in combination with heart-friendly garlic, to Indian meat dishes.

3.6.14 Muttai Kootu (Poached Eggs in Tamarind Sauce)

Preparation Time	:	15 min
Soaking Time	:	10 min
Cooking Time	:	25 min

Serves 4

Ingredients

3 handfuls/180 g/6 oz sambhar onions
1 tsp cumin seeds
A sprig of curry leaves
A lime-sized ball/30 g/1 oz tamarind
1 cup/250 ml/8 fl oz hot water
2 tsp/10 ml/ 1/3 fl oz oil
1/2 tsp turmeric powder
1/4 tsp red chilli powder
1 cup/250 ml/8 fl oz water
1 tsp/5 g/ 1/6 oz sugar
Salt to taste
4 medium/180 g/6 oz eggs

(1) Grind the sambhar onions, cumin seeds and curry leaves together to a coarse paste.

(2) Soak the tamarind in 1/2 cup hot water for 10 minutes. Squeeze to extract pulp. Add another 1/2 cup hot water to the same tamarind and extract pulp a second time.

(3) Heat a wide pan, then add the oil. When the oil begins to smoke, add the ground paste and fry for about 5 minutes. Add the turmeric powder and red chilli powder. Fry for 1 minute. Add the tamarind extract, 1 cup water, sugar and salt. Bring to the boil, then lower the heat and simmer for 5 minutes. Crack the eggs, one at a time, into the hot sauce, allowing 1 or 2 minutes between each addition. Allow the eggs to cook in the sauce, then pick up the vessel and swirl the contents once or twice. Do not use a spoon to stir.

(4) Serve hot with rice or chappatis.

Per Serving			
Kilocalories	153	Vitamin C	1 mg
Protein	7 g	Vitamin A (as carotene)	334 mcg
Fat	9 g	Vitamin A (as retinol)	162 mcg
Carbohydrate	12 g	Fibre	1 g
Calcium	60 mg	Cholesterol	225 mg
Phosphorus	134 mg		
Iron	3 mg	1,000 mcg = 1 mg	

Cooking Hints

It is also possible to poach fish in this manner. Substitute 500 g/1.1 lb fleshy fish for the 4 eggs in Meen Kootu. If sambhar onions are not available, use 2 medium Bombay onions (180 g/6 oz) instead.

3.6.15 Akoori (Masala Scrambled Eggs)

Preparation Time	:	10 min
Cooking Time	:	15 min

Serves 4

Ingredients

4 medium/180 g/6 oz eggs
Salt to taste
2 tsp/10 ml/ 1/3 fl oz oil
2 medium/180 g/6 oz Bombay onions, finely chopped
1 whole pod/10 g/ 1/3 oz garlic, finely chopped
1/2" or 1 cm piece/4 g/ 1/8 oz fresh ginger, finely chopped
2 medium/5 g/ 1/6 oz green chillies, deseeded and finely chopped
1/2 tsp cumin seeds
Pinch of turmeric powder
2 medium/120 g/4 oz ripe tomatoes, diced
1/2 tsp sugar
1/2 bundle/15 g/ 1/2 oz coriander leaves, finely chopped

(1) Whisk the eggs with a little salt until well blended.

(2) Heat a pan, then add the oil. Add the onions and fry until just brown. Add the garlic, ginger, green chillies, cumin seeds and turmeric powder. Fry for 1 minute. Add the tomatoes and sugar. Cook until the tomatoes are mushy.

(3) Remove from the fire and add the well-beaten eggs. Stirring continuously return the pan to the fire and scramble the eggs until well done but soft and moist. Garnish with the coriander leaves. Serve on toast for breakfast.

Per Serving			
Kilocalories	138	Vitamin C	20 mg
Protein	7 g	Vitamin A (as carotene)	1,766 mcg
Fat	9 g	Vitamin A (as retinol)	162 mcg
Carbohydrate	8 g	Fibre	1 g
Calcium	71 mg	Cholesterol	225 mg
Phosphorus	140 mg		
Iron	2 mg	1,000 mcg = 1 mg	

Matters of Interest

In many Parsee homes, the day begins with this interesting form of scrambled eggs. To make this dish even more substantial, boil 1 large (125 g/4 oz) potato, peel, dice, and add it along with the tomatoes. Proceed as indicated in the recipe.

Adding potatoes is also a good way to reduce the number of eggs, besides increasing vitamin C. Although egg is a wonderful source of high quality protein which has been awarded the highest biological value of 100 because it is almost fully utilized in the human body, its protein content is perfectly counterbalanced by its fat content—6 g of each in a medium egg. This fat content is not only high but also contains large amounts of cholesterol—225 to 300 mg per egg. All the cholesterol in egg is concentrated in the yolk.

Egg also provides vitamin A in its two natural forms—as the precursor or provitamin called carotene, and as retinol, the vitamin itself. Retinol is found only in animal fats, though carotene, the more abundant in Nature, is found in both animal and vegetable foods.

3.7 Raitas
Salads
Chutneys
Preserves

3.7.1   Tamatar Piyaz ka Raita (Tomato and Onion Salad in Curds)

Preparation Time   :   12 min
Cooking Time   :   Nil

Serves 4

Ingredients

2 large/250 g/8 oz Bombay onions, thinly sliced
Pinch of cumin seeds, powdered
Salt to taste
1 cup/250 ml/8 fl oz curds, lightly beaten (from skimmed milk)
2 medium/120 g/4 oz ripe tomatoes, diced
2 medium/5 g/ 1/6 oz green chillies, finely chopped
1/2 bundle/15 g/ 1/2 oz coriander leaves, finely chopped

(1)   *Rinse the sliced onions in boiled, cooled water. Drain.*
(2)   *Add the powdered cumin seeds and salt to the beaten curds. Stir in the sliced onions, tomatoes, green chillies and coriander leaves.*
(3)   *Serve with mutton biriyani or chicken curry.*

Per Serving			
Kilocalories	57	Iron	1 mg
Protein	3 g	Vitamin C	22 mg
Fat	Less than 0.5 g	Vitamin A (as carotene)	1,496 mcg
Carbohydrate	11 g	Fibre	1 g
Calcium	126 mg	Cholesterol	1 mg
Phosphorus	97 mg	1,000 mcg = 1 mg	

Nutrition Notes

Salads prepared from curds are known as raitas in the north and pachadis in the south. This fresh salad is usually served with biriyani or any other meat dish high in fat because it acts as a broom, sweeping the fat along, thereby reducing the amount absorbed into the body.

Notice that the seeds of the tomatoes have not been discarded. They serve as a laxative.

3.7.2 Vellarikkai Pachadi (Cucumber and Curds Salad)

Preparation Time　　:　　12 min
Cooking Time　　　　:　　12 min

Serves 6

Ingredients

1 large/660 g/1 lb 6 oz cucumber (preferably the orange-skinned variety)
1 1/2 whole pods/15 g/ 1/2 oz garlic
2 medium/5 g/ 1/6 oz green chillies
1 tsp mustard seeds
1/2 tsp cumin seeds
A sprig of curry leaves
1 tsp/5 ml/ 1/6 fl oz oil
1/2 tsp mustard seeds
4 tbsp/60 ml/2 fl oz water
Salt to taste
1/2 cup/125 ml/4 fl oz curds, lightly beaten (from skimmed milk)

(1) *Wash and peel the cucumber. Remove both ends (to avoid any bitter taste) and core of seeds. Dice. Set aside.*

(2) *Grind the garlic, green chillies, 1 tsp mustard seeds, cumin seeds and curry leaves together to a smooth paste, adding a little water.*

(3) *Heat a pan, then add the oil. Add 1/2 tsp mustard seeds. When the mustard seeds begin to splutter, add the cucumber, water and salt. Cook covered until the cucumber is tender.*

(4) *Stir in the ground paste. Simmer for 2 minutes.*

(5) *Remove from the fire. Cool. Stir the beaten curds into the cooked and cooled cucumber. Taste for salt and adjust the seasoning. Serve with any meat dish.*

Per Serving			
Kilocalories	27	Iron	0.5 mg
Protein	1 g	Vitamin C	6 mg
Fat	1 g	Vitamin A (as carotene)	55 mcg
Carbohydrate	4 g	Fibre	Trace
Calcium	34 mg	Cholesterol	Trace
Phosphorus	45 mg	1,000 mcg = 1 mg	

Cucumber Comfort

With its high water content and small amounts of numerous minerals, cucumber is ideal for the hot summer months when body fluids and salts lost through sweating have to be replaced. And being wonderfully low in calories, its intake does not have to be monitored closely either.

This pachadi is popular in the hot, humid coastal districts of Tamil Nadu. If cucumber is not available, substitute with snake gourd.

3.7.3 Fresh Moong Usal (Sprouted Green Gram Salad)

Preparation Time	:	10 min
Soaking Time	:	12 hours *or* Overnight
Sprouting Time	:	24 hours minimum
Cooking Time	:	Nil

Serves 4

Ingredients

1 cup/240 g/8 oz whole green gram, cleaned and washed
1 medium/90 g/3 oz Bombay onion, finely chopped
2 medium/5 g/ 1/6 oz green chillies, finely chopped
1 1/2 tsp/7.5 ml/ 1/4 fl oz lime juice
Salt to taste

(1) *Soak the green gram in generous amounts of water for 12 hours, preferably overnight.*

(2) *Drain and wrap the soaked gram in a damp cloth. Hang up in a warm place for 24 hours or until sprouts appear. Keep the cloth moist at all times.*

(3) *Mix the sprouted green gram, chopped onion and green chillies together. Drizzle with the lime juice and salt. Serve with any meal that is high in fat.*

Per Serving			
Kilocalories	213	Iron	3 mg
Protein	15 g	Vitamin C	10 mg
Fat	1 g	Vitamin A (as carotene)	87 mcg
Carbohydrate	37 g	Fibre	3 g
Calcium	87 mg		
Phosphorus	208 mg	1,000 mcg = 1 mg	

The Awakening

Sprouting is a process by which the dormant seed begins to grow. The "activated" seed needs a number of nutrients for its own growth which become available to man if sprouts are consumed.

Starch is converted to simple sugars that are more easily assimilated in the human gut. Maltose or malt sugar is one such sugar and is found only in sprouted (malted) grains and pulses. Similarly, proteins are available in the form of amino acids, the building blocks of proteins.

The vitamin and mineral content is also greatly enhanced. While dried pulses contain no vitamin C at all, on sprouting, it is manufactured in the seed, a benefit that is passed on to human beings if the sprouts are eaten raw or lightly cooked. Twenty four hours after germination, the vitamin C content is about 8 mg per 100 g of the pulse. At the end of 48 hours, it is 12 mg for the same weight. If sprouting is continued up to 72 hours, 100 g of sprouts will contain as much as 14 mg of vitamin C.

The iron in pulses is largely bound to phytates, compounds that render iron unavailable for absorption. Sprouting breaks this bond, and the iron is readily utilized in the body, especially since the vitamin C also present creates the right environment for absorption.

For longer sprouts, extend the sprouting time. However, the cloth should always be kept moist if growth is to be encouraged. Most whole pulses and legumes can be sprouted.

This salad, high in carbohydrate and protein but low in fat, is recommended for all ages—for children to meet their protein and energy requirements, and for adults to meet their calorie needs through carbohydrates.

All pulses and legumes contain soluble fibre which is extremely beneficial in lowering elevated blood cholesterol and blood glucose levels.

3.7.4 Cachumber (Fresh Vegetable Relish)

Preparation Time : 20 min
Cooking Time : Nil

Serves 8

Ingredients

1 tender/600 g/1 1/4 lb cucumber
2 medium/180 g/6 oz Bombay onions, finely chopped

2 medium/120 g/4 oz ripe tomatoes, diced
1/2 bundle/15 g/ 1/2 oz coriander leaves, finely chopped
2 medium/5 g/ 1/6 oz green chillies, deseeded and finely chopped
1 tbsp/15 ml/ 1/2 fl oz lime juice
Pinch of salt

(1) Wash and peel the cucumber. Remove both ends (to avoid any bitter taste) and core of seeds. Cube.

(2) Mix all the ingredients together. Serve with any fatty dish or meal.

Per Serving			
Kilocalories	22	Iron	1 mg
Protein	1 g	Vitamin C	14 mg
Fat	Trace	Vitamin A (as carotene)	748 mcg
Carbohydrate	5 g	Fibre	0.5 g
Calcium	28 mg		
Phosphorus	28 mg	1,000 mcg = 1 mg	

Waste Woes

About 240 g/8 oz is lost to the peel and seeds of cucumber which are normally thrown away. However, there are foods that suffer less wastage such as radishes, carrots and raw mangoes. These may replace cucumber or be included in the relish. And, the bonus will be the additional benefit of more nutrients.

Cachumber is a pan-Indian dish, with minor regional variations adding variety to the basic recipe given here.

3.7.5 Potato and Groundnut Salad

Preparation Time : 5 min
Cooking Time : 14 min

Serves 4

Ingredients

2 large/250 g/8 oz potatoes
1 cup or 6 handfuls/180 g/6 oz shelled groundnuts
1 medium/90 g/3 oz Bombay onion, finely chopped
1/2 bundle/15 g/ 1/2 oz coriander leaves, finely chopped
2 medium/5 g/ 1/6 oz green chillies, deseeded and finely chopped

1 1/2 tsp/7.5 ml/ 1/4 fl oz lime juice
Pinch of black salt
Salt and pepper to taste

(1) *Scrub the potatoes. Place them in a pressure-cooker together with 1/2 cup groundnuts and sufficient water. Close the cooker. Bring to maximum pressure over high heat, then lower the flame and pressure-cook for 5 minutes. Remove from the fire. Allow the pressure inside the cooker to dissipate, then peel and cube the potatoes. Tip the cooked groundnuts into a sieve to drain.*

(2) *Roast the remaining 1/2 cup groundnuts, without oil, until they begin to crackle —about 5 minutes. Remove the papery skin and crush coarsely.*

(3) *Mix all the ingredients together. Serve as a cold salad either separately or with a rice meal.*

Per Serving			
Kilocalories	331	Iron	2 mg
Protein	13 g	Vitamin C	21 mg
Fat	18 g	Vitamin A (as carotene)	617 mcg
Carbohydrate	29 g	Fibre	2 g
Calcium	63 mg		
Phosphorus	202 mg	1,000 mcg = 1 mg	

Peanut Prattle

Though groundnuts are very high in fat (40 g fat per 100 g of groundnuts), much of it is fortunately unsaturated and they contain practically no cholesterol. Moreover, groundnuts have numerous other nutritional benefits that justify their unstinted use in cooking. Groundnuts have good amounts of protein, carbohydrates, vitamins (fat soluble vitamin E and water soluble B vitamins including vitamin B_1, vitamin B_3, the highest in all foods except liver, vitamin B_6, folic acid and pantothenic acid) and minerals (phosphorus, copper, manganese, zinc, chromium and molybdenum).

3.7.6   Kosumberi (Cucumber and Split Green Gram Salad)

Preparation Time   :   10 min
Soaking Time   :   4 hours
Cooking Time   :   Nil

Serves 8

Ingredients

1 cup/240 g/8 oz green gram dhal (without husk), cleaned and washed
1 large/660 g/1 lb 6 oz cucumber
2 medium/180 g/6 oz Bombay onions, finely chopped
4 medium/10 g/ 1/3 oz green chillies, finely chopped
Salt to taste

(1) *Soak the green gram dhal in generous amounts of water for 4 hours. Drain.*

(2) *Wash and peel the cucumber. Cut off both ends to avoid any bitter taste. Remove the core of seeds. Cube.*

(3) *Mix all the ingredients together. Add salt. Serve with any meat dish.*

Per Serving			
Kilocalories	123	Iron	2 mg
Protein	8 g	Vitamin C	8 mg
Fat	Trace	Vitamin A (as carotene)	45 mcg
Carbohydrate	22 g	Fibre	1 g
Calcium	39 mg		
Phosphorus	147 mg	1,000 mcg = 1 mg	

A Woman's Lot

For a long time it has been known that vitamin and mineral supplements taken in the week preceding and during menstruation considerably lessen the symptoms of bloating, cramping and discomfort experienced by a vast majority of women. Beside the minerals indicated, green gram dhal is a very good source of all the minerals and electrolytes except iodine and cobalt, and vitamin B_1, vitamin B_2, vitamin B_3, vitamin B_6, pantothenic acid, biotin and especially folic acid of the B complex group. Green chillies also contain vitamin B_2, besides being an outstanding repository for magnesium, copper, potassium and vitamin C. Therefore, it comes as no surprise that this salad, little known outside the southern state of Karnataka, is recommended for women plagued with premenstrual syndrome (PMS) and its associated troubles.

3.7.7 Coconut Chutney

Preparation Time : 15 min
Cooking Time : 5 min

Serves 6

Ingredients

1/2 medium shell/90 g/3 oz freshly grated coconut
3 tbsp or 2 handfuls/30 g/1 oz roasted bengal gram
2 medium/5 g/ 1/6 oz green chillies
A sprig of curry leaves
A marble-sized ball of tamarind
1 1/2 cups/375 ml/12 1/2 fl oz water
Salt to taste
2 tsp/10 ml/ 1/3 fl oz oil
1/2 tsp mustard seeds
2 whole dried red chillies
1 tsp black gram dhal (without husk)

(1) *Grind the coconut, roasted bengal gram, green chillies, curry leaves and tamarind together to a smooth paste, adding a little water. Stir in 1 1/2 cups water and salt. Set aside.*

(2) *Heat a pan, then add the oil. Add the mustard seeds and red chillies torn in two. When the mustard seeds begin to splutter, add the black gram dhal and fry until golden. Remove from the fire and stir in the diluted ground masala.*

(3) *Serve cold with rice iddlis and dosais.*

Per Serving			
Kilocalories	106	Iron	1 mg
Protein	2 g	Vitamin C	1 mg
Fat	8 g	Vitamin A (as carotene)	62 mcg
Carbohydrate	6 g	Fibre	1 g
Calcium	9 mg		
Phosphorus	58 mg	1,000 mcg = 1 mg	

What's Good For You

Excess coconut in the diet is not healthy because of its high content of saturated fat. This recipe has been included only because iddlis and dosais are traditionally served with coconut chutney and sambhar in South India. Try to avoid the chutney, and eat them only with sambhar. Fortunately, coconut has only minute amounts of cholesterol.

However, if you feel you must eat the traditional way, be sure to eat this chutney not later than eleven in the morning. It is then likely that most of the calories will be burnt during the course of the day when work is inevitable.

3.7.8   Curry Leaf Chutney

Preparation Time	:	15 min
Cooking Time	:	2 min

Yield 45 g/1 1/2 oz

Ingredients

1 tsp/5 ml/ 1/6 fl oz oil
1/2" or 1 cm piece/4 g/ 1/8 oz fresh ginger, chopped
1/2 tsp cumin seeds
1 whole dried red chilli
2 garlic cloves, chopped
1 cup or 5 large sprigs/30 g/1 oz curry leaves, picked and washed
A marble-sized ball of tamarind
1 1/2 tsp/7.5 g/ 1/4 oz sugar
1/4 tsp salt

(1)   Heat a pan, then add the oil. Add the ginger, cumin seeds, red chilli and garlic. When the cumin seeds change colour, add the curry leaves, stir quickly, and remove from the fire.

(2)   Grind all the ingredients together to a smooth paste, adding a little water. Serve with hot rice and ghee, dosais or parathas.

Per Teaspoon			
Kilocalories	14	Iron	Trace
Protein	Trace	Vitamin C	Trace
Fat	1 g	Vitamin A (as carotene)	701 mcg
Carbohydrate	2 g	Fibre	Trace
Calcium	29 mg		
Phosphorus	3 mg	1,000 mcg = 1 mg	

What's in a Curry Leaf

The curry leaf, used to flavour most South Indian dishes, is an outstanding source of carotene which is converted to vitamin A in the human body. Being fat soluble, the practice of tempering actually facilitates absorption—a pointer to the wisdom of Indian cooking.

3.7.9 Mint Chutney

Preparation Time   :   12 min
Cooking Time   :   Nil

Yield 60 g/2 oz

Ingredients

1 bundle/30 g/1 oz mint leaves, washed and cleaned
2 garlic cloves
1 medium green chilli
1 tsp/5 g/ 1/6 oz sugar
1/2 tsp salt
1 tsp/5 ml/ 1/6 fl oz lime juice

(1) *Strip the mint leaves from the stalks. Retain the tender tips of the shoots.*
(2) *Grind all the ingredients together, adding the lime juice to get a fairly liquid paste.*
(3) *Serve with aloo paratha or mutton tikkis or vegetable cutlets, besides other recipes as indicated in the book.*

Per Teaspoon			
Kilocalories	3	Iron	Trace
Protein	Trace	Vitamin C	1 mg
Fat	Negligible	Vitamin A (as carotene)	479 mcg
Carbohydrate	1 g	Fibre	Negligible
Calcium	6 mg		
Phosphorus	2 mg	1,000 mcg = 1 mg	

A Hint of Mint

Mint is a natural digestive, and should be served with greasy, fried foods to eliminate the uncomfortable feeling of fullness that accompanies most fatty meals. It also helps to transport fat out of the body.

3.7.10 Tomato Chutney

Preparation Time   :   5 min
Cooking Time   :   10 min

Serves 4

Ingredients

About 8 medium/500 g/1.1 lb ripe tomatoes, coarsely chopped
2 tsp/10 ml/ 1/3 fl oz oil
1/2 tsp mustard seeds
1 medium/90 g/3 oz Bombay onion, finely chopped
2 medium/5 g/ 1/6 oz green chillies, deseeded and finely chopped
1/4 tsp turmeric powder
Salt to taste
1 tsp/5 g/ 1/6 oz sugar
1/2 bundle/15 g/ 1/2 oz coriander leaves, finely chopped

(1) *Liquidize the chopped tomatoes in a blender/mixer at the lowest speed for about 10 seconds.*

(2) *Heat a pan, then add the oil. Add the mustard seeds. When the mustard seeds begin to splutter, add the onion and fry until soft. Add the puréed tomatoes, green chillies, turmeric powder and salt. Simmer for 5 minutes.*

(3) *Sprinkle with the sugar and coriander leaves. Simmer for 1 minute. Remove from the fire. Serve with plain fried rice or chappatis.*

Per Serving			
Kilocalories	66	Iron	1 mg
Protein	2 g	Vitamin C	43 mg
Fat	3 g	Vitamin A (as carotene)	4,355 mcg
Carbohydrate	9 g	Fibre	1 g
Calcium	78 mg		
Phosphorus	40 mg	1,000 mcg = 1 mg	

Food Wise

The tomatoes have been puréed complete with the seeds and skin to get the benefit of fibre, vitamins and minerals present in those parts that are usually discarded. Tomato seeds are a good laxative. If a blender/mixer is not available, chop the tomatoes very fine to get the same effect.

3.7.11 Coriander Chutney

Preparation Time : 12 min
Cooking Time : Nil

Yield 120 g/4 oz

Ingredients

4 bundles/120 g/4 oz coriander leaves, washed and cleaned
1 whole pod/10 g/ 1/3 oz garlic
2 medium/5 g/ 1/6 oz green chillies, deseeded
1/2 tsp cumin seeds
A marble-sized ball of tamarind
1 tsp/5 g/ 1/6 oz sugar
1/2 tsp salt

(1) *Pick only the coriander leaves and the tender tips of the shoots.*

(2) *Grind the coriander leaves, garlic, green chillies, cumin seeds and tamarind together to a smooth paste without adding any water. Add the sugar and salt. Mix to blend.*

(3) *Serve as a dip with any savoury dish instead of tomato ketchup. Coriander chutney also makes an excellent filling for sandwiches.*

Per Teaspoon			
Kilocalories	3	Iron	Negligible
Protein	Trace	Vitamin C	4 mg
Fat	Negligible	Vitamin A (as carotene)	380 mcg
Carbohydrate	1 g	Fibre	Negligible
Calcium	5 mg		
Phosphorus	4 mg	1,000 mcg = 1 mg	

Cooking Tips

If a mixer/blender is used to prepare this chutney, place all the ingredients except the cumin seeds in the jar. Select the lowest speed and blend for 1 minute. For the next 30 seconds, start at the lowest speed and advance to the highest. Stop the mixer and scrape down the sides of the jar. Test for smoothness. Use lemon juice, not water, if some wetness is needed to get the right texture. Powder the cumin seeds and mix into the chutney.

Wash the grinding stone or mixer with a little water after the chutney has been removed. Add it to curries and dhals. It will give them a tangible "lift".

About 60 g/2 oz is wasted as roots and inedible stalks from 4 bundles of coriander leaves.

Nutrition and Health

Coriander is a very good source of vitamin A (as carotene) and vitamin C. Most of the vitamins and minerals found in green leafy vegetables are likely to be present in coriander leaves too, though much of the calcium could be bound to substances called oxalates which will prevent its utilization in the gut.

Substituting lemon juice for tamarind will further augment the vitamin C content of coriander chutney. Or 2 tsp vinegar may be used instead. Vinegar by itself contributes no nutrients, but like all sour foods it protects the water soluble vitamins of the B complex group and vitamin C from degradation.

Coriander is a medicinal herb and should be eaten as often as possible as a tonic. Additionally, it is believed to lessen the severity of epileptic fits, and coriander chutney is usually recommended as a means of ensuring a high intake. Coriander leaves are otherwise almost always employed as a garnish, and the vitamin C they contain helps to convert iron from vegetable sources to the form that is readily absorbed.

3.7.12 Imli ki Chutney (Sweet and Sour Tamarind Sauce)

Preparation Time	:	5 min
Soaking Time	:	10 min
Cooking Time	:	10 min

Yield 1 cup/250 ml/8 fl oz

Ingredients

A lime-sized ball/30 g/1 oz tamarind
1 cup/250 ml/8 fl oz hot water
4 tbsp/60 g/2 oz powdered jaggery
1/2 tsp cumin seeds, powdered
1/4 tsp red chilli powder
1/2 tsp salt

(1) Soak the tamarind in 1/2 cup hot water for 10 minutes. Rub vigorously between the fingers and squeeze to extract pulp. Add another 1/2 cup hot water to the same tamarind and extract pulp a second time.

(2) *Place the tamarind extract, jaggery, powdered cumin seeds, red chilli powder and salt in a pan. Bring to the boil. Boil vigorously for 2 minutes, then turn off the heat.*

(3) *Strain and serve with chhole or sundal.*

Per Tablespoon			
Kilocalories	20	Iron	Trace
Protein	Negligible	Vitamin C	Negligible
Fat	Nil	Vitamin A (as carotene)	1 mcg
Carbohydrate	5 g	Fibre	Trace
Calcium	6 mg		
Phosphorus	4 mg	1,000 mcg = 1 mg	

Notes of Interest

Both tamarind and jaggery enjoy an ubiquitous presence in cooking in every region of India. They are of nutritional significance because they contain iron — the contribution of 2 tbsp (30 ml/1 fl oz) of imli ki chutney will be almost 1 g, which is rather high since iron is not widely available in foods. Moreover, tamarind being acidic presents the right environment for the conversion of complex ferric iron salts to ferrous iron, the form which is absorbed in the human gut. Sour foods like tamarind also assist in the absorption of calcium and magnesium.

Besides, the acidic medium that tamarind provides has a protective effect on the vitamins of the B complex group (except folic acid, pantothenic acid and vitamin B_{12}) and vitamin C that are destroyed by light, high cooking temperatures, prolonged heating or when foods are reheated.

Old tamarind is believed to promote healing of stomach and gut ailments. The tartaric acid in tamarind helps to prevent the formation of kidney stones.

3.7.13 Devil's Chutney

Preparation Time	:	7 min
Cooking Time	:	1 min

Yield 60 g/2 oz

Ingredients

4 whole dried red chillies, deseeded
3 tbsp plus 1 tsp/50 g/1 2/3 oz seedless raisins
1 whole pod/10 g/ 1/3 oz garlic

1" or 2.5 cm piece/8 g/ 1/4 oz fresh ginger
A marble-sized ball of tamarind
1 tsp/5 g/ 1/6 oz sugar
1/4 tsp salt
1 tsp vinegar

(1) Roast the red chillies lightly, without oil, until crisp.
(2) Grind all the ingredients together to get a thick paste using only vinegar to moisten.
(3) Serve with mutton biriyani or plain/vegetable fried rice.

Per Teaspoon			
Kilocalories	17	Iron	Trace
Protein	Trace	Vitamin C	Trace
Fat	Negligible	Vitamin A (as carotene)	1 mcg
Carbohydrate	4 g	Fibre	Trace
Calcium	5 mg		
Phosphorus	7 mg	1,000 mcg = 1 mg	

An Acquaintance with Iron

This chutney is recommended especially for its iron content. Two teaspoons (10 g/ 1/3 oz) provide almost 1 g of iron which is pretty good since iron in Nature is rather poorly distributed in foods.

Raisins are a very good source of iron. Dried dates too contain large amounts of iron and some fibre, and can be included in this chutney. However, it must be remembered that being dried fruits, they are also high in calories. On an average, 2 tbsp/30 g/1 oz of any dried fruit will give 100 kilocalories.

Tamarind is also a good source of iron.

3.7.14 Date Chutney

Preparation Time	:	20 min
Soaking Time	:	15 min
Cooking Time	:	10 min

Yield 360 g/12 oz

Ingredients

250 g/8 oz dried dates

3 whole dried red chillies
1/2 cup/125 ml/4 fl oz vinegar, preferably brown
2 whole pods/20 g/ 2/3 oz garlic
1" or 2.5 cm piece/8 g/ 1/4 oz fresh ginger
1 tsp cumin seeds
4 tbsp/60 g/2 oz sugar
2 tsp salt

(1) *Stone the dates and chop coarsely.*

(2) *Soak the red chillies in the vinegar for 15 minutes.*

(3) *Grind the red chillies, garlic, ginger and cumin seeds together to a paste, adding a little vinegar. Do not use water.*

(4) *Dissolve the sugar in the remaining vinegar (used to soak the chillies) over gentle heat. Bring to the boil and add the ground paste. Lower the heat and simmer for 2 minutes. Add the salt.*

(5) *Add the pitted dates and cook until the mixture begins to lump together.*

(6) *Remove from the fire and fill into a sterilized jar while still hot.*

Per Tablespoon			
Kilocalories	37	Iron	1 mg
Protein	Trace	Vitamin C	Trace
Fat	Negligible	Vitamin A (as carotene)	2 mcg
Carbohydrate	9 g	Fibre	Trace
Calcium	10 mg		
Phosphorus	7 mg	1,000 mcg = 1 mg	

Top Tip

Buy stoned dates as they give better value for money even if they are slightly more expensive. With the stones, the wastage can be as much as 60 g/2 oz for every 250 g/8 oz.

Nutrition Notes

Dates are an excellent source of iron. Compared with fresh dates, dried dates contain more than double of most nutrients except fat which is present in equal amounts in both. All dried fruits are low-fat sources of high energy, containing about 75 g of carbohydrate per 100 g of dried fruit, and less than 1 g of fat.

3.7.15 Amla Murraba (Indian Gooseberry Preserve)

Preparation Time	:	15 min
Soaking Time	:	48 hours (2 days)
Cooking Time	:	1 hour

Yield 60 pieces

Ingredients

About 60 marble-sized/500 g/1.1 lb Indian gooseberries
A generous pinch of slaked lime (calcium hydroxide used with betel leaf)
1 kg/2.2 lb sugar
1 cup/250 ml/8 fl oz water

(1) *Wash the gooseberries, remove the stalks and prick all over with a fork.*

(2) *Immerse the gooseberries completely in water containing a generous pinch of slaked lime (sufficient to make the water milky in appearance). Leave undisturbed in a cool place for 2 days. (The gooseberries should be very firm when pressed between thumb and forefinger.)*

(3) *Pour off the lime water and wash the gooseberries well. Spread out on a cloth to dry.*

(4) *Place the sugar and 1 cup water in a wide pan. Stir over low heat until the sugar dissolves. Bring to the boil. Add the gooseberries. Cook over moderate heat, stirring continuously, until the syrup is thick and the two-thread consistency is reached. To test for this stage, a drop of cooled sugar syrup is placed between thumb and forefinger. When pressed together and drawn apart, two distinct threads will take form. The murraba is now ready — the sugar will not crystallize out but will remain in solution (syrup).*

(5) *Allow the foam to subside, then bottle in sterilized jars while still hot.*

Per Murraba			
Kilocalories	71	Iron	Trace
Protein	Negligible	Vitamin C	50 mg
Fat	Nil	Vitamin A (as carotene)	1 mcg
Carbohydrate	18 g	Fibre	Trace
Calcium	6 mg		
Phosphorus	2 mg	1,000 mcg = 1 mg	

Nature's Vitamin Pill

There is much debate over the amount of vitamin C that remains after such prolonged cooking. Some claim that none is lost while others say that since vitamin C is so easily destroyed by heat, nothing of nutritional significance could remain, especially since the Indian gooseberries in amla murraba are also exposed to light and alkali (slaked lime), both well known as agents of destruction of vitamin C.

Whatever the argument, though, it must be mentioned that the Indian gooseberry has a vitamin C content only next to the West Indian cherry which is believed to have the highest concentration of this vitamin in any food at 1,000 mg per 100 g of the edible portion. The same weight of Indian gooseberries (about 12 marble-sized ones) provides 600 mg of vitamin C, which is 15 times the daily adult Indian requirement (40 mg).

The Indian gooseberry is believed to be a very natural vitamin pill. One amla murraba in the morning is considered insurance against a lifetime of illness.

The murraba syrup makes a refreshing drink that could help replace electrolytes (especially potassium that is present in Indian gooseberry at 225 mg per 100 g of the edible portion) and water lost through sweating on a hot day. Simply mix 1 tsp of the delicately flavoured syrup in a glass of water and drink it.

In countries where chewing betel leaves is habitual, the use of slaked lime contributes to the intake of calcium. However, it has not been considered for these calculations.

3.8 Snacks

3.8.1 Sweet Potato Balls

Preparation Time : 15 min
Cooking Time : 20 min

Makes 25

Ingredients

About 5 tubers/1 kg/2.2 lb sweet potatoes
1 cup or 6 handfuls/180 g/6 oz shelled groundnuts
5 tbsp/75 g/2 1/2 oz powdered jaggery
6 tbsp/30 g/1 oz freshly grated coconut
1 tbsp/15 g/ 1/2 oz sugar

(1) Wash the sweet potatoes. Place them in a pressure-cooker together with sufficient water. Close the cooker. Bring to maximum pressure over high heat, then lower the flame and pressure-cook for 5 minutes. Remove from the fire. Allow the pressure inside the cooker to dissipate, then peel and mash the sweet potatoes until smooth. Divide into 25 portions.

(2) Roast the groundnuts, without oil, until they begin to crackle. Remove the papery skin and crush coarsely.

(3) Mix the jaggery with the groundnuts. Divide into 25 portions.

(4) Flatten a portion of the mashed sweet potato. Place a portion of the groundnut-jaggery mixture in the centre. Work the edges of the mashed sweet potato to enclose the mixture. Form into a ball.

(5) Combine the grated coconut and sugar. Roll each ball in the sweetened coconut. Serve for tea or as a mid-morning snack.

Per Piece			
Kilocalories	108	Iron	Trace
Protein	2 g	Vitamin C	10 mg
Fat	4 g	Vitamin A (as carotene)	880 mcg
Carbohydrate	17 g	Fibre	1 g
Calcium	27 mg		
Phosphorus	51 mg	1,000 mcg = 1 mg	

Nutrition Notes

Note that it is possible to increase the number of calories without the addition of visible fat. Almost half the weight of groundnuts and fresh coconut may be attributed to fat.

The orange variety of sweet potato is an excellent source of carotene, the precursor of vitamin A.

3.8.2   Khandvi (Savoury Curd and Gram Flour Roll-Ups)

Preparation Time   :   15 min
Cooking Time   :   30 min

Serves 6

Ingredients

2 medium/5 g/ 1/6 oz green chillies
1/2" or 1 cm piece/4 g/ 1/8 oz fresh ginger
1 cup/120 g/4 oz bengal gram flour
1 1/2 cups/375 ml/12 1/2 fl oz water
1/2 tsp turmeric powder
A generous pinch of asafoetida powder
Salt to taste
1 1/2 cups/375 ml/12 1/2 fl oz sour curds, lightly beaten (from skimmed milk)
2 tsp/10 ml/ 1/3 fl oz oil
1/2 tsp mustard seeds
1/2 bundle/15 g/ 1/2 oz coriander leaves, finely chopped

(1)   Grind the green chillies and ginger together to a smooth paste.

(2)   Add the ground paste, bengal gram flour, water, turmeric powder, asafoetida powder and salt to the beaten curds. Mix to get a smooth batter.

(3)   Place the mixture in a wide pan and stir continuously over low, steady heat. Do not allow it to boil.

(4)   When the mixture is quite thick and begins to hold its form, test for doneness by spreading a little of the paste on a plate. Let it cool for about 1 minute. If it can then be rolled and lifted, then the khandvi is ready.

(5)   Spread the mixture as thinly as possible (about 1 to 2 mm thick) over a clean, flat, smooth surface (polished marble, granite or cuddapah work surfaces are ideal) with the back of a spoon or with a spatula. Allow to cool completely, then cut into strips, 2" (5 cm) wide. Roll up as tightly as possible and arrange on a serving plate.

(6)   Heat a frying pan, then add the oil. Add the mustard seeds. When the mustard seeds begin to splutter, draw off the heat and dribble them over the khandvi rolls. Sprinkle with the chopped coriander leaves. Serve at once. Ideal as a teatime snack.

Per Serving			
Kilocalories	109	Iron	1 mg
Protein	6 g	Vitamin C	5 mg
Fat	3 g	Vitamin A (as carotene)	421 mcg
Carbohydrate	15 g	Fibre	Trace
Calcium	91 mg	Cholesterol	1 mg
Phosphorus	125 mg	1,000 mcg = 1 mg	

Notes of Interest

This delicacy was created by India's vegetarian chefs par excellence — the people of Gujarat. Children and invalids in particular will enjoy the subtle, piquant flavour of khandvi.

In the hot weather, the curds tend to get increasingly sour, so khandvi is best enjoyed as soon as it is made.

Khandvi is usually served with a garnish of fresh coconut scrapings beside the coriander leaves. It has been deliberately omitted to avoid the inclusion of saturated fat which is the major component of coconut.

3.8.3 Oopooma (Savoury Semolina Mix)

Preparation Time : 5 min
Cooking Time   : 20 min

Serves 6

Ingredients

1 handful/30 g/1 oz shelled groundnuts
2 cups/420 g/14 oz semolina
2 tbsp/30 ml/1 fl oz oil
1/4 tsp mustard seeds
2 medium/5 g/ 1/6 oz green chillies, deseeded and finely chopped
A sprig of curry leaves, finely chopped
4 cups/1 litre/1.6 pints hot water
Salt to taste

(1) *Roast the groundnuts, without oil, until they begin to crackle. Remove the papery skin and set aside.*

(2) *In a heavy kadai, roast the semolina over low heat without adding any oil until it just begins to change colour. Remove from the fire and set aside.*

(3) *Return the kadai to the fire. Add the oil. When the oil begins to smoke, add the mustard seeds. When the mustard seeds begin to splutter, add the chopped green chillies and curry leaves. Fry for 30 seconds. Gradually pour in 4 cups hot water. Add salt. Bring to the boil, and maintain a rolling boil. Taste for salt and adjust the seasoning until a trifle salty.*

(4) *Lower the heat and add the roasted semolina to the boiling water in a steady stream. Stir vigorously to avoid lumps. Cook until all the water is absorbed. Remove from the fire and add the roasted groundnuts.*

(5) *Serve hot or cold for breakfast or at teatime.*

Per Serving			
Kilocalories	318	Iron	1 mg
Protein	9 g	Vitamin C	1 mg
Fat	8 g	Vitamin A (as carotene)	55 mcg
Carbohydrate	54 g	Fibre	Trace
Calcium	17 mg		
Phosphorus	91 mg	1,000 mcg = 1 mg	

South Indian Fast Food

South of The Vindhyas, oopooma enjoys universal appeal as a fast food. As it does not spoil easily, it is also a favoured packed food for long-distance trips.

The mixture of hot water and semolina tends to bubble and plop spewing hot blobs of molten oopooma in all directions. While it is possible to master the art of dodging these missiles, there is a milder way to get oopooma done.

Follow steps 1 and 2 of the recipe. Then add enough salted hot water to the roasted semolina and mix until it begins to resemble moist breadcrumbs.

Heat the oil in a kadai and proceed with the tempering, adding mustard seeds, green chillies and curry leaves to the hot oil. Stir in the moistened semolina and cook for about 6 to 8 minutes. Serve garnished with the roasted groundnuts.

By this method, oopooma will have a powdery texture in contrast to the consistency of a mash in the former.

For festive occasions, substitute cashew nuts and raisins for the groundnuts. Fry them in the hot oil until golden, drain and set aside for the garnishing. To the same oil, add the mustard seeds and proceed as indicated in the recipe.

For a Fruit Oopooma, chop fresh pineapple, grapes and orange segments, sprinkle with sugar and add to the oopooma before taking it off the fire. These fruit will further enrich this dish with vitamin C and carotene (the precursor of vitamin A).

Substituting whey (obtained from making paneer—Recipe No: 3.11.3) for hot water improves the nutritional quality of oopooma by adding valuable proteins, minerals and vitamins.

3.8.4   Chiwda (Mixture)

Preparation Time   :   2 min
Cooking Time   :   20 min

Yield 225 g/7 1/2 oz

Ingredients

1 cup/100 g/3 1/3 oz rice flakes
2 handfuls/60 g/2 oz shelled groundnuts
2 tsp/10 ml/ 1/3 fl oz oil
Pinch of turmeric powder
2 medium/5 g/ 1/6 oz green chillies, deseeded and finely chopped
A sprig of curry leaves, finely chopped
3 tbsp or 2 handfuls/30 g/1 oz roasted bengal gram
1 tbsp/15 g/ 1/2 oz raisins
1 tbsp/15 g/ 1/2 oz sugar
1/2 tsp chiwda masala powder (Recipe No: 3.11.8)
Salt to taste

(1)   Pick the rice flakes clean. Do not wash. Set aside.

(2)   Roast the groundnuts, without oil, until they begin to crackle. Remove the papery skin and set aside.

(3)   In a heavy kadai, roast the rice flakes for about 3 minutes. Sprinkle with the oil and turmeric powder. Add the green chillies and curry leaves. When the chillies are quite dry, add the roasted bengal gram and groundnuts. Keep stirring until the rice flakes are very crisp but before they revert to the original grain. Add the raisins, sugar, chiwda masala powder and salt. Mix well.

(4)   Remove from the fire and set aside until cool. Store in an airtight container. Serve for tea or with drinks.

Per Tablespoon			
Kilocalories	67	Iron	2 mg
Protein	2 g	Vitamin C	Trace
Fat	3 g	Vitamin A (as carotene)	24 mcg
Carbohydrate	9 g	Fibre	Trace
Calcium	7 mg		
Phosphorus	39 mg	1,000 mcg = 1 mg	

Top Tip

Chiwda is to North India what mixture is to South India. It is usually deep-fried, but can also be dry-roasted as in this recipe.

This easy-to-make snack can be prepared in advance and stored. It will keep for about 1 week. To blend the contents, keep the tin tightly shut and roll it each time before serving.

3.8.5   Plain Dosai (Rice and Pulse Pancake)

Preparation Time	:	20 min
Soaking Time	:	6 hours
Leavening Time	:	12 hours *or* Overnight
Cooking Time	:	1 hour

Makes 25

Ingredients

3 cups/720 g/1 1/2 lb uncooked parboiled rice, cleaned and washed

1 cup/180 g/6 oz black gram dhal (without husk), cleaned and washed

1 tsp fenugreek seeds

2 1/2 cups/625 ml/1 pint water

Salt to taste

1 small potato, washed

4 tbsp/60 ml/2 fl oz oil

(1) *Soak the rice separately, and the black gram dhal and fenugreek seeds together, in generous amounts of water for 6 hours.*

(2) *Drain the rice and dhal completely. In a mixer, starting at the lowest speed, grind the rice to a smooth paste separately, adding 1 1/2 cups water, a little at a time. Gradually increase the speed as the paste gets smoother. Set aside.*

(3) *Grind the dhal and fenugreek seeds together to a smooth paste in the mixer at the lowest speed initially, but gradually progressing to the highest, adding 1 cup water, a little at a time.*

(4) *Mix both batters together. Add the salt and more water, if necessary, to get a batter of pouring consistency. Set aside to ferment for 12 hours or overnight in a vessel large enough to allow the batter to rise. Keep in a warm place.*

(5) *Heat a tawa reserved only for dosai making. (Do not use a tawa that is put to other uses such as chappati making.) To test if the tawa is ready for use, sprinkle with a few drops of water. If it sizzles, then lower the heat and proceed with making the dosais.*

(6) *Take the potato, slice off one end, pierce it with a fork and dip it in the oil. Rub it over the surface of the tawa. Wait for the oil to smoke. Without stirring the fermented batter too much, pour a ladleful on the hot tawa. Spread outwards in a continuous, circular motion using the back of the ladle until the batter covers most of the tawa surface. Dribble oil along the edges of the dosai.*

(7) *When the surface of the dosai appears dry, insert a spatula under it and turn it over. Cook for 2 minutes until crisp.*

(8) *Serve in traditional South Indian style with sambhar and coconut chutney either for breakfast, tiffin (mid-morning) or tea.*

Per Dosai			
Kilocalories	147	Iron	1 mg
Protein	4 g	Vitamin C	Nil
Fat	3 g	Vitamin A (as carotene)	3 mcg
Carbohydrate	27 g	Fibre	Trace
Calcium	14 mg		
Phosphorus	70 mg	1,000 mcg = 1 mg	

Dosai Cooking Dos

All forms of dosai probably originated in South India where rice is the staple. However, because of its immense popularity, dosai has become synonymous with Indian vegetarian cooking.

Set aside a tawa only for dosai making. It defeats the purpose of making a perfect dosai if the tawa is put to other uses. After every use, the tawa should be wiped clean with paper or cloth, smeared with 2 drops vegetable oil and stored.

If the tawa has to be washed, do so in hot, soapy water and rinse clean. Then, "season" it by first heating it through. When all the water has evaporated, spread 2 drops vegetable oil over the hot surface. When the oil begins to smoke, take the tawa off the fire, cool and store.

Sprinkling water over the tawa not only indicates readiness for use but also prevents overheating.

Using a potato to spread the oil on the tawa has two purposes. First, it restricts the amount of oil used. Second, it provides a glaze over the surface, allowing the batter to be spread evenly and perfectly. Use the same potato until none is left, slicing off the portion last used to expose a fresh surface every time it gets roasted. An onion also serves the same purpose.

Make sure that the ratio of rice to dhal is always 3:1 or 4:1 for dosais. This makes them thinner and crispier. Diluting the batter further will also give a crispier dosai but do not dilute too much as large, bald patches will appear while spreading.

Extra batter may be stored conveniently in the refrigerator (not freezer). It will keep without souring for about 4 days.

3.8.6 Masala Dosai
(Rice and Pulse Pancake with Potato filling)

Preparation Time	:	25 min
Soaking Time	:	6 hours
Leavening Time	:	12 hours *or* Overnight
Cooking Time	:	1 hour 30 min

Makes 25

Ingredients

Dosai Batter
As indicated in the recipe for plain dosai (Recipe No: 3.8.5)
Potato Masala
As indicated in the recipe for potato masala (Recipe No: 3.5.5). Double all the ingredients to obtain sufficient filling for 25 dosais.

(1) *Heat a tawa (reserved only for dosai making) and sprinkle with a few drops of water. If it sizzles, then lower the heat and proceed with dosai making.*

(2) *Cut the end off a potato, pierce it with a fork and dip it in the oil. Rub it over the surface of the tawa. When the oil begins to smoke, pour a ladleful of the dosai batter on the tawa and spread outwards in a continuous, circular motion with the back of the ladle. Dot the edges of the dosai with oil.*

(3) *When the surface appears dry and the edges brown, spread 2 tbsp of the prepared potato masala (kept ready on the side) over one half of the dosai. Fold the other half over to enclose the filling.*

(4) *Serve with sambhar and coconut chutney. For masala dosai, the coconut chutney should be thick and pasty. Reduce the amount of water mentioned in the recipe. Ideal for breakfast or tea.*

Per Masala Dosai			
Kilocalories	196	Iron	1 mg
Protein	4 g	Vitamin C	8 mg
Fat	4 g	Vitamin A (as carotene)	38 mcg
Carbohydrate	37 g	Fibre	Trace
Calcium	25 mg		
Phosphorus	92 mg	1,000 mcg = 1 mg	

3.8.7 Fruit Chaat (Indian Fruit Salad)

Preparation Time   :   30 min
Cooking Time   :   Nil

Serves 6

Ingredients

1 small/750 g/1 lb 9 oz pineapple, washed
1 small/1 kg/2.2 lb ripe but firm papaya, washed
1/4 large/1 1/4 kg/2 lb 10 oz watermelon, washed
2 medium/250 g/8 oz apples, washed
2 medium/120 g/4 oz guavas, washed
2 medium/120 g/4 oz oranges
1 tbsp/15 ml/ 1/2 fl oz lime juice
1/2 tsp kala (chaat) masala (Recipe No: 3.11.10)
A generous pinch of salt
12 toothpicks

(1) *Remove the base of the pineapple and discard. Stand the pineapple upright. Hold the crown firmly and cut away the peel, straight down, using a sharp knife. Remove the crown and "eyes". Cut in half lengthways. Slice each half across into 12 pieces. Set aside.*

(2) *Peel the papaya and cut in half. Remove the seeds. Cut into bite-sized cubes.*

(3) *Cut the watermelon into fingers, about 2" (5 cm) long and 1/2" (1 cm) thick. Discard the green rind. Remove as many seeds as possible.*

(4) *Quarter the apples and core. Do not peel. Cube.*

(5) *Top and tail the guavas. Cube.*

(6) *Peel the oranges and slice each into 6 wheels. Remove the pips.*

(7) *Place the papaya, watermelon, apples and guavas in a bowl. Pour over the lime juice and toss well together.*

(8) *Take 6 individual serving dishes. Arrange 4 half slices of pineapple in each. Heap the chopped fruit in the centre. Top with 2 wheels of orange. Drizzle with the kala masala and salt. Stick 2 toothpicks in the fruit. Serve as a midday refresher.*

Per Serving			
Kilocalories	132	Iron	11 mg
Protein	2 g	Vitamin C	150 mg
Fat	1 g	Vitamin A (as carotene)	4,046 mcg
Carbohydrate	30 g	Fibre	3 g
Calcium	60 mg		
Phosphorus	51 mg	1,000 mcg = 1 mg	

Fruit for Health

Fruit chaat is regular street fare in much of North and Western India, though it is a rather unhygienic way of getting so many valuable nutrients. The safe option is to prepare it at home.

Carotene, the precursor of vitamin A, is essential for good vision and healthy skin. More recently, it is believed, along with vitamin C, to reduce the risk of heart attacks, strokes and cancer, and to delay the onset of cataracts. Papaya and orange (and ripe mango which may also be included) are excellent sources of carotene. Watermelon contains no carotene, and pineapple, though deceptively yellow, has rather low levels of this provitamin of vitamin A.

Guava is an excellent source of vitamin C, and to a much lesser extent, papaya and pineapple.

Though fruits are considered poor sources of iron, watermelon holds the sole distinction of a fruit (except dried fruits) that makes a fair contribution of iron to the diet. The green rind of watermelon can be chopped up and added to curries like sambhar.

Fruits are exceedingly good sources of potassium, and also contain large amounts of fibre which promotes good health by facilitating elimination, preventing the uptake of fat in the intestines, and by reducing blood cholesterol and blood glucose levels.

3.8.8 Dal Dhokli (Wheat Flour Dumpling Squares in Dhal Sauce)

Preparation Time : 40 min
Soaking Time   : 30 min
Cooking Time   : 40 min

Serves 6

Ingredients

A lime-sized ball/30 g/1 oz tamarind

1 cup/250 ml/8 fl oz hot water
1 cup/240 g/8 oz red gram dhal, cleaned and washed
2 1/2 cups/625 ml/1 pint water
1 whole pod/10 g/ 1/3 oz garlic, finely chopped
1" or 2.5 cm piece/8 g/ 1/4 oz fresh ginger, finely chopped
2 medium/5 g/ 1/6 oz green chillies, finely chopped
1/2 tsp cumin seeds, powdered
1/2 tsp turmeric powder
1/2 tsp red chilli powder
Salt to taste
1/2 tsp cumin seeds, powdered
1/2 tsp turmeric powder
1 cup/180 g/6 oz wholemeal wheat flour
1/2 cup/125 ml/4 fl oz cold water
Flour for dredging
6 cups/1 1/2 litres/2 1/2 pints hot water
1 medium/60 g/2 oz ripe tomato, diced
3 tbsp/45 g/1 1/2 oz powdered jaggery
1 handful/30 g/1 oz shelled groundnuts
1/2 bundle/15 g/ 1/2 oz coriander leaves, finely chopped
1 medium/90 g/3 oz Bombay onion, finely chopped
1 medium/30 g/1 oz lime, cut into 6 wedges

(1) Soak the tamarind in 1/2 cup hot water for 10 minutes. Squeeze to extract pulp. Add another 1/2 cup hot water to the same tamarind and extract pulp a second time.

(2) Soak the red gram dhal in 2 1/2 cups water for 30 minutes. Place the dhal, soaking water, chopped garlic, ginger, green chillies, 1/2 tsp powdered cumin seeds, 1/2 tsp turmeric powder, 1/2 tsp red chilli powder and salt in the body of a pressure-cooker. Close the cooker. Bring to maximum pressure over high heat, then lower the flame and pressure-cook for 5 minutes. Remove from the fire and allow the pressure inside the cooker to dissipate.

(3) Add salt, 1/2 tsp powdered cumin seeds and 1/2 tsp turmeric powder to the wholemeal wheat flour. Mix well. Make a stiff dough with about 1/2 cup cold water. Divide into 3 portions. Dredge with flour and roll out each portion as thinly as possible. Cut into 2" (5 cm) squares (or diamonds). Set aside.

(4) Place the cooked dhal in a very wide pan. Dilute it with 6 cups hot water. Pour in the tamarind extract. Add the diced tomato, jaggery and shelled groundnuts. Bring to the boil, then lower the heat and simmer. Drop the wheat flour squares, well apart, into the bubbling dhal sauce to prevent them from sticking together. After the last addition, bring to the boil and continue cooking for a further 10 minutes. Sprinkle with the chopped coriander leaves and remove from the fire.

(5) *Spoon into individual bowls. Garnish with the chopped onion and add a squeeze of lime. Serve hot.*

Per Serving			
Kilocalories	323	Iron	4 mg
Protein	15 g	Vitamin C	11 mg
Fat	3 g	Vitamin A (as carotene)	764 mcg
Carbohydrate	59 g	Fibre	2 g
Calcium	82 mg		
Phosphorus	273 mg	1,000 mcg = 1 mg	

Food Wise

In true Gujarati style, each bowl of dal dhokli is usually served with a generous dollop of ghee gently melting into the hot sauce. Naturally, better sense prevailed in presenting this recipe without the ghee, for the health of your heart. Much of the fat indicated comes from groundnut. Dal dhokli is a meal in itself and can be served for Sunday brunch or for a very filling high tea.

3.8.9 Rice Iddli (Steamed Rice Cake)

Preparation Time	:	20 min
Soaking Time	:	6 hours
Leavening Time	:	12 hours *or* Overnight
Cooking Time	:	30 min

Makes 24

Ingredients

2 cups/480 g/1 lb uncooked parboiled rice, cleaned and washed
1 cup/180 g/6 oz black gram dhal (without husk), cleaned and washed
1 3/4 cups/450 ml/ 3/4 pint water
Salt to taste
1 tsp/5 ml/ 1/6 fl oz refined oil

(1) *Soak the rice and dhal separately in generous amounts of water for 6 hours.*

(2) *Drain the rice and dhal completely. In a mixer, (the motor of a blender may not take the strain of this grinding), grind the dhal to a smooth paste separately, adding 3/4 cup water, a little at a time. Blend at the lowest speed initially, and gradually progress to the highest as the paste gets smoother.*

(3) *Grind the rice next, separately, to a little coarser paste, adding 1 cup water. Blend at the lowest speed, and progress to the highest. Add more water if necessary to get a batter of thick consistency.*

(4) *Mix both batters together. Add salt. Set aside to ferment for 12 hours or overnight in a vessel large enough to allow the batter to rise. Keep in a warm place.*

(5) *Lightly grease an iddli mould of 12-iddli capacity with the refined oil. Place the mould in the body of a pressure-cooker that contains sufficient water (about 2 cups). Allow to heat through. Take it out and without mixing the fermented batter, pour a ladleful into each mould. Steam, without the weight, for 15 minutes or until a skewer pushed through the centre of an iddli comes out clean. (The iddlis will take between 8 and 15 minutes to get done depending on the size of the mould.) Prepare another batch of iddlis using the same batter.*

(6) *Serve with sambhar and coconut chutney or with 2 tsp milagai podi mixed to a paste with a little gingelly oil.*

Per Iddli			
Kilocalories	97	Iron	0.5 mg
Protein	3 g	Vitamin C	Nil
Fat	Trace	Vitamin A (as carotene)	3 mcg
Carbohydrate	20 g	Fibre	Trace
Calcium	13 mg		
Phosphorus	58 mg	1,000 mcg = 1 mg	

What Better Nutrition?

This breakfast dish is of South Indian origin.

Iddlis ideally demonstrate how cereals and pulses can be combined to make up for the inherent imbalance of essential amino acids (the building blocks of proteins) that is a feature of each group separately. In combination, however, this is more than amply compensated for.

Iddlis are perfect for little children and for the sick as they are low in fat and are easily digested. Their bland flavour is especially appealing.

Though parboiled rice is preferred, raw rice may also be used. To soften iddlis, add 1 handful puffed rice or 1 handful cooked rice when the rice is being ground.

Dhokla is a Gujarati variation of iddli. Mix 1 cup (250 ml/8 fl oz) water and 3/4 cup (187.5 ml/6 1/4 fl oz) sour curds (from skimmed milk) together. Prepare the dhal and rice batters as instructed in the iddli recipe using the curds mixture. Allow to ferment. Grease a dhokla mould or a pressure-cooker container. Steam the fermented batter for 15 minutes in two batches. Cut the dhokla into big chunks and arrange them on a serving dish.

Heat a pan, then add 1 tsp (5 ml/ 1/6 fl oz) refined oil. Add 1/2 tsp mustard seeds, 2 medium (5 g/ 1/6 oz) green chillies, slit lengthways and a generous pinch of asafoetida powder. When the mustard seeds begin to splutter, remove the pan from the fire and stir in 1/2 tsp sugar, the juice of 1/2 lime, 1 tbsp water and a pinch of salt. Mix until dissolved and dribble the mixture over the dhoklas kept ready. Sprinkle with 1/2 bundle (15 g/ 1/2 oz) chopped coriander leaves. Serve immediately with coriander chutney.

3.8.10 Vegetable Cutlet

Preparation Time	:	40 min
Resting Time	:	30 min
Cooking Time	:	50 min

Makes 12

Ingredients

4 large/500 g/1.1 lb potatoes
Salt to taste
2 tsp/10 ml/ 1/3 fl oz refined oil
1 medium/90 g/3 oz Bombay onion, finely chopped
2 medium/5 g/ 1/6 oz green chillies, deseeded and finely chopped
5 small/120 g/4 oz carrots, finely diced
About 8/90 g/3 oz beans, finely chopped
1 handful/30 g/1 oz shelled peas
2 tbsp/30 ml/1 fl oz hot water
Pinch of turmeric powder
Salt to taste
1 tsp/5 ml/ 1/6 fl oz lime juice
1/2 bundle/15 g/ 1/2 oz coriander leaves, finely chopped
1 tbsp/15 g/ 1/2 oz refined wheat flour
2 tbsp/30 ml/1 fl oz refined oil

(1) *Scrub the potatoes. Place them in a pressure-cooker together with sufficient water. Close the cooker. Bring to maximum pressure over high heat, then lower the flame and pressure-cook for 7 minutes. Remove from the fire. Allow the pressure inside the cooker to dissipate, then peel, add a little salt and mash the potatoes until very smooth. Divide into 12 portions.*

(2) *Heat a kadai, then add 2 tsp refined oil. Add the chopped onion and green chillies. When the onion is soft, add the carrots, beans and peas. Fry for 2 minutes. Stir in the hot water, turmeric powder and salt. Cook uncovered until the vegetables are tender and all the moisture is absorbed. Sprinkle with the lime juice and coriander leaves. Mix well and remove from the fire. Divide into 12 portions.*

(3) *Shape the mashed potato into 12 logs and fill the centre of each with a portion of the vegetable mixture. Work the edges of the mashed potato to enclose the filling. Roll up and flatten into 3" × 2" (7.5 cm × 5 cm) oblong cutlets. Dust with the refined wheat flour. Cover and set aside for 30 minutes, preferably in the refrigerator.*

(4) *Heat a frying pan, then add 1 tsp oil. Lower the heat and arrange 6 cutlets in the hot oil. Dribble another 1 tsp oil between the cutlets, and allow to brown. Flip over and add another 1 tsp oil to brown the other side. Place on absorbent paper to drain.*

(5) *Prepare the remaining 6 cutlets. Serve hot with mint chutney.*

Per Cutlet			
Kilocalories	98	Iron	1 mg
Protein	2 g	Vitamin C	13 mg
Fat	4 g	Vitamin A (as carotene)	1,097 mcg
Carbohydrate	15 g	Fibre	1 g
Calcium	23 mg		
Phosphorus	92 mg	1,000 mcg = 1 mg	

Health Hint

It was possible to use only 2 tbsp oil to brown the cutlets because the frying pan was well-seasoned. Always heat the frying pan first, then add oil. This evaporates any moisture that might be present in the pores of the metal which is the main reason why food sticks to the pan. Consequently, less fat is needed. Non-stick cookware is another alternative to reduce fat in cooking.

3.8.11 Rava-Semiya Iddli
(Savoury Steamed Semolina and Vermicelli Cake)

Preparation Time	:	10 min
Resting Time	:	2 hours
Cooking Time	:	30 min

Makes 16

Ingredients

1 cup/210 g/7 oz semolina
2 cups/80 g/2 2/3 oz fine vermicelli, crumbled
Salt to taste
2 1/2 cups/625 ml/1 pint sour curds, lightly beaten (from skimmed milk)
Warm water, if necessary
2 tsp/10 ml/ 1/3 fl oz refined oil
1/2 tsp mustard seeds
1 tsp black gram dhal (without husk)
2 medium/5 g/ 1/6 oz green chillies, deseeded and finely chopped
1" or 2.5 cm piece/8 g/ 1/4 oz fresh ginger, finely chopped
A sprig of curry leaves, finely chopped

(1) *Roast the semolina and vermicelli separately over low heat, without oil, until golden. Set aside.*

(2) *Add the salt to the beaten curds. Stir in the roasted semolina and vermicelli. Add a little warm water, if necessary, to get a thick, pasty batter. Set aside for 2 hours.*

(3) *Lightly grease an iddli mould with a little of the refined oil. Place the mould in the body of a pressure-cooker that contains sufficient water (about 2 cups). Allow to heat through.*

(4) *In the meantime, heat the remaining refined oil in a frying pan and add the mustard seeds. When the mustard seeds begin to splutter, add the black gram dhal, chopped green chillies, ginger and curry leaves. Fry until the ginger is cooked. Stir into the batter. Mix well, taste for salt and adjust the seasoning.*

(5) *Take the iddli mould out of the pressure-cooker. Place a ladleful of the batter in each mould. Steam, without the weight, for 15 minutes or until a skewer pushed through the centre of an iddli comes out clean. (The iddlis will take between 8 and 15 minutes to get done depending on the size of the mould.)*

(6) *Serve with vegetable stew or mutton curry. As a school lunch, pack with a little mint chutney or coriander chutney.*

Per Iddli			
Kilocalories	82	Iron	Trace
Protein	3 g	Vitamin C	1 mg
Fat	1 g	Vitamin A (as carotene)	21 mcg
Carbohydrate	16 g	Fibre	Negligible
Calcium	51 mg	Cholesterol	1 mg
Phosphorus	55 mg	1,000 mcg = 1 mg	

Cooking Hints

Also of South Indian origin, rava-semiya iddlis are a variation of the more popular rice iddlis. They are easier to make, and require no time for leavening.

To ensure that these iddlis are perfect, it is important that the ratio of semolina to vermicelli is a constant 1:2 *by volume*. Use coarse semolina. Sift to remove the fine flour, if necessary.

Designed for Diabetics

Diabetics, in particular, should be encouraged to eat these iddlis as both semolina and vermicelli are wheat products that are more beneficial in maintaining blood glucose levels within acceptable limits than rice, for example, which raises blood sugar levels too rapidly, necessitating greater caution. Besides, the necessary calories are largely provided by carbohydrates which is a very good thing. These iddlis, being very low in fat, are additionally advantageous for diabetics with a weight problem.

3.8.12 Khichidi (Savoury Rice and Pulse Snack)

Preparation Time	:	5 min
Soaking Time	:	4 hours
Cooking Time	:	30 min

Serves 6

Ingredients

1 cup/240 g/8 oz uncooked parboiled rice, cleaned and washed
1 cup/240 g/8 oz whole green gram, cleaned and washed
4 1/2 cups/1 1/8 litres/1.8 pints hot water
2 medium/5 g/ 1/6 oz green chillies, slit lengthways
1/2 tsp turmeric powder
Pinch of asafoetida powder
Salt to taste

(1) Soak the rice and green gram together in 4 1/2 cups hot water for 4 hours.

(2) Place the rice, green gram and soaking water in the body of a pressure-cooker of minimum 7 1/2-litre capacity. Add the green chillies, turmeric powder, asafoetida powder and salt. Close the cooker. Bring to maximum pressure over high heat, then lower the flame and pressure-cook for 10 minutes. Remove from the fire. Allow the pressure inside the cooker to dissipate, then open and fluff up the khichidi with a fork.

(3) Serve hot with fresh curds.

Per Serving			
Kilocalories	272	Iron	2 mg
Protein	12 g	Vitamin C	1 mg
Fat	1 g	Vitamin A (as carotene)	58 mcg
Carbohydrate	54 g	Fibre	2 g
Calcium	54 mg		
Phosphorus	188 mg	1,000 mcg = 1 mg	

Health Notes

Khichidi, along with iddli and dosai, is a fine example of how the essential amino acids (the building blocks of protein) lacking in one source are compensated for by another. Rice lacks two essential amino acids, namely, lysine and threonine, but in combination with green gram which has no methionine, the deficiencies in each individual group are more than made up for.

In this recipe, parboiled rice and whole green gram have been used in preference to the more usual raw rice and husked green gram dhal. These substitutions raise the nutritive values of this dish significantly.

If parboiled rice is not available, use raw rice, but reduce the water by 1/2 cup (125 ml/4 fl oz).

The combination of whole green gram and rice is also more attractive than split green gram and rice. If the green gram can be sprouted first, then the vitamin C content will, additionally, be enhanced.

Common to North India, very often, khichidi is served during illness like fevers or to settle an upset stomach because of its bland flavour and easy digestibility. During fevers, when a high-protein, high-carbohydrate, low-fat diet is essential, this food is ideal. Before cooking, add a raw potato, cut into quarters, to further increase the carbohydrate and vitamin C content—both nutrients are vital for healing and recovery. For those who would prefer khichidi as a filling snack, it can be lightly tempered with 1/2 tsp cumin seeds in 2 tsp (10 ml/ 1/3 fl oz) hot oil, and garnished with chopped coriander leaves.

3.8.13 Thayir Semiya (Vermicelli in Curds)

Preparation Time	:	8 min
Cooking Time	:	15 min
Before Serving	:	1 hour

Serves 4

Ingredients

1 tbsp/15 ml/ 1/2 fl oz refined oil
1/2 tsp mustard seeds
1 medium green chilli, deseeded and finely chopped
1/2" or 1 cm piece/4 g/ 1/8 oz fresh ginger, finely chopped
A sprig of curry leaves, finely chopped
2 tbsp/15 g/ 1/2 oz broken cashew nuts
1 tbsp/15 g/ 1/2 oz raisins
1 1/2 cups/60 g/2 oz fine vermicelli, crumbled
1 cup/250 ml/8 fl oz hot water
1/2 cup/125 ml/4 fl oz warm skimmed milk
1 tbsp/15 g/ 1/2 oz sugar
Salt to taste
1 cup/250 ml/8 fl oz curds, lightly beaten (from skimmed milk)

(1) *Heat a wide pan, then add the oil. Add the mustard seeds. When the mustard seeds begin to splutter, add the chopped green chilli, ginger and curry leaves. Fry for 1 minute. Add the cashew nuts and raisins. Fry until the cashew nuts are just golden. Sprinkle with the vermicelli and fry until all the ingredients are well-blended. Pour in 1 cup hot water to soften the vermicelli. Add the milk, sugar and salt. Bring to the boil, then turn off the heat.*

(2) *When the vermicelli is lukewarm, stir in the beaten curds. Taste for salt and adjust the seasoning. Keep unrefrigerated for 1 hour before serving. (Beyond 1 hour, it will have to be refrigerated as the curds may sour too much especially in the warm weather.) Serve chilled if preferred.*

Per Serving			
Kilocalories	164	Iron	1 mg
Protein	5 g	Vitamin C	2 mg
Fat	6 g	Vitamin A (as carotene)	70 mcg
Carbohydrate	24 g	Fibre	Trace
Calcium	124 mg	Cholesterol	2 mg
Phosphorus	119 mg	1,000 mcg = 1 mg	

Nutrition Notes

Whole milk has four times as much fat and seven times as much cholesterol as skimmed milk. To reduce the fat content of milk, after boiling, cool it and place it in the refrigerator. Skim off the cream that rises to the surface. Repeat two or three times.

While the Tamils will lay claim to this dish which is akin to thayir saadam (curd rice), South Indians from the four other states will probably recognize it as their own, though known by a different name.

3.8.14   Tandoori Paneer ka Tikka (Grilled Cottage Cheese Squares)

Preparation Time	:	5 min
Marination Time	:	3 hours
Cooking Time	:	20 min

Makes 16

Ingredients

250 g/8 oz Indian cottage cheese
1 whole pod/10 g/ 1/3 oz garlic
1/2 tsp cumin seeds
10 black peppercorns
1/2 tsp garam masala (Recipe No: 3.11.6)
1/2 tsp mango powder
Salt to taste
1/2 cup/125 ml/4 fl oz curds, lightly beaten (from skimmed milk)
4 skewers
1 tsp/5 ml/ 1/6 fl oz oil

(1)   *Cut the cottage cheese into 1" (2.5 cm) squares of 1" (2.5 cm) thickness.*

(2)   *Grind the garlic, cumin seeds and peppercorns together to a smooth paste.*

(3)   *Add the ground paste, garam masala, mango powder and salt to the beaten curds. Mix well. Taste for salt and adjust the seasoning.*

(4)   *Immerse the cottage cheese in the marinade placed in a stainless steel or glass bowl. Cover and leave in the refrigerator for 3 hours. At the end of every hour, turn the pieces of cottage cheese over in the marinade so that all the sides are evenly coated.*

(5)   *Heat a gas tandoor (or grill) for 10 minutes or until very hot. Lower the heat. Lightly*

grease 4 skewers with the oil and thread 4 tikkas on each. Place them in the tandoor and raise the heat. Cover and cook for 2 minutes over high heat. Lower the heat and baste the tikkas with the remaining oil. Every 2 minutes, turn the tikkas over so that every side is exposed equally to the hottest part of the tandoor.

(6)   Slip the tikkas off the skewers. Serve as a starter or with drinks.

Per Tikka			
Kilocalories	47	Vitamin C	1 mg
Protein	3 g	Vitamin A (as carotene)	Nil
Fat	4 g	Vitamin A (as retinol)	17 mcg
Carbohydrate	1 g	Fibre	Nil
Calcium	42 mg	Cholesterol	9 mg
Phosphorus	31 mg		
Iron	Negligible	1,000 mcg = 1 mg	

Top Tip

Part of the North Indian tandoor repertoire, these tikkas may be prepared over an open barbecue spit too.

Health Pointer

In this recipe, the cottage cheese is a commercial product prepared from whole milk which has taken the fat and cholesterol levels rather high.

Cottage cheese can be prepared at home quickly and cheaply, both in terms of cost and fat, by using skimmed milk. It is recommended that home-made cottage cheese prepared from skimmed milk be used in cooking (Recipe No: 3.11.3).

3.8.15   Poha (Savoury Rice Flakes)

Preparation Time   :   10 min
Cooking Time   :   20 min

Serves 4

Ingredients

2 cups/200 g/6 2/3 oz rice flakes
1 large/125 g/4 oz potato
1 handful/30 g/1 oz shelled groundnuts
1 tsp cumin seeds, crushed
Pinch of asafoetida powder

2 tsp/10 ml/ 1/3 fl oz oil
1/2 tsp mustard seeds
1/4 tsp turmeric powder
1 tsp/5 g/ 1/6 oz sugar
Salt to taste
1 1/2 tsp/7.5 ml/ 1/4 fl oz lime juice
1/2 bundle/15 g/ 1/2 oz coriander leaves, finely chopped

(1) *Clean, wash and place the rice flakes in a colander lined with cloth to drain.*

(2) *Scrub the potato. Place it in a pressure-cooker together with sufficient water. Close the cooker. Bring to maximum pressure over high heat, then lower the flame and pressure-cook for 7 minutes. Remove from the fire. Allow the pressure inside the cooker to dissipate, then peel and cube the potato.*

(3) *Roast the groundnuts, without oil, until they begin to crackle. Remove the papery skin and set aside.*

(4) *Mix the crushed cumin seeds and asafoetida powder together. Set aside.*

(5) *Heat a wide pan, then add the oil. Add the mustard seeds. When the mustard seeds begin to splutter, add the cooked potato and turmeric powder. Mix well to blend. Stir in the moist rice flakes. Sprinkle with the cumin seed-asafoetida powder, sugar and salt. Stir once and draw off the fire.*

(6) *Drizzle with the lime juice. Garnish with the roasted groundnuts and chopped coriander leaves. Serve for tea or as a mid-morning snack.*

Per Serving			
Kilocalories	276	Iron	10 mg
Protein	6 g	Vitamin C	12 mg
Fat	6 g	Vitamin A (as carotene)	570 mcg
Carbohydrate	49 g	Fibre	1 g
Calcium	28 mg		
Phosphorus	162 mg	1,000 mcg = 1 mg	

Cooking Hints

Always cook more potatoes than necessary and store the balance, covered, in the refrigerator/freezer. These can be easily incorporated in recipes, saving much time.

Poha can be made in half the time given if one pre-cooked potato is available. This wonderful snack that comes to us courtesy the Maharashtrians, can be prepared to feed unexpected guests or eternally famished children because it is so easily made.

The Heart of the Matter

Rice flakes contain a very high percentage of iron (20 mg per 100 g of flakes). This makes them one of the best foods for iron from non-animal sources. Persons with a tendency to iron deficiency anaemia, especially teenage girls and pregnant women, are advised to eat rice flakes as often as possible.

Rice flakes, as a low-sodium cereal product high in potassium and magnesium, are recommended for persons with chronic heart disease. As these people have to watch their sodium intake (particularly if complications include high blood pressure) and are often prescribed diuretics (drugs that reduce fluid retention) which deplete the body of potassium, rice flakes are the healthy alternative that accommodates all these considerations. Moreover, magnesium and potassium (with calcium) have a regulatory effect on the heartbeat.

Fluid retention that is sometimes a complication of pregnancy may be managed by increasing rice flakes in the diet, since medication, unless carefully monitored, is seldom prescribed. Additionally, rice flakes contain a fair amount of vitamin B_3.

3.9 Sweets

3.9.1   Gajjar ka Halwa (Carrot Halwa)

Preparation Time   :   5 min
Cooking Time   :   35 min

Serves 4

Ingredients

About 11 medium/500 g/1.1 lb carrots, washed and peeled
2 tbsp/15 g/ 1/2 oz broken cashew nuts
4 small, green cardamoms
2 cups/500 ml/16 fl oz skimmed milk
3/4 cup/180 g/6 oz sugar
1 tbsp/15 ml/ 1/2 fl oz refined oil
1 tbsp/15 g/ 1/2 oz raisins

(1)   Top and tail the carrots. Place them in a pressure-cooker container. Do not add extra water to the carrots. Pour sufficient water in the body of the pressure-cooker. Lower the container into the pressure-cooker. Close the cooker. Bring to maximum pressure over high heat, then lower the flame and pressure-cook for 3 minutes. Remove from the fire. Allow the pressure inside the cooker to dissipate, then mash the carrots coarsely with a fork.

(2)   Lightly roast the cashew nuts, without oil, until they begin to change colour. Set aside.

(3)   Remove the seeds from the cardamom pods and powder coarsely.

(4)   Heat the milk and sugar together in a heavy-bottomed pan. Stir until the sugar dissolves.

(5)   Add the mashed carrots and stir continuously until the milk is absorbed. Stir in the refined oil, raisins, cashew nuts and cardamom powder. When the mixture rolls into a ball, remove from the fire. Transfer to a serving bowl. Serve hot or cold as a dessert.

Per Serving			
Kilocalories	343	Iron	2 mg
Protein	5 g	Vitamin C	5 mg
Fat	6 g	Vitamin A (as carotene)	11,052 mcg
Carbohydrate	67 g	Fibre	2 g
Calcium	261 mg	Cholesterol	3 mg
Phosphorus	795 mg	1,000 mcg = 1 mg	

Nutrition Talk

Gajjar ka halwa is a sweet popular in North India. It is possible to make it with no fat at all. However, carotene being fat soluble is better absorbed if a little oil is present. Substituting whole milk for skimmed milk will ensure that the carotene is absorbed without added fat, besides providing 261 mcg of vitamin A (as retinol) per 500 ml of milk. This volume of whole milk will, additionally, provide 21 g of mostly saturated fat which carries a load of 68 mg of cholesterol as against 10 mg of cholesterol from skimmed milk.

Carrots provide the "vision" vitamin as its precursor beta carotene. Carrots also increase the number of red blood cells, reduce the risk of heart attacks, strokes and cancer, help to develop immunity against upper respiratory tract infections, and, keep the skin looking young and healthy.

Use tender carrots. Less sugar will then have to be added.

3.9.2 Ravo (Semolina Pudding)

Preparation Time	:	10 min
Resting Time	:	1 hour
Cooking Time	:	15 min
Chilling Time	:	2 hours minimum

Serves 4

Ingredients

2 cups/500 ml/16 fl oz cold skimmed milk
4 tbsp/60 g/2 oz sugar
2 tbsp/30 g/1 oz semolina
1 tsp/5 g/ 1/6 oz ghee
Pinch of salt
A few drops of rose essence
Pinch of freshly grated nutmeg
1 tbsp or about 12/15 g/ 1/2 oz almonds, blanched and slivered
1 tbsp/15 g/ 1/2 oz raisins

(1) *Place the milk, sugar, semolina, ghee and salt in a pan and set aside for 1 hour.*

(2) *Place the pan over low heat. Gradually bring the mixture to the boil and stir until it thickens. Draw off the fire. Stir in the essence and nutmeg. Mix well.*

(3) *Spoon the ravo into individual bowls. Set aside to cool. Sprinkle with the*

almonds and raisins. Chill for at least 2 hours before serving. Traditionally served at breakfast on auspicious occasions among the Parsees.

Per Serving			
Kilocalories	169	Vitamin C	1 mg
Protein	5 g	Vitamin A (as carotene)	Negligible
Fat	4 g	Vitamin A (as retinol)	8 mcg
Carbohydrate	30 g	Fibre	Trace
Calcium	165 mg	Cholesterol	6 mg
Phosphorus	142 mg		
Iron	1 mg	1,000 mcg = 1 mg	

Good Health

Animal fats contain significant amounts of cholesterol. Dietary cholesterol can be reduced if refined oil (or any vegetable oil) is used instead of ghee. However, hydrogenated vegetable fats like vanaspati, although they contain almost no cholesterol, are made up of saturated fatty acids which are implicated in heart and related disease conditions.

3.9.3 Payir Payasam (Whole Green Gram in Sweetened Milk Sauce)

Preparation Time	:	10 min
Soaking Time	:	2 hours
Cooking Time	:	20 min

Serves 6

Ingredients

1 cup/240 g/8 oz whole green gram, cleaned and washed

2 tbsp/30 g/1 oz sago, cleaned

2 cups/500 ml/16 fl oz water

A generous pinch of salt

3/4 cup/180 g/6 oz powdered jaggery

1 cup/250 ml/8 fl oz water

3 small, green cardamoms

1 tbsp/15 ml/ 1/2 fl oz refined oil

1 tsp/5 g/ 1/6 oz ghee

2 tbsp/30 g/1 oz raisins

2 tbsp/15 g/ 1/2 oz broken cashew nuts

1 cup/250 ml/8 fl oz hot skimmed milk

3 cloves, crushed

(1)   Soak the green gram and sago together in 2 cups water for 2 hours. Place
      the green gram, sago, soaking water and salt in the body of a pressure-cooker.
      Close the cooker. Bring to maximum pressure over high heat, then lower the
      flame and pressure-cook for 5 minutes. Remove from the fire. Allow the
      pressure inside the cooker to dissipate.

.(2)   Dissolve the jaggery in 1 cup water over moderate heat. Bring to the boil.
      Strain and set aside.

(3)   Remove the seeds from the cardamom pods and powder.

(4)   Heat the refined oil and ghee together in a pan. Lower the heat and add the
      raisins and cashew nuts. Fry until the nuts are golden. Stir in the cooked gram
      and sago. Pour in the jaggery syrup. Bring to the boil, then add the hot milk.
      Simmer for 5 minutes. Sprinkle with the cardamom powder and crushed
      cloves. Remove from the fire.

(5)   Serve hot on special occasions or to welcome guests into the home.

Per Serving			
Kilocalories	338	Vitamin C	0.5 mg
Protein	11 g	Vitamin A (as carotene)	39 mcg
Fat	5 g	Vitamin A (as retinol)	5 mcg
Carbohydrate	62 g	Fibre	2 g
Calcium	130 mg	Cholesterol	3 mg
Phosphorus	196 mg		
Iron	3 mg	1,000 mcg = 1 mg	

Food Wise

For a truly authentic South Indian flavour, substitute 3 cups (750 ml/1 1/4 pints)
coconut milk (Recipe No: 3.11.2) for 2 cups (500 ml/16 fl oz) water and 1 cup
(250 ml/8 fl oz) skimmed milk. Pressure-cook the green gram and sago in the
second and third coconut extracts. Add the thick first milk just before taking
the payasam off the fire.

Coconut milk is high in saturated fat which is a major contributing factor in the
aetiology of heart disease. Hence, in this recipe, skimmed milk was used
instead.

Chopped ripe banana or jackfruit is sometimes added before serving, being
fruits common to this region.

3.9.4 Chikki (Gingelly Seed Candy)

Preparation Time   :   15 min (over 2 days)
Cooking Time   :   25 min

Makes 30

Ingredients

1 3/4 cups/250 g/8 oz gingelly seeds, preferably white
1 tsp/5 ml/ 1/6 fl oz refined oil
500 g/1.1 lb jaggery, crumbled
1/2 cup/125 ml/4 fl oz water
1/2 tsp dried ginger, powdered

(1) Clean and wash the gingelly seeds to remove sand and grit. Spread out on a cloth and dry in the sun, or place in an oven after it has been turned off so that the wet seeds will dry slowly and the dissipating heat is not wasted.

(2) The next day, grease a 12" x 8" (30 cm x 20 cm) stainless steel or baking tray with the refined oil. Set aside.

(3) Roast the gingelly seeds in a kadai, without oil, until the raw taste is removed — about 8 minutes.

(4) Dissolve the jaggery in 1/2 cup water over low heat. Strain.

(5) Boil the jaggery syrup until it is reduced to the soft ball stage (a drop of the syrup in a bowl of cold water will form a soft, pliable ball that holds its shape).

(6) Stir in the roasted gingelly seeds and powdered dried ginger. Pour immediately into the prepared tray. Mark into squares when almost set. Allow to cool, then break up and store in an airtight container.

Per Chikki Square			
Kilocalories	112	Iron	1 mg
Protein	2 g	Vitamin C	Nil
Fat	4 g	Vitamin A (as carotene)	5 mcg
Carbohydrate	18 g	Fibre	Trace
Calcium	134 mg		
Phosphorus	54 mg	1,000 mcg = 1 mg	

Cooking Hints

The gingelly seeds should be cleaned, washed and dried the previous day as otherwise the roasting time will be more than doubled.

An equal amount of roasted groundnuts or roasted bengal gram may be substituted for the gingelly seeds. Or a mix of all three can be made into a particularly delicious chikki.

Health Wise

Almost half the weight of gingelly seeds is fat, but highly desirable, since it is made up largely of mono- and polyunsaturated fatty acids (PUFA), besides essential fatty acids (EFA) that the diet must provide as they are not synthesized in the body.

Gingelly seeds are also rich in vitamin E, and, vitamin B_1 and folic acid of the B complex group.

Gingelly seeds are a virtual storehouse of minerals too. Calcium, phosphorus, copper, zinc, manganese, molybdenum and chromium are some of the minerals that are present in them. The highest concentration of zinc in vegetable foods is probably found in gingelly seeds other than wheat germ.

Jaggery provides some calcium, phosphorus, iron and potassium.

The seemingly insignificant dried ginger makes a contribution too. It contains magnesium and manganese, and, some amounts of copper, zinc and chromium. Dried ginger is also an effective analgesic and anti-inflammatory agent.

Variations of chikki such as rewri, gazak and til pappad, employing gingelly seeds and jaggery, appear in shops only in the cold, winter months of North India, as they help to lubricate and reduce the pain of arthritic joints, in addition to providing the necessary heat to keep warm.

3.9.5 Phirni (Sweetened Rice Pudding)

Preparation Time	:	5 min
Cooking Time	:	30 min
Chilling Time	:	2 hours minimum

Serves 4

Ingredients

2 cups/500 ml/16 fl oz skimmed milk
4 tbsp/60 g/2 oz sugar
2 tbsp/30 g/1 oz rice flour
A few drops of rose essence

1 tbsp or about 12/15 g/ 1/2 oz almonds, blanched and slivered
1 tbsp/15 g/ 1/2 oz pistachios, crushed
Silver edible foil

---

(1) *Bring the milk to the boil in a pan. Lower the heat and add the sugar. Stir until the sugar dissolves. Gradually add the rice flour, a little at a time, to prevent lumping. Stirring continuously, cook until the mixture thickens. Remove from the fire.*

(2) *Cool the mixture to room temperature. Stir in the essence.*

(3) *Transfer to individual bowls. Decorate with the nuts and silver edible foil. Chill before serving.*

Per Serving			
Kilocalories	170	Iron	1 mg
Protein	5 g	Vitamin C	1 mg
Fat	4 g	Vitamin A (as carotene)	5 mcg
Carbohydrate	28 g	Fibre	Trace
Calcium	166 mg	Cholesterol	3 mg
Phosphorus	158 mg	1,000 mcg = 1 mg	

Time Saving Cooking

Traditionally, uncooked rice is soaked in water for at least 2 hours, then drained and ground to a smooth paste before it is used to make phirni. In this recipe, rice that had been previously ground and stored as rice flour was used—a convenient and easy way to have a delicious dessert ready in no time.

Nutritionally Speaking

Though no fat has been added in the preparation of this sweet, (even the milk is skimmed), the fat indicated has crept in "invisibly" through the nuts used as a garnish. Many foods (nuts and oilseeds in particular) that are not visibly oily are responsible for a high degree of unintended fat intake.

3.9.6   Paal Kolukattai (Rice Dumplings in Sweetened Milk Sauce)

Preparation Time	:	30 min
Cooking Time	:	25 min

Serves 6

Ingredients

3 tbsp/15 g/ 1/2 oz freshly grated coconut
2 1/2 tbsp/37.5 g/1 1/4 oz sugar
2 cups/360 g/12 oz roasted rice flour
A generous pinch of salt
Sufficient hot water to make the dough
1 cup/250 ml/8 fl oz skimmed milk
2 cups/500 ml/16 fl oz water
9 1/2 tbsp/142.5 g/4 3/4 oz sugar
Pinch of salt

(1)   Add the grated coconut and 2 1/2 tbsp sugar to the rice flour. Mix well. Dissolve a generous pinch of salt in the hot water. Gradually add the hot, salted water to the rice flour mixture to get a soft, pliable dough.

(2)   Divide the dough into small logs and pinch off marble-sized portions. Roll up into balls and set aside.

(3)   Place the milk, water and 9 1/2 tbsp sugar in a very wide pan and bring to the boil. Add a pinch of salt. Lower the heat and simmer. Press the rice dumplings between thumb and forefinger to flatten them, then drop them, one by one, into the bubbling milk sauce. Drop them well apart so that they do not stick to each other. Allow 3 minutes between each batch. Complete in 4 batches.

(4)   Do not stir the dumplings with a spoon when they are cooking. Instead, pick up the pan and swirl the contents before each new addition. After the last addition, simmer for 5 minutes until the milk sauce is thick and the last batch is well cooked.

(5)   Serve hot for breakfast or tea.

Per Serving			
Kilocalories	350	Iron	1 mg
Protein	5 g	Vitamin C	Trace
Fat	1 g	Vitamin A	Nil
Carbohydrate	80 g	Fibre	Trace
Calcium	59 mg	Cholesterol	1 mg
Phosphorus	130 mg	1,000 mcg = 1 mg	

Cooking Tip

This form of rice dumpling is typical of fare common to the southern tip of coastal Tamil Nadu, where rice and coconut are the basic ingredients in almost all the sweets prepared in this region.

The rice flour used in this recipe was made from parboiled rice. However, raw rice may be substituted for it. Roast the rice flour until a nice aroma arises, cool completely and store it in an airtight container. It will keep for many months and can be used whenever needed without any further cooking or roasting.

3.9.7   Kulfi (Indian Ice-cream)

Preparation Time	:	5 min
Cooking Time	:	35 min
Freezing Time	:	4 hours minimum

Makes 8

Ingredients

2 cups/500 ml/16 fl oz skimmed milk
5 tbsp/75 g/2 1/2 oz sugar
Pinch of salt
1 tbsp/15 g/ 1/2 oz rice flour
Warm water
1 tbsp/15 g/ 1/2 oz pistachios, finely chopped
1 tbsp or about 12/15 g/ 1/2 oz almonds, blanched and ground
A few drops of kewra essence

(1) *Bring the milk to the boil in a pan. Add the sugar and salt. Lower the heat and continue to simmer until reduced by half. Stir occasionally.*

(2) *Make a thick paste of the rice flour with a little warm water. Add it to the milk. Stirring continuously, cook until it thickens. Add the chopped pistachios and almond paste. Mix well and remove from the fire.*

(3) *Cool to room temperature, then pour into cone-shaped kulfi moulds (ice-cream moulds of any shape will also do), allowing sufficient space for the kulfi to expand on cooling. Freeze until very hard.*

(4) *To unmould, roll each mould between your palms and tap the kulfi out into individual dessert bowls. Sprinkle with the essence. Slice quickly (as it melts rather fast) in half lengthways. Serve at once.*

Per Kulfi			
Kilocalories	86	Iron	Trace
Protein	3 g	Vitamin C	1 mg
Fat	2 g	Vitamin A (as carotene)	3 mcg
Carbohydrate	14 g	Fibre	Negligible
Calcium	83 mg	Cholesterol	1 mg
Phosphorus	76 mg	1,000 mcg = 1 mg	

Top Tip

For a smoother kulfi, substitute cornflour for rice flour.

3.9.8　Guava Cheese

Preparation Time　:　25 min
Cooking Time　　　:　2 hours 20 min

Makes 50—Yield 1 kg/2.2 lb

Ingredients

About 14 medium/1.1 kg/2 lb 5 oz ripe guavas
1 cup/250 ml/8 fl oz water
5 cups/1.2 kg/2 1/2 lb sugar
2 tbsp/30 ml/1 fl oz lime juice
Pinch of salt
5 tsp/25 ml/ 5/6 fl oz refined oil

(1) *Wash and top the guavas. Chop them coarsely. Place the chopped guavas and 1 cup water in the body of a pressure-cooker. Close the cooker. Bring to maximum pressure over high heat, then lower the flame and pressure-cook for 6 minutes. Remove from the fire. Allow the pressure inside the cooker to dissipate. Rub the cooked guavas through a sieve to remove the seeds.*

(2) *Place the guava pulp, sugar, lime juice, salt and 4 tsp refined oil in a wide, heavy-bottomed pan. Cook over moderate heat, stirring continuously. In about 2 hours, the mixture will leave the sides of the pan and roll into a ball.*

(3) *Grease 2 trays of approximate dimensions 15" x 10" (37.5 cm x 25 cm) with the remaining 1 tsp refined oil. Pour the guava cheese into them and spread evenly with a spatula. Allow to set. Cut into squares when cool.*

Per Piece			
Kilocalories	109	Iron	Trace
Protein	Negligible	Vitamin C	4 mg
Fat	1 g	Vitamin A (as carotene)	88 mcg
Carbohydrate	26 g	Fibre	1 g
Calcium	14 mg		
Phosphorus	5 mg	1,000 mcg = 1 mg	

Fruit Cheese

The people linked to this unusual fruit cheese in India are the nuns in convents in the hill stations, and the Anglo-Indians.

The weights may look a trifle odd, but guava cheese is ideally prepared *by volume*. Equal volume measures of guava pulp and sugar give a quality product.

For a dark maroon cheese, choose deep-red guavas. The white variety will yield a much paler, pinkish cheese.

At one stage, the mixture bubbles vigorously, and it becomes almost impossible to continue stirring with the hot, bubbling guava cheese plopping all over the place. Since cooking cannot be halted, the alternative is to slip on an oven mitten, or, if one is not available, a clean, old sock (better two) that will prevent scalds and burns.

The vitamin C mentioned in the nutritive value table is indicative of what guavas and limes in these amounts will provide under normal circumstances. However, given the time taken to arrive at the setting point of guava cheese, all the vitamin C present may possibly be destroyed because of the prolonged heating, except for the fact that the acidic medium provided by lime juice could inhibit this effect.

3.9.9 Sheer Korma (Vermicelli in Sweetened Milk Sauce)

Preparation Time	:	10 min
Cooking Time	:	40 min
Chilling Time	:	2 hours minimum

Serves 6

Ingredients

4 small, green cardamoms
3 cups/750 ml/1 1/4 pints skimmed milk

5 tbsp/75 g/2 1/2 oz sugar
Pinch of salt
2 tsp/10 ml/ 1/3 fl oz refined oil
1 tsp/5 g/ 1/6 oz ghee
1 tbsp/15 g/ 1/2 oz raisins
2 tbsp/15 g/ 1/2 oz broken cashew nuts
1 tbsp or about 12/15 g/ 1/2 oz almonds, blanched and slivered
1 tbsp/15 g/ 1/2 oz piyal seeds
1 1/2 cups/60 g/2 oz fine vermicelli, crumbled
1 cup/250 ml/8 fl oz hot water
Pinch of freshly grated nutmeg
Pinch of saffron
Silver edible foil

(1) *Remove the seeds from the cardamom pods and powder.*

(2) *Place the milk, sugar and salt in a pan. Bring to the boil. Lower the heat and continue to simmer, stirring occasionally to break the surface skin.*

(3) *Heat the refined oil and ghee together in another wide pan. Add the raisins, cashew nuts, almonds and piyal seeds. Fry until the nuts are golden. Drain and set aside.*

(4) *To the same oil, add the vermicelli and fry until golden. Pour in 1 cup hot water to soften the vermicelli. Bring to the boil.*

(5) *Add the cooked vermicelli, cardamom powder and nutmeg to the milk simmering on the fire. When the original quantity is reduced by half, add the fried raisins, nuts, piyal seeds and saffron. Remove from the fire.*

(6) *Transfer to a serving bowl. Allow to cool, then chill for at least 2 hours. Cover with silver edible foil and serve.*

Per Serving			
Kilocalories	199	Vitamin C	1 mg
Protein	6 g	Vitamin A (as carotene)	2 mcg
Fat	7 g	Vitamin A (as retinol)	5 mcg
Carbohydrate	29 g	Fibre	Trace
Calcium	170 mg	Cholesterol	5 mg
Phosphorus	161 mg		
Iron	1 mg	1,000 mcg = 1 mg	

Weight Watchers, Beware!

This festive dessert may be attributed to the Muslims in the country, and is a rich variation of the North Indian kheer and South Indian payasam.

Almost half the weight of nuts is made up of fat. As nuts are traditionally used to garnish Indian desserts, a brisk 20-minute walk after a sweet dessert will help burn 100 kcal. A lazier walk with a dog for half an hour will expend 70 kcal.

3.9.10 Rosogulla (Cottage Cheese Ball) in Sugar Syrup

Preparation Time	:	10 min
Dripping Time	:	1 hour
Cooking Time	:	45 min
Chilling Time	:	2 hours minimum

Makes 14

Ingredients

---

4 cups/1 litre/1.6 pints skimmed milk
1 tbsp/15 ml/ 1/2 fl oz lime juice
1/2 tsp refined wheat flour
1 cup/240 g/8 oz sugar
3 cups/750 ml/1 1/4 pints water
A few drops of rose essence or rose water

---

(1)   Bring the milk to the boil in a saucepan. Remove from the fire and stir in the lime juice. When the milk curdles, pour it into a colander lined with muslin cloth or hang up to drain. Leave undisturbed for 1 hour. Squeeze out any remaining liquid. The soft crumbly cheese that remains is chenna. Set the whey aside. Tip the chenna into a bowl.

(2)   Add the refined wheat flour and 1 tsp sugar to the chenna. Knead thoroughly until soft and smooth. Divide into 14 portions. Roll up into balls the size of large marbles making sure that the surface is absolutely smooth.

(3)   Place the remaining sugar and water in a wide saucepan. (The rosogullas will expand as they cook.) Dissolve the sugar over low heat, then raise the flame and boil for 5 minutes. Drop the rosogullas into the boiling syrup, one at a time. Maintain a steady boil for about 10 minutes after the last addition. When the rosogullas are about the size of a walnut, press each one down gently with the back of a spoon to ensure that they are spongy and absorb the syrup. Cook for a further 10 minutes, pressing them down every few minutes. Remove from the fire. When still warm, sprinkle with the rose essence or rose water.

(4)   Serve chilled with generous amounts of syrup.

Per Rosogulla			
Kilocalories	90	Iron	Trace
Protein	2 g	Vitamin C	1 mg
Fat	Negligible	Vitamin A (as carotene)	Negligible
Carbohydrate	21 g	Fibre	Nil
Calcium	88 mg	Cholesterol	1 mg
Phosphorus	65 mg	1,000 mcg = 1 mg	

Cooking Hints

Cow's milk was used for this recipe. The yield, therefore, was about half of what buffalo's milk would have given.

The rosogullas may be made larger if so desired, but the pan should also be large enough to accommodate them comfortably or they will stick to each other.

Do not disturb the rosogullas until they are well cooked (about 10 minutes after the last addition) or they will disintegrate.

The syrup must be thin and light. If it gets too thick, dilute with more hot water.

Nutrition Notes

Some loss of protein and a good deal of vitamin C is to be expected as the whey is drained away and not utilized in the making of rosogullas.

Never discard whey. Cook vegetables, rice or dhal with it. Use it in curries instead of water or knead it into dough. It contains the more valuable proteins in milk, namely, lactalbumins and lactoglobulins.

3.9.11 Shrikand (Sweetened Cream Cheese)

Preparation Time	:	10 min
Dripping Time	:	4 hours
Cooking Time	:	Nil
Chilling Time	:	2 hours minimum

Serves 4

Ingredients

2 small, green cardamoms
4 cups/1 litre/1.6 pints freshly set curds (from skimmed milk)
5 tbsp/75 g/2 1/2 oz sugar, powdered
Dash of saffron powder (optional)

(1) *Remove the seeds from the cardamom pods and powder.*

(2) *Line a colander with a piece of muslin cloth. Tip the curds into it, and allow to drip for 4 hours. Squeeze dry. Rub the cream cheese through a sieve to get an absolutely smooth texture. Alternatively, blend in a mixer/blender. Do not discard the whey.*

(3) *Gradually whisk the powdered sugar, cardamom powder and saffron powder, if used, into the cream cheese.*

(4) *Chill thoroughly. Serve with either hot puris or as a dessert.*

Per Serving			
Kilocalories	147	Iron	0.5 mg
Protein	6 g	Vitamin C	3 mg
Fat	Trace	Vitamin A	Nil
Carbohydrate	30 g	Fibre	Nil
Calcium	302 mg	Cholesterol	5 mg
Phosphorus	225 mg	1,000 mcg = 1 mg	

Cooking Tip

For this recipe, the curds were made from cow's milk. Use buffalo's milk for higher yield.

Good Health

Puris are deep-fried, dough rounds made from either refined or wholemeal wheat flour. They are well known in the Indian bread repertoire. In keeping with the aspect of reduced fat intake which governed the selection of recipes for this book, the making of puris has not been included.

Use the whey to cook vegetables or add it to curries. It contains the more valuable of the milk proteins, namely, lactalbumins and lactoglobulins, besides vitamins of the B complex group present in curds.

Sound Indian Food Sense

For an entirely different and refreshing flavour, prepare Aam ki Shrikand. Stir 1 puréed ripe mango into the shrikand before chilling.

The addition of ripe mango has the benefit of providing beta carotene, the provitamin of vitamin A, while curds promotes its absorption with two factors, namely, protein and fat.

3.9.12 Rava Ladoo (Sweet Semolina Ball)

Preparation Time : 25 min
Cooking Time   : 10 min

Makes 35

Ingredients

10 small, green cardamoms
3 cups/630 g/1 lb 5 oz semolina
1 cup/240 g/8 oz sugar
2 tbsp/30 ml/1 fl oz refined oil
1 tsp/5 g/ 1/6 oz ghee
2 tbsp/15 g/ 1/2 oz broken cashew nuts
1 tbsp/15 g/ 1/2 oz raisins
1/2 tsp salt
4 tbsp/60 ml/2 fl oz hot skimmed milk

(1) Remove the seeds from the cardamom pods and powder.

(2) In a heavy kadai, roast the semolina over low heat, without oil, until it just begins to turn golden and a nice aroma arises. Remove from the fire and set aside to cool.

(3) Mix the semolina and sugar together. Place half the amount in a mixer/blender. Blend at the lowest speed for 30 seconds. Open the jar, stir the contents and blend again, at the same speed, for another 30 seconds. Prepare the balance semolina-sugar mixture.

(4) Heat the oil and ghee together in a wide pan. Add the cashew nuts and raisins and fry until the cashew nuts turn light brown. Draw the pan off the fire. Stir in the powdered semolina and sugar, salt and cardamom powder.

(5) Gradually stir in the hot milk until the mixture is crumbly and resembles moist breadcrumbs.

(6) Shape into lime-sized balls when still hot, rolling them as tightly as possible with the fingers of one hand.

(7) Serve for tea or for festive occasions. Do not keep for more than 2 days.

Per Ladoo			
Kilocalories	103	Vitamin C	Negligible
Protein	2 g	Vitamin A (as carotene)	Trace
Fat	1 g	Vitamin A (as retinol)	1 mcg
Carbohydrate	21 g	Fibre	Negligible
Calcium	6 mg	Cholesterol	Trace
Phosphorus	22 mg		
Iron	Trace	1,000 mcg = 1 mg	

Health Hint

Traditionally, in South India, ghee is used to bind the semolina and sugar together, not milk. In view of the ill effects of this saturated, cholesterol-rich animal fat on one's health, skimmed milk was used as a healthy and wholesome alternative. This does not compromise the final product in any physical attribute whatsoever. Ghee has been used here only as a flavouring.

3.10 Drinks

3.10.1 Lassi (Sweetened Buttermilk)

Preparation Time	:	6 min
Cooking Time	:	Nil
Chilling Time	:	30 min

Serves 4

Ingredients

4 tbsp/60 g/2 oz sugar
Pinch of salt
1 cup/250 ml/8 fl oz water
3 cups/750 ml/1 1/4 pints curds (from skimmed milk)

(1) *Dissolve the sugar and salt in 1 cup water.*

(2) *Whisk the curds lightly, gradually beating in the sweetened water.*

(3) *Pour into 4 tall glasses and chill for 30 minutes. Serve on a hot day.*

Per Glass			
Kilocalories	114	Iron	Trace
Protein	5 g	Vitamin C	2 mg
Fat	Trace	Vitamin A	Nil
Carbohydrate	24 g	Fibre	Nil
Calcium	227 mg	Cholesterol	4 mg
Phosphorus	169 mg	1,000 mcg = 1 mg	

Cooking Tips

To avoid chilling time, whisk in 6 ice cubes and serve. If a mixer/blender is used, select the whipping blade and blend all the ingredients together at low speed for 30 seconds. Repeat once more.

Traditionally, lassi is prepared by churning whole-milk curds, and serving it with a generous dollop of cream. If this method is chosen, be careful with speed and time when using a mixer/blender. Butter will separate out if either is exceeded.

Good Health

Lassi served with a meal rich in iron will facilitate iron absorption in the gut, particularly if the iron is from vegetable sources like green leafy vegetables. Lassi is better tolerated than milk because during fermentation the sugar in milk (lactose) is converted to lactic acid. Curds prepared from whole milk will have a higher fat and cholesterol content.

3.10.2 Kokum Saar (Digestive Drink)

Preparation Time	:	20 min
Soaking Time	:	30 min
Cooking Time	:	20 min

Serves 6

Ingredients

3 cups/750 ml/1 1/4 pints hot water
1/2 large shell/120 g/4 oz freshly grated coconut, coarsely ground
5 pieces dried kokum (no English equivalent)
1 cup/250 ml/8 fl oz hot water
2 medium/5 g/ 1/6 oz green chillies, deseeded and finely chopped
3 garlic cloves, crushed
A few coriander leaves, finely chopped
Salt to taste

(1) *Add 1 cup hot water to the ground coconut. Mix well, then squeeze to extract the first milk. Repeat twice more, adding 1 cup hot water each time to the same coconut. Strain and set aside.*

(2) *Soak the kokum pieces in 1/2 cup hot water for 30 minutes. Rub vigorously between the fingers and squeeze to extract pulp. Add another 1/2 cup hot water to the same kokum. Extract pulp a second time. Strain and set aside.*

(3) *Mix all the ingredients together and place the pan over low heat. Gradually raise the flame until the kokum drink comes to the boil.*

(4) *Remove from the fire. Cool to room temperature. Serve at the end of a heavy meal.*

Per Serving			
Kilocalories	89	Iron	Trace
Protein	1 g	Vitamin C	1 mg
Fat	8 g	Vitamin A (as carotene)	45 mcg
Carbohydrate	3 g	Fibre	Negligible
Calcium	3 mg		
Phosphorus	49 mg	1,000 mcg = 1 mg	

Kokum—The Unusual Ingredient

Kokum saar is an excellent digestive and is usually served after a rich meal, especially one that is heavy on meat. It is common to the west coast of India, particularly Maharashtra. Ironic though it may sound, coconut milk in Indian cuisine is considered "light" even though it is a concentrated source of fat. This (mis)conception is potentially dangerous as it leads to unlimited use of coconut in cooking. However, coconut has insignificant amounts of cholesterol.

Kokum (the condiment) is a natural antihistamine and is used to give relief from mild (food/insect bite) allergies. Kokum derives from the same family that gives us the Malabar tamarind (*kodampuli* in Malayalam) and the delectable mangosteen.

3.10.3 Filter Coffee (South Indian Drip Coffee)

Preparation Time	:	5 min
Steeping Time	:	45 min
Cooking Time	:	15 min

Serves 6

Ingredients

4 heaped tsp/20 g/ 2/3 oz freshly ground coffee
10 tbsp/150 ml/ 1/4 pint boiling water
4 tbsp/60 g/2 oz sugar
3 1/2 cups/900 ml/1 1/2 pints skimmed milk

(1) *Place the freshly ground coffee in a coffee filter of 150 ml capacity. Cover with the boiling water. Allow to steep for 45 minutes.*

(2) *Take 6 glasses of 150 ml capacity. Place 2 tsp sugar in each. Bring the milk to the boil, then remove from the fire and divide it equally between the 6 glasses. Add 5 tsp of the coffee filtrate or decoction to the milk in each glass. Mix by transferring the coffee from the glass to another that is empty until nice and frothy. Serve immediately.*

Per Glass			
Kilocalories	83	Iron	Trace
Protein	4 g	Vitamin C	2 mg
Fat	Trace	Vitamin A	Nil
Carbohydrate	17 g	Fibre	Nil
Calcium	181 mg	Cholesterol	3 mg
Phosphorus	135 mg	1,000 mcg = 1 mg	

Curious about Coffee?

In a departure from more familiar coffee making, in South India, coffee is added to milk and not vice versa.

Coffee is never mixed by stirring with a spoon. Instead, South Indians traditionally serve coffee in stainless steel tumblers that sit in a crucible called *dabara* of the same capacity. By transferring the coffee from the tumbler to the *dabara* (jocularly called "boxing" coffee, an art that has some experts being able to "stretch" the stream of steaming coffee to up to a yard!), it is well blended and cooled to the right temperature at the same time.

It is not necessary to make the decoction up into coffee as soon as it is prepared. It can be stored and a little used only when required.

Coffee powder contains fibre but is of no dietary significance since it is not consumed. Instant coffee ensures that this benefit is not lost.

The caffeine content of coffee varies. Drip coffee (as given here) has the most, followed in descending order by percolated, instant and decaffeinated.

3.10.4 Chhaas (Unsweetened Buttermilk)

Preparation Time : 15 min
Cooking Time : Nil
Chilling Time : 2 hours minimum

Serves 4

Ingredients

1/2" or 1 cm piece/4 g/ 1/8 oz fresh ginger
2 garlic cloves
2 medium/5 g/ 1/6 oz green chillies, deseeded
A small sprig of curry leaves
3 cups/750 ml/1 1/4 pints curds (from skimmed milk)
1 cup/250 ml/8 fl oz cold water
Salt to taste
Dash of kala (chaat) masala (Recipe No: 3.11.10)
Pinch of black salt

(1) *Grind the ginger, garlic, 1 chilli and half the curry leaves together to a paste.*

(2) *Chop the remaining chilli and curry leaves finely.*

(3) *Whisk the curds lightly, and gradually beat in the cold water.*

(4) *Add the ground paste and chopped ingredients.*

(5) *Stir in the salt, kala masala and black salt. Whip until frothy. Pour into 4 tall glasses and serve chilled.*

Per Glass			
Kilocalories	56	Iron	0.5 mg
Protein	5 g	Vitamin C	3 mg
Fat	Trace	Vitamin A (as carotene)	57 mcg
Carbohydrate	9 g	Fibre	Trace
Calcium	227 mg	Cholesterol	4 mg
Phosphorus	170 mg	1,000 mcg = 1 mg	

Cooking Hints

To avoid chilling time, whisk in 6 ice cubes and serve. If a mixer/blender is used, select the whipping blade and blend the curds and cold water together at low speed for 30 seconds. Add the ground paste and chopped ingredients, and blend for another 30 seconds. Stir in the salt, kala masala and black salt. Serve chilled.

Beauty Tip

This immensely refreshing drink does wonders for the skin. During summer, before the skin is left dehydrated and wrinkled, drink tall glasses of chhaas as often as possible. Make a great quantity and store it in the refrigerator in advance.

Nutrition Notes

Not only do curds contain vitamins of the B complex group, but the bacteria present in them also encourage the intestinal bacteria to manufacture some B vitamins. Further, since curds have live bacteria, they help to break down complex milk sugar (lactose) to lactic acid, thereby preventing fermentation by intestinal bacteria.

Milk protein is also partly digested by the action of the bacteria in curds. Moreover, the presence of these bacteria hinders the growth of the undesirable ones. That is why curds, not milk, are recommended during illness. Especially when powerful antibiotics have destroyed many of the bacteria naturally present in the gut, consumption of curds helps to restore the balance.

Curds are also a natural antihistamine and cause none of the allergic reactions that might occur when milk is consumed.

3.10.5 Tarbooz ka Sharbat (Watermelon Refresher)

Preparation Time   :   25 min
Cooking Time   :   Nil
Chilling Time   :   2 hours minimum

Serves 6

Ingredients

1/2 large/2 1/2 kg/5 1/4 lb watermelon
4 tbsp/60 g/2 oz sugar
1 tbsp/15 ml/ 1/2 fl oz lime juice
8 ice cubes
A few drops of rose or kewra essence
Pinch of salt
Crushed ice

(1) *Wash the watermelon and cut away the rind. Remove as many seeds as possible. Chop coarsely.*

(2) *Place half the amount of watermelon, sugar, lime juice and ice cubes in a mixer/blender. Blend at the lowest speed for 15 seconds. Open the jar, stir the contents, and blend again for 15 seconds. Pour into a tall jar. Repeat with the remaining half of the same ingredients.*

(3) *Add the essence and salt. Stir well. Cover and chill for at least 2 hours.*

(4) *To serve, pour into 6 tall, thin glasses and top with crushed ice.*

Per Glass			
Kilocalories	76	Iron	17 mg
Protein	0.5 g	Vitamin C	4 mg
Fat	0.5 g	Vitamin A (as carotene)	Trace
Carbohydrate	17 g	Fibre	0.5 g
Calcium	27 mg		
Phosphorus	27 mg	1,000 mcg = 1 mg	

Summer Cooler

Sharbat made from all fruit juices is an ideal thirst quencher in summer. Thirst is the natural response to replace lost body fluids. With the mercury rising, profuse sweating causes loss of not only water but the electrolytes sodium, potassium and chloride as well. If these are not replaced, the symptoms of dehydration like disorientation will be manifested.

Under temperate conditions, a safe guide to avert this problem is to consume as much fluid as the daily calorie requirement. For example, if one's daily calorie requirement is 2,000 kcal, then the fluid intake per day should be at least 2 litres. Naturally, this intake has to be increased in summer or after strenuous exercise. A combination of both will necessitate the consumption of huge amounts of fluids well in excess of the daily average. However, large amounts of fluids consumed at one time are less beneficial than the frequent intake of smaller quantities.

The bright red colour of watermelon may be attributed to lycopene, a carotene that is not converted to vitamin A in the body.

3.10.6 Falooda (Sweet Indian Milk Drink with Cornflour Drops)

Preparation Time	:	20 min
Soaking Time	:	15 min
Cooking Time	:	25 min
Chilling Time	:	2 hours

Serves 4

Ingredients

2 cups/500 ml/16 fl oz skimmed milk
4 tbsp/60 g/2 oz sugar
1 cup/250 ml/8 fl oz water
1 tbsp/15 g/ 1/2 oz falooda seeds
2 tbsp/15 g/ 1/2 oz cornflour
1 1/2 cups/375 ml/12 1/2 fl oz water
1 tray ice cubes
1/2 tsp rose essence
A few drops of cochineal

(1) Bring the milk to the boil in a saucepan. Remove from the fire and add the sugar. Stir until the sugar dissolves. Set aside to cool.

(2) Add 1 cup water to the falooda seeds. Set aside for 15 minutes until the seeds swell completely.

(3) Make a paste of the cornflour with a little water. Stir in the remaining 1 1/2 cups water. Place on the fire and bring to the boil. Continue boiling for about 10 minutes or until the mixture is thick and pasty.

(4) Reserve 8 ice cubes and place the rest in a pan. Place a colander or sieve with wide mesh over the pan containing the ice cubes. Pour the cornflour

paste into the colander or sieve and rub with the back of a spoon so that drops of the paste fall on the ice and solidify. Allow the ice to melt, then pour through a strainer and collect the cornflour bits (falooda).

(5) *Mix all the ingredients together except the 8 ice cubes kept in reserve. Chill for 2 hours. Stir well and fill three-quarters of 4 tall glasses with the drink. Add 2 ice cubes in each glass. Serve with a thick finger of vanilla ice-cream in each drink. (Do not forget to put a tall spoon in each glass for the falooda.)*

*Per Glass			
Kilocalories	109	Iron	Trace
Protein	4 g	Vitamin C	1 mg
Fat	Trace	Vitamin A	Nil
Carbohydrate	23 g	**Fibre	Trace
Calcium	152 mg	Cholesterol	3 mg
Phosphorus	126 mg	1,000 mcg = 1 mg	

*   Values do not include nutritive contribution of ice-cream.
** Fibre content of falooda seeds not available.

Cooking Notes

The traditional recipe for falooda calls for the use of rose syrup. As it is a concentrated source of sugar and unnecessarily increases the calorie tally, it has been avoided in this recipe. For those who do not wish to depart from standard practice, the use of 3 tbsp (45 ml/1 1/2 fl oz) rose syrup per glass is recommended. The alternative method described here, though economical on calories, does not compromise the final product in any way and few can tell the difference, if at all.

To many, the method of obtaining the falooda will appear time-consuming and tedious. A quicker way is to boil 1/2 cup (20 g/ 2/3 oz) thick vermicelli in 1 cup (250 ml/8 fl oz) water and stir it in with the other ingredients. The effect is not exactly similar, but is no less delicious and saves many minutes in preparation and cooking.

For a fresh, fruity finish, add 3 tbsp (45 g/1 1/2 oz) chopped watermelon to each glass before serving.

Fibre Wonder

Flea or falooda seeds are a very good source of soluble fibre. They are excellent for preventing constipation and are particularly recommended for anyone who eats a highly refined diet.

Falooda seeds are considered cooling. They help to heal boils in the mouth formed from the use of antibiotics—mix a tablespoon of falooda seeds in a glass of water and allow sufficient time for them to swell before consumption.

3.11 Common Extracts
Masalas

3.11.1 Ghee (Clarified Butter)

Preparation Time   :   Nil
Cooking Time   :   15 min

Yield 410 g/14 oz

Ingredients

500 g/1.1 lb fresh unsalted butter
A large sprig of curry leaves or drumstick leaves

(1) *Place a heavy-bottomed, wide pan on the fire with the butter. Stir continuously over medium heat.*

(2) *When the butter begins to froth, and the milk solids turn golden-brown, add the curry leaves or drumstick leaves and turn off the heat.*

(3) *Stir for 2 minutes longer until the foam subsides. Bottle immediately in a sterilized jar, straining out the milk solids and leaves.*

*Per Tablespoon			
Kilocalories	135	Vitamin A (as retinol)	90 mcg
Fat	15 g	Cholesterol	38 mg
		1,000 mcg = 1 mg	

* Values do not include nutritive contribution of curry leaves or drumstick leaves.

The Indian Touch

Curry leaves or drumstick leaves impart a fine flavour to ghee and are also known to preserve it. Additionally, carotene, which is fat soluble, is drawn from the leaves and adds to the vitamin A already available in ghee.

Fresh betel leaves (2 for 500 g butter should be adequate) also prevent ghee from going rancid.

3.11.2 Coconut Milk

Preparation Time : 20 min
Cooking Time : 5 min

Yield 3 cups/750 ml/1 1/4 pints

Ingredients

3 cups/750 ml/1 1/4 pints hot water
1/2 large shell/120 g/4 oz freshly grated coconut, coarsely ground

(1) *Add 1 cup hot water to the ground coconut. Mix well. Put the mixture through a strainer and squeeze to extract the first milk. (This first extract is also known as Coconut Cream.)*

(2) *Repeat twice more, adding 1 cup hot water each time to the same coconut. Use as a base for curries and gravies instead of water.*

Normally, the second and third extracts are used to cook food in. The first, thick milk is added last, just as the food gets cooked and is about to be drawn off the fire before serving.

Per Cup (250 ml/8 fl oz)			
Kilocalories	178	Iron	1 mg
Protein	2 g	Vitamin C	Trace
Fat	17 g	Vitamin A	Nil
Carbohydrate	5 g	Fibre	Nil
Calcium	4 mg		
Phosphorus	96 mg	1,000 mcg = 1 mg	

Coconut in Cooking

A mixer/blender may also be used to extract coconut milk. Place the grated coconut in the mixer with 1 cup (250 ml/8 fl oz) hot water and blend at the lowest speed for 2 minutes. Repeat until all 3 cups (750 ml/1 1/4 pints) of coconut milk are extracted.

Throughout the west coast of India and in parts of the east, coconut milk is the all-purpose cooking medium for meat, fish, vegetables and even for some sweets. This does not appear difficult to understand in the light of the following facts:

Coconut milk is the most convenient substitute for milk as it poses none of the problems associated with milk such as curdling.

With its high fat content, extra fat is seldom added to cooking because prolonged heating draws the fat out of the coconut milk. This feature is particularly exploited in the making of halwas in parts of South India.

From the standpoint of nutrition, though coconut milk contains a vegetable fat (generally recommended over animal fats), this vegetable source of fat has a greater proportion of lauric acid, less desirable because it is a saturated fatty acid commonly associated with heart and related diseases. Its use should, therefore, be restricted as much as possible.

Strangely, coconut in combination with fish and seafood does not have as detrimental an effect, possibly because of the high content of the more beneficial, health-promoting unsaturated Omega-3 fatty acids present in these foods. In this book, coconut has been freely used in this combination.

Coconut milk (and oil) contains negligible amounts of cholesterol.

3.11.3 Paneer (Indian Cottage Cheese)

Preparation Time	:	5 min
Dripping Time	:	1 hour
Cooking Time	:	15 min
Setting Time	:	2 hours

Yield 120 g/4 oz

Ingredients

4 cups/1 litre/1.6 pints skimmed milk
1 tbsp/15 ml/ 1/2 fl oz lime juice

(1) *Bring the milk to the boil in a saucepan. Remove from the fire and stir in the lime juice. When the milk curdles, pour it into a colander lined with muslin cloth or hang up to drain. Leave undisturbed for 1 hour. Squeeze out any remaining liquid. The soft, crumbly cheese that remains is Chenna, the main ingredient in sweets like rosogulla. (Do not discard the whey but collect it in a pan.)*

(2) *To make paneer, roll the chenna into a ball. Wrap the muslin cloth around it, draw up the ends and twist them securely on top to enclose the ball of chenna. Place it under a wooden board. Place a heavy weight on the board. Leave undisturbed for 2 hours. Remove the board and muslin. Cut the cheese into any desired shape. By adjusting the heaviness of the weight (any heavy object will do) and the time, the paneer can be made softer or harder. Paneer moulds are also available.*

Per 120 g/4 oz			
Kilocalories	290	Iron	2 mg
Protein	25 g	Vitamin C	10 mg
Fat	1 g	Vitamin A	Nil
Carbohydrate	46 g	Fibre	Nil
Calcium	1,200 mg	Cholesterol	20 mg
Phosphorus	900 mg	1,000 mcg = 1 mg	

Cooking Tips and Nutrition Notes

Cow's milk was used to make the paneer in this recipe. The yield will be almost double with buffalo's milk. Buffalo's milk has a higher content of all the major nutrients including fat (except iron which is the same for both). However, buffalo's milk has less carotene, B vitamins, vitamin C, sodium and potassium than cow's milk.

Whey that has been saved from a previous batch of paneer-making can be used instead of lime juice to curdle milk, particularly if it is allowed to sour. The resultant chenna will be much softer and is especially suitable for making spongy rosogullas.

Paneer contains mainly casein, a protein that is less superior and not as easily digested in the human gut as the proteins found in the liquid whey. Besides, vitamin B_{12} is bound to whey proteins. This is the reason why every attempt should be made to reuse the whey in cooking.

3.11.4 Tamarind Extract

Preparation Time	:	10 min
Soaking Time	:	10 min
Cooking Time	:	3 min

Yield 1 cup/250 ml/8 fl oz

Ingredients

A lime-sized ball/30 g/1 oz tamarind
1 cup/250 ml/8 fl oz hot water

(1) Soak the tamarind in 1/2 cup hot water for 10 minutes. Rub vigorously between the fingers and squeeze to extract pulp.

(2) Add another 1/2 cup hot water to the same tamarind and extract pulp a second time. Use as desired.

Per Cup (250 ml/8 fl oz)			
Kilocalories	85	Iron	5 mg
Protein	1 g	Vitamin C	1 mg
Fat	Negligible	Vitamin A (as carotene)	18 mcg
Carbohydrate	20 g	Fibre	2 g
Calcium	51 mg		
Phosphorus	33 mg	1,000 mcg = 1 mg	

Talking Tamarind

Tamarind contains tartaric acid, an organic acid that alters the composition of urine, making it more alkaline. This in turn appears to discourage the formation of kidney stones, if tamarind is used regularly in cooking. Rasam, in which tamarind is a major ingredient, could be the reason for the lower incidence of kidney stones among South Indians who include it habitually in their diets.

Try to use tamarind that is many seasons old. Old tamarind is a curative for stomach ailments.

3.11.5 Curds (Live Or Bio-Yoghurt)

Preparation Time	:	5 min
Cooking Time	:	15 min
Setting Time	:	3 to 12 hours

Yield 4 cups/1 litre/1.6 pints

Ingredients

4 cups/1 litre/1.6 pints skimmed milk
1 tbsp/15 ml/ 1/2 fl oz curds (starter)

(1)   Boil the milk and cool until lukewarm.

(2)   Smear the sides of a (preferably ceramic) bowl with the curds starter. Pour in the warm milk.

(3)   Stand covered in a warm place. The curds will set in about 3 to 6 hours. In cooler climes, the time for setting could take as long as 12 to 16 hours. Place in the refrigerator to prevent further souring. Use a little of these curds as starter to prepare the next batch.

Set curds in an unglazed earthen vessel. It will remain delightfully cool even if not refrigerated (but fermentation will continue increasing the sourness of the curds) and will be thick enough to cut with a knife.

Per Cup (250 ml/8 fl oz)			
Kilocalories	74	Iron	0.5 mg
Protein	6 g	Vitamin C	3 mg
Fat	Trace	Vitamin A	Nil
Carbohydrate	12 g	Fibre	Nil
Calcium	305 mg	Cholesterol	5 mg
Phosphorus	228 mg	1,000 mcg = 1 mg	

Know Your Curds

Whole milk will provide vitamin A both in the form of carotene, its precursor, and as retinol, the vitamin itself. Both are present in milk fat which is removed when milk is skimmed.

The conversion of milk to curds is brought about by a little organism called *Lactobacillus* of which there are many kinds. While nutritionally the value of curds is no more than the milk from which it is prepared, it has certain other beneficial, largely therapeutic, properties.

The complex form of nutrients present in milk is broken down to simpler, more easily digestible components when milk is converted into curds. Lactose or milk sugar is one of them. On conversion, lactic acid results, which is less acidic than is commonly believed. Not surprisingly, therefore, curds are recommended for such intestinal disorders as dysentery and peptic ulcers. Lactic acid also favours the absorption of iron.

Lactobacillus also encourages the growth of those bacteria in the human gut that manufacture some of the vitamins of the B complex group while inhibiting the multiplication of the less desirable ones.

Curds also restore the balance of intestinal flora when antibiotics, prescribed indiscriminately in modern-day treatment of illness, have eliminated many of those naturally present in the human gut.

Curds are also a natural antihistamine and are better tolerated than milk. Even people who complain of lactose intolerance (insufficient production of lactase, the enzyme that splits lactose), can freely consume curds with no fear of the accompanying undesirable and uncomfortable symptoms of diarrhoea and abdominal distension.

Curds are, additionally, believed to aid in the prevention of cancer of the colon.

3.11.6 Garam Masala (Indian Spice Mix)

Preparation Time   :   5 min
Cooking Time   :   5 min

Yield 120 g/4 oz

Ingredients

40 small/15 g/ 1/2 oz green cardamoms
4 tbsp/20 g/ 2/3 oz black peppercorns
3 tbsp/30 g/1 oz cumin seeds
3 tbsp/30 g/1 oz cloves
3 tbsp/15 g/ 1/2 oz broken cinnamon sticks
2 regular/10 g/ 1/3 oz nutmegs, broken into small pieces (optional)
3 tbsp/5 g/ 1/6 oz mace, crumbled (optional)

(1) *Remove the seeds from the cardamom pods.*

(2) *Roast the cardamom seeds, peppercorns, cumin seeds, cloves and cinnamon sticks, and, nutmegs and mace, if used, together over low heat, without oil, until the cumin seeds begin to change colour. Do not brown.*

(3) *Powder all the roasted spices together until fine. Sieve. Grind the coarser bits a second time until smooth. Store in an airtight container.*

Per Teaspoon (Inclusive of Optional Ingredients)			
Kilocalories	17	Iron	0.5 mg
Protein	0.5 g	Vitamin C	Trace
Fat	1 g	Vitamin A (as carotene)	26 mcg
Carbohydrate	2 g	Fibre	1 g
Calcium	38 mg		
Phosphorus	12 mg	1,000 mcg = 1 mg	

Spice of Life

If a mixer/blender or spice grinder is used for grinding, blend for 1 minute at the lowest speed. (If different blades are available, select the one recommended for dry grinding.) Sieve and grind the coarser bits again at the same speed for the same length of time.

To make a smaller amount of garam masala:

> Lightly roast 8 cloves, 2 big, brown cardamoms or 6 small, green ones (seeds only), 2" or 5 cm stick cinnamon, 1/2 tsp cumin seeds and 1 tsp black peppercorns (about 80) together, without oil, until the cumin seeds begin to darken. Grind to a powder. The yield will be about 1 tbsp garam masala which should be sufficient for 4 to 6 preparations. Any that is left over can be conveniently stored.

Garam masala is the preferred spice powder in North Indian cooking. The mix in garam masala is especially designed to promote good health.

Its most important function is to stimulate gastric secretion which in turn improves appetite. No less important, and perfectly complementary, are the digestive and carminative properties of the spices used in garam masala. Interestingly, cumin seeds or jeera probably got their name from the word "jeeranum" which in Tamil means digestion.

Most of these spices provide the minerals calcium, manganese, iron, magnesium, copper, chromium, phosphorus, sodium and potassium. Since spices are used regularly in Indian cooking, their contribution of these minerals, however small, cannot be ignored.

Gentle roasting brings out the flavour and aroma of essential oils present in spices. Additionally, the roasting of spices and condiments like cardamom, coriander, cumin, black pepper, red pepper, anise and fennel helps to increase the availability of acetylcholine and its precursor choline, two compounds which are an integral part of all cells in the human body, and of the nervous tissue in particular, as acetylcholine assists in the transmission of nerve impulses. These substances are probably released from their bound form or are developed chemically when spices are roasted.

3.11.7 Milagai Podi (Spicy Dhal Powder for Iddlis)

Preparation Time	:	5 min
Cooking Time	:	25 min

Yield 345 g/11 1/2 oz

Ingredients
_____

1/2 cup/120 g/4 oz bengal gram dhal, cleaned

1/2 cup/120 g/4 oz red gram dhal, cleaned

1/2 cup/90 g/3 oz black gram dhal (without husk), cleaned

15 whole dried red chillies

1/2 cup or 2 1/2 large sprigs/15 g/ 1/2 oz curry leaves
1/2 tsp asafoetida powder
Salt to taste

(1) *Roast the dhals separately, without oil, until light brown and well done — about 7 minutes each. (A single grain should have a hard, almost unyielding feel when bitten upon, not soft and chewy.) Cool.*

(2) *Remove the stalks of the red chillies. Roast the red chillies and curry leaves together over low heat, without oil, until the curry leaves are crisp and crumbly. Cool.*

(3) *Place all the ingredients except the salt in a mixer (the motor of a blender may not take the strain of this grinding), and blend at the lowest speed for 1 minute. Open the jar, stir the contents and blend again at the same speed for 1 minute.*

(4) *Stir in the salt and store in an airtight container.*

(5) *Serve 1 or 2 tsp of milagai podi mixed in gingelly oil with iddlis.*

Per Tablespoon			
Kilocalories	51	Iron	1 mg
Protein	3 g	Vitamin C	Negligible
Fat	Less than 0.5 g	Vitamin A (as carotene)	152 mcg
Carbohydrate	9 g	Fibre	Trace
Calcium	18 mg		
Phosphorus	49 mg	1,000 mcg = 1 mg	

Food Wise

Iddlis are typically eaten with milagai podi in Tamil Nadu. Some prefer a sweet and sour milagai podi. To achieve this, take a large marble-sized ball of tamarind and toast it, without burning, on a hot tawa until as much moisture as possible is removed. Add 2 tbsp (30 g/1 oz) powdered jaggery to the cooled tamarind and grind them with the rest of the ingredients. The tamarind-jaggery milagai podi has the additional benefit of more iron.

3.11.8 Chiwda Masala Powder

Preparation Time   :   5 min
Cooking Time   :   Nil

Yield 15 g/ 1/2 oz

Ingredients

1 tsp cumin seeds
40 black peppercorns
1/2" or 1 cm stick cinnamon
1/4 tsp carum seeds
1/4 tsp black salt
2 tsp/5 g/ 1/6 oz mango powder
1/4 tsp red chilli powder

(1)   Powder the cumin seeds, peppercorns, cinnamon, carum seeds and black salt together. Mix in the remaining ingredients until well blended. Store in an airtight container. Use as directed by a specific recipe, or to flavour roasted nuts.

Indian Food Sense

Carum seeds are used in home medicine to reduce the pain and gripes that accompany indigestion and colic.

Seemingly insignificant ingredients like black salt used in Indian cooking have been found to have antioxidant activity which helps to prevent or reduce the incidence of inflammatory or degenerative disease conditions.

3.11.9 Sambhar Podi (South Indian Curry Powder)

Preparation Time   :   10 min
Cooking Time   :   30 min

Yield 340 g/11 oz

Ingredients

2 cups/150 g/5 oz coriander seeds
1 tbsp/15 g/ 1/2 oz uncooked raw rice

1 tbsp/15 g/ 1/2 oz bengal gram dhal
1 tbsp/15 g/ 1/2 oz black gram dhal (without husk)
1 tbsp/15 g/ 1/2 oz red gram dhal
3 tbsp/45 g/1 1/2 oz fenugreek seeds
1 1/2 tbsp/15 g/ 1/2 oz mustard seeds
2 tbsp/20 g/ 2/3 oz cumin seeds
2 tbsp/10 g/ 1/3 oz black peppercorns
2 cups/60 g/2 oz whole dried red chillies
1/2 cup or 2 1/2 large sprigs/15 g/ 1/2 oz curry leaves
1 tsp asafoetida powder

(1) Roast the coriander seeds, without oil, until a nice aroma arises. Cool.

(2) Roast the raw rice, bengal gram dhal, black gram dhal and red gram dhal separately, without oil, until light brown and hard with an almost unyielding feel when bitten upon. Cool.

(3) Roast the fenugreek seeds and mustard seeds together until the fenugreek seeds begin to change colour. Cool.

(4) Roast the cumin seeds and peppercorns together until the cumin seeds begin to darken. Cool.

(5) Remove the stalks of the red chillies. Roast the red chillies and curry leaves together over low heat until the curry leaves are crisp and crumbly. Cool.

(6) Place all the ingredients in a mixer (the motor of a blender may not take the strain of this grinding), and blend at the lowest speed for 30 seconds or until well blended. Blend again at the same speed for 1 minute. Open the jar, stir the contents, and blend further at the lowest speed for 1 1/2 minutes and at high speed for 30 seconds until soft and powdery.

(7) Store in an airtight container and use when required.

Per Tablespoon			
Kilocalories	50	Iron	1 mg
Protein	3 g	Vitamin C	1 mg
Fat	2 g	Vitamin A (as carotene)	222 mcg
Carbohydrate	6 g	Fibre	3 g
Calcium	70 mg		
Phosphorus	61 mg	1,000 mcg = 1 mg	

Cooking Notes

To make a smaller amount of sambhar podi:

> Roast 2 tbsp (10 g/ 1/3 oz) coriander seeds, 1 1/2 tsp fenugreek seeds, 1/2 tsp cumin seeds, 1/2 tsp mustard seeds, 1 tbsp (15 g / 1/2 oz) bengal gram dhal, 10 black peppercorns and a few curry leaves separately. Cool. Add 1/2 tsp red chilli powder and a pinch of asafoetida powder. Powder all the ingredients together until fine. Use what is required and store the balance in an airtight container.

Nutrition Notes

Drying of fresh spices and condiments concentrates nutrients, which is why the same weight of the dried and fresh ingredient will show a greater nutritive value in the former. Dried spices and condiments represent only one-fifth of the fresh form, and drying lowers the values of some nutrients like the water soluble vitamin C.

Choline, a substance that becomes more readily available when spices and condiments are roasted, prevents the accumulation of fat in the liver. Choline is also involved in the transport of fat and cholesterol in the bloodstream.

Fenugreek seeds are especially well known for their blood glucose and blood cholesterol lowering effects, a result of the large amounts of soluble fibre present in them.

Mustard seeds are believed to contain substances which prevent cancer.

3.11.10 Kala (Chaat) Masala

Preparation Time	:	3 min
Cooking Time	:	5 min

Yield 10 g/ 1/3 oz

Ingredients

2 tsp coriander seeds
1 tsp cumin seeds
1 tbsp/5 g/ 1/6 oz black peppercorns

(1) *Roast all the ingredients together, without oil, over low heat until a nice aroma arises. Powder coarsely and store in an airtight container.*

(2) *Sprinkle over curds and chaat preparations.*

Spices and Health

Kala masala powder may be found on many a kitchen shelf in North India.

This combination of spices is commonly used as a seasoning to flavour fresh fruit and vegetable salads, curds, and, drinks like unsweetened fresh lime juice and buttermilk because coriander seeds, cumin seeds and black pepper are digestive and carminative. Further, cumin seeds protect against the effects of exposure to the hot, summer sun, while coriander seeds have cooling and diuretic properties.

Section 4

Select Bibliography

Agarwal, D.K., Agarwal, K.N., Upadhyay, S.K., Mittal, R., Prakash, R. and Rai, S., Physical and Sexual Growth Pattern of Affluent Indian Children from 5 to 18 Years of Age, *Indian Pediatrics* (Journal of the Indian Academy of Pediatrics), Vol:29, October 1992, No:10, pp 1203–1282.

Arnott, A., (1979), *Fruits of the Earth,* A.R. Mowbray & Co. Ltd., London and Oxford.

Bellamy, Carol, (1998), *The State of the World's Children—Summary*, United Nations Children's Fund, New York.

Charley, H., (1970), *Food Science*, John Wiley and Sons, Inc., New York.

Chopra, R.N., Nayar, S.L. and Chopra, I.C., (1992), *Glossary of Indian Medicinal Plants*, Council of Scientific and Industrial Research, New Delhi.

Davidson, S., Passmore, R., Brock, J.F. and Truswell, A.S., (1975), *Human Nutrition and Dietetics*, 6th Ed., The English Language Book Society and Churchill Livingstone, Great Britain.

Dietary Guidelines for Indians—A Manual, (1998), National Institute of Nutrition, Hyderabad, India.

Frazier, W.C. and Westhoff, D.C., (1978), *Food Microbiology*, 3rd (TMH) Ed., Tata McGraw-Hill Publishing Co. Ltd., New Delhi.

Gopalan, C., Rama Sastri, B.V. and Balasubramanian, S.C., (1995), *Nutritive Value of Indian Foods*, Rvsd Ed., National Institute of Nutrition, Indian Council of Medical Research, Hyderabad, India.

Guyton, A.C., (1976), *Textbook of Medical Physiology*, 5th Ed., W.B. Saunders Co., Philadelphia.

Hazarika, S., (1987), *Bhopal—The Lessons of a Tragedy*, Penguin Books (India) Private Ltd., New Delhi.

Inhibition of LDL Oxidation by Phenolic Substances in Red Wine : A Clue to the French Paradox? *Nutrition Reviews*, Vol:51, June 1993, No:6, pp 185–187.

Krause, M.V. and Mahan, L.K., (1984), *Food, Nutrition and Diet Therapy—A Textbook of Nutritional Care*, 7th Ed., W.B. Saunders Co., Philadelphia.

Mannar, M.G.V. and Dunn, J.T., (1995), *Salt Iodization for the Elimination of Iodine Deficiency*, International Council for Control of Iodine Deficiency Disorders (ICCIDD), The Netherlands.

Mathew, Anila E., Trace Elements in Health and Disease (Part–I), *Nutrition* (A Quarterly Publication of the National Institute of Nutrition, Hyderabad, India), Vol:33, January 1999, No:1, pp 23–32.

Mathew, Anila E., Trace Elements in Health and Disease (Part–II), *Nutrition* (A Quarterly Publication of the National Institute of Nutrition, Hyderabad, India), Vol:33, April 1999, No:2, pp 26–32.

Mathur, Pulkit, Natural Antioxidants in Our Diet, *Nutrition* (A Quarterly Publication of the National Institute of Nutrition, Hyderabad, India), Vol:31, October 1997, No:4, pp 10–17.

Nutrient Requirements and Recommended Dietary Allowances for Indians—A Report of the Expert Group of the Indian Council of Medical Research, (1995), Indian Council of Medical Research, New Delhi.

Paul, P.C. and Palmer, H.H., (1972), *Food Theory and Applications*, John Wiley and Sons, Inc., New York.

Peter, K.V., Bioinformatics on Tree Spices, *Indian Spices*, Vol:36, January–March 1999, No:1, pp 16–18.

Pinstrup-Andersen, Per, Pelletier, David and Alderman, Harold, (Eds.), (1997), *Child Growth and Nutrition in Developing Countries—Priorities for Action*, Oxford University Press, Delhi.

Premalatha, R., Nutrition in Normal Pregnancy and Lactation, *A Manual of Second Regional Workshop on "Planning Diet for Health"*, March 1999, pp 3–7.

Robinson, C.H. and Lawler, M.R., (1982), *Normal and Therapeutic Nutrition*, 16th Ed., Macmillan Publishing Co., Inc., New York.

Robinson, C.H., Lawler, M.R., Chenoweth, W.L. and Garwick, A.E., (1986), *Normal and Therapeutic Nutrition*, 17th Ed., Prentice-Hall, Inc., Upper Saddle River, NJ.

Stryer, Lubert, (1981), *Biochemistry*, 2nd Ed., W.H. Freeman and Company, New York.

Swaminathan, M., (1978), *Handbook of Food and Nutrition–Part II*, Ganesh and Co., Madras, India.

Tortora, G.J. and Anagnostakos, N.P., (1981), *Principles of Anatomy and Physiology*, 3rd Ed., Harper and Row, Publishers, New York.

Weil, Andrew, (1995), *Spontaneous Healing—How to Discover and Enhance Your Body's Natural Ability to Maintain and Heal Itself*, Little, Brown and Company, London.

Yudkin, J., (1986), *The Penguin Encyclopaedia of Nutrition*, Penguin Books Ltd., Harmondsworth, England.

Section 5

Appendices

5.1 GLOSSARY OF INGREDIENTS

English	Hindi	Tamil
Cereals and Grain Products		
Bajra/Pearl millet	Bajra	Cambu
Cornflour/Cornstarch	Makai ka atta	Makka mavoo
Jowar	Juar	Cholam
Maize/Corn	Maka/Bhutta	Makka cholam
Ragi/Finger millet	Madua/Mohua	Kezhvaragu
Rice flakes/Beaten rice	Chiwda/Powva	Aval
Rice flour	Chawal ka atta	Arisi mavoo
Rice, parboiled	Usna/Sela chawal	Puloongal arisi
Rice, puffed	Murrmura	Pori
Rice, raw	Chawal	Pacha arisi
Semolina	Sooji/Rava	Ravai
Vermicelli	Sev/Seviyan	Semiya
Wheat	Gehun	Godumai
Wheat flour, refined	Maida	Maida mavoo
Wheat flour, wholemeal	Atta	Godumai mavoo
Wheat germ	—	Godumai mulai
Dairy Products		
Butter	Makhan	Vennai
Butter, clarified/Butter oil/Samna	Ghee	Neyyi
Buttermilk	Matta/Chaas/Lassi	Moru
Cottage cheese	Chenna/Paneer	Paal katti
Cream	Malai	Aadai
Curds/Yoghurt	Dahi	Thayir
Milk	Doodh	Paal
Milk, buffalo's	Bhains ka doodh	Erumaipaal
Milk, cow's	Ghai ka doodh	Pasumpaal
Whole milk solids/Dried milk lump	Khoya/Mawa	Thirattu paal
Fish and Seafood		
Bombay duck	Bombil	Vangaravasi
Catfish	Shingala	Keluthi
Crab	Kenkra/Kekre	Nandoo

English	Hindi	Tamil
Fish	Machhi	Meen
Hilsa	Hilsa	Oolum
Mackerel	Kaulagedar (Marathi)	Kanankeluthi
Mullet	—	Madavai
Pomfret	Pamflet/Halva	Vavval
Prawn/Shrimp	Jinga	Iraal
Ravas/Indian salmon	Ravas (Marathi)	Puzhakkala
Rohu	Rohu	—
Sardine	Pedwa (Marathi)	Seedai
Seer/Kingfish	Surmai	Vanjram
Shark	Waghsheer (Marathi)	Soorah
Sole	Morrul	Virahl

Flesh Foods (Eggs, Meat, Poultry)

English	Hindi	Tamil
Brain	Bheja/Magz	Moolai
Chicken	Murghi	Kozhi
Egg	Anda/Bhaida	Muttai
Egg yolk	Anda ki zardi	Manjal karu
Kidney	Gurda	—
Liver	Kaleji	Eeral
Meat, beef	Ghai ka gosht	Mattu eraichi
Meat, buffalo	Bhains ka gosht	Erumai eraichi
Meat, minced	Kheema	Kothu kari
Mutton (Goat/Lamb)	Bhakri ka gosht	Attiraichi
Pork	Suar ka gosht/Shikar	Panni eraichi/Panni kari

Fruits

English	Hindi	Tamil
Apple	Seb	Apple
Apricot	Khoomani/Khoobani	—
Bael fruit	Bel	Bilwa pazham
Banana/Plantain	Kela/Kele	Vazha pazham
Cashew fruit	Kaju phal	Mundiri pazham
Cherry	Alubalu	—
Custard apple/Sugar apple	Seethaphal/Sharifa	Seetha pazham
Date, dried	Kharak/Chhuara	—
Date, fresh	Khajur	Pericham pazham
Fig	Anjeer	Athi pazham
Gooseberry, cape	Rasbari	Tholthakkali
Gooseberry, Indian	Amla	Nellikai
Gooseberry, star	Harfarowrie	Aranelli
Grape	Angoor	Drakshai
Guava	Amrood	Koiyya pazham
Jackfruit	Kathal	Pala pazham
Jambu fruit	Jamun	Naga pazham
Lime, juice	Nimbu ka ras	—
Lime, sour	Nimbu	Elumicham pazham
Lime, sweet	Musambi/Musammi	Sathukudi
Loquat	Lokat	Lakot pazham
Mango, raw	Aam	Mangai

English	Hindi	Tamil
Mango, ripe	Aam	Maam pazham
Mangosteen	Mangusthan	Mangusthan
Melon, musk/Cantaloupe	Kharbooja	Mulam pazham
Melon, water	Tarbooz	Darbusini
Mulberry	Shahtoot	Musukkottai pazham
Olive	Zaitun	—
Olive, wild/Indian	—	Vikki pazham
Orange	Narangi/Santra	Kichili pazham/Kamala orange
Palmyra fruit	Tar	Panai nungu
Papaya	Papita	Pappali
Peach	Aarhoo	Pichis pazham
Pear	Nashpati	Berikai
Pineapple	Ananas	Anasi pazham
Plum	Alubokhara	Alapagoda
Pomegranate	Anar	Mathulam pazham
Pummelo	Chakotra	Bamblimas
Raisin	Kishmish	Drakshai
Sapota	Chickoo	Sapota
Woodapple	Kaith	Vilam pazham
Zizyphus/Indian plum	Ber	Elanthapazham
Nuts and Oilseeds		
Almond	Badam	Vadam kottai
Areca nut/Betel-nut	Supari	Paaku
Cashew nut	Kaju	Mundiri paruppoo
Coconut, dessicated	Nariyal ka burada	—
Coconut, dry	Copra	Copra
Coconut, fresh	Nariyal	Thengai
Coconut, milk/cream	Nariyal ka doodh	Thengapaal
Coconut, tender	Nariyal	Elanee
Coconut, water	Nariyal ka pani	llaneer
Flea/Falooda/Basil seeds	Sabja/Tukmeria ka beej	Tirnutpatchi
Gingelly/Sesame seeds	Til	Elloo
Groundnut/Peanut	Moongphali	Verkadalai/Nilakkadalai
Linseed seeds/Flax	Alsi	Alshi vidai
Mustard seeds (black)	Sarson	Kadugoo
Mustard seeds (reddish-brown)	Rai	Kadugoo
Pistachio nut	Pista	Pista
Piyal seeds	Chironji/Charoli	Sarai parupoo/Mowda
Psyllium/Plantain/Spogel seeds	Isabgol/Ispaghul	Ishappukol
Safflower seeds	Kardi/Kusumbh	Sendurakan
Sunflower seeds	Surya mukhi	Suryakanthi
Walnut	Akhrot	Akrottu
Pulses and Legumes		
Bengal gram dhal	Chane ki dhal	Kadalai parupoo
Bengal gram flour	Besan	Kadalai mavoo
Bengal gram, roasted	Bhuna chana	Pottukadalai

English	Hindi	Tamil
Bengal gram, whole/ Chickpeas/Garbanzos	Chana/Kabuli chana	Kothukadalai
Black gram dhal	Urad dhal	Uluntham parupoo
Cow-peas	Lobia	Karamani
Field beans	Sem	Mocha kottai
French beans/Red kidney beans, dried	Rajmah	Rajmah
Green gram dhal	Moong dhal	Payatham parupoo
Green gram, whole/Mung beans	Moong	Pasipayir
Lentils	Masoor	—
Lentils, split	Masoor dhal	Mysore parupoo
Peas, dried	Sukhe mattar	Pattani
Peas, fresh	Hari mattar	Pattani
Red gram dhal/Pigeon-peas/ Congo peas/Cadjan peas	Arhar ki dhal/Tur dhal	Tuvaram parupoo
Soya beans	Bhatmas	—
Spices, Condiments and Herbs		
Anise/Aniseed	Velaiti saunf/Badian	Shombu
Asafoetida	Hing	Perungkayam
Basil, holy/Indian	Tulsi	Tulasi
Bay leaf, Indian/Cassia leaf	Tej patta	Brinji elai
Black pepper/Peppercorns	Kali mirch	Milagoo
Caraway seeds	Shiajeera	Seemai sombu
Cardamom, brown	Bari ellaichi/Moti ellaichi	Periyayelam
Cardamom, green	Chhoti ellaichi	Elakkai
Carum seeds/Bishop's weed/Ajowan	Ajwain	Omum
Chilli, green	Hari mirch	Pachai milagai
Chilli, red/Cayenne pepper	Laal mirch	Milagai
Chilli, whole dried red	Sookhi laal mirch	Vattal
Cinnamon	Dalchini	(Lavanga) Pattai
Cloves	Lavang	Kramboo
Coriander leaves/ Cilantro/Chinese parsley	Hara dhania	Kothamalli
Coriander seeds	Dhania	Kothamallividai
Cumin seeds, white	Sufeid jeera	Jeeragam
Curry leaves/Sweet neem	Gandhela/Karipatta	Kariveppilai
Fennel	Saunf	Sombu
Fenugreek seeds	Methi	Venthayam
Garcinia indica (no English equivalent)	Kokum	Murgal
Garlic	Lehsan	Ullipoondu
Ginger, dried	Sonth	Chukku
Ginger, fresh	Adrak	Inji
Mace	Javithri	Jathipatri
Mango powder	Amchoor	—
Mint	Pudina	Pudina
Nutmeg	Jaiphal	Jathikkai
Onion seeds/Nigella seeds/ Black cumin	Kalonji/Kalajira	Karunjiragam/ Seemai jeeragam

English	Hindi	Tamil
Pomegranate seeds (powder)	Anardhana	—
Poppy seeds	Postdana/Khus khus	Khasakhasa
Saffron	Kesar/Zaffran	Kungamapoo
Tamarind	Imli	Puli
Turmeric	Haldi	Manjal

Vegetables

Leafy Vegetables

English	Hindi	Tamil
Amaranth	Chaulai saag	Thandukeerai/ Mullakeerai
Betel leaves	Paan ka patta	Vethlai
Cabbage	Bandh gobi	Muttaikose
Drumstick leaves	Saijan patta	Murungai keerai
Fenugreek leaves	Methi saag	Venthiya keerai
Lettuce	Salad patta	Salathu/Salad keerai
Spinach	Palak	Pasali keerai

Other Vegetables

English	Hindi	Tamil
Ash gourd	Petha	Posinikkai
Beans	Sem	Beans
Beans, broad/Fava beans	Bakla/Papdi/Sem	Avarai
Beans, cluster	Guar ki phalli	Kothavara
Beans, double	Chastang	—
Bitter gourd	Karela	Pavakkai
Bottle gourd	Lowki/Dudhi	Shorakkai
Brinjal/Aubergine/Eggplant	Baingan	Kathirikkai
Cauliflower	Phool gobi	Kovippoo
Chilli, capsicum/Paprika/ Red, green, yellow peppers	Simla/Sagiya mirch	Koda milagai
Cucumber	Khira/Kakdi	Vellarikkai
Drumstick	Saijan ki phalli	Murungakkai
Gherkin	Konduri	Kovakkai
Knol-khol/Kohlrabi	Kohl-rabi/Kadam ghatgobi	Knol-khol
Ladies fingers/Gumbo/Okra	Bhindi	Vendakkai
Marrow, chow-chow	Chow-chow	Seemai kathirikka
Mushroom	Kukurmutta/Guchi	Kalan
Parwar	Parwal	—
Plantain, flower	Kela ka phool	Vazhapoo
Plantain, green	Hara kela	Vazhakkai
Plantain, stem	Kele ka tana	Vazhai thandu
Pumpkin, red	Laal kaddu/Kaddu	Parangikkai
Pumpkin, white/Field pumpkin/ Vegetable marrow	Safeid kaddu/Kumra	Suraikayi
Ridge gourd	Torai	Pirkkankkai
Round gourd	Tinda	—
Snake gourd	Chachinda/Chirchira	Podalangai
Tomato	Tamatar	Thakkali
Water chestnut	Shingara	Singhara

English	Hindi	Tamil
Root Vegetables and Tubers		
Beetroot	Chukandar	Beetroot
Carrot	Gajjar	Carrot
Colocasia/Taro	Arvi/Ghuiyan	Seppang kizhangoo
Onion, Bombay/big	Piyaz	Periya vengayam
Onion, sambhar/small/Shallot	—	Chinna vengayam
Onion, spring/Scallion	Hara piyaz	Vengaya thandu
Potato	Aloo	Urula kizhangoo
Radish	Mooli	Mullangi
Sweet potato	Shakarkand	Shakkaravalli kizhangoo
Tapioca/Cassava	Simla aloo	Maravalli kizhangoo
Turnip	Shalgam	—
Yam, elephant	Zimikand/Sooran	Senai kizhangoo
Yam, ordinary	—	Karunai kizhangoo
Miscellaneous		
Alum	Phitkari	Padigaaram
Arrowroot	Araroht/Tikhor	Kuva mavoo
Baking soda/Sodium bicarbonate	Pakane ka soda/Meetha soda	Soda uppoo
Bread	Roti/Double roti	Rotti
Citric acid	Nimbu ka tejab/Nimbu ka sat	Elimicha uppoo
Edible foil, gold	Sone ka warq	Ponn thagadoo
Edible foil, silver	Chaandi ka warq	Velli thagadoo
Gelatin	Sares	—
Griddle	Tawa	Tawa
Honey	Shahad	Thain
Ice	Baraf	Ice katti
Ice-cream, Indian	Kulfi	Kulfi
Jaggery/Unrefined cane or palm sugar	Gur	Vellam
Kewra/Fragrant screw pine essence	Kewra arq/Ruh kewra	—
Kewra/Fragrant screw pine water	Kewra jal	—
Lime, slaked/Calcium hydroxide	Chunna	Chunam
Mixed seed kernels, dried (pumpkin, musk melon, watermelon and cucumber)	Char maghaz	—
Mixed spices/Indian spice mix	Garam masala	—
Oil	Tel	Ennai
Oil, olive	Zetoon ka tel	—
Pickle	Acchaar	Oorgai
Rose essence	Ruh gulab	Roja sathoo
Rose water	Gulab jal	Paneer
Sago	Sabudana	Javvarisi
Salt, black	Kala namak	Karupoo uppoo
Salt, table/cooking (Sodium chloride)	Namak	Uppoo
Sugar, brown	Boora shakkar	Cheeni sarkarai
Sugar-candy	Mishree	—

English	Hindi	Tamil
Sugar cane	Ganna	Karumbu
Sugar, castor	Pithi sakkar/Barik chini	—
Sugar syrup	Chasnee/Sheera	Sarkarai pagoo
Sugar, white	Cheeni/Shakkar	Sarkarai
Tartaric acid	Imli ka sat	—
Vinegar	Sirka	Surukka/kaadi
Wok	Kadai	Eerhumbu chutty
Yeast	Khamir	Khadi

5.2 FOOD SOURCES OF PROTEINS, CARBOHYDRATES AND FATS

Rating	Proteins	Carbohydrates	Fats
Excellent	Egg	Sugar	Ghee
	Milk	Jaggery	Cooking oils
	Milk products	Honey	Butter
	Fish	Sago	Margarine
	Meat	Wheat	Vanaspati
	Poultry	Rice	Cocoa butter
	Soya beans	Semolina	
	Wheat germ	Dried fruits	
	Liver	Pulses	
		Bread	
		Dried peas and beans	
Good	Yeast	Tapioca	Walnuts
	Pulses	Fresh dates	Dry coconut
	Dried peas and beans	Yam	Almonds
	Rice	Colocasia	Pistachio nuts
	Ragi	Fresh water chestnuts	Gingelly seeds
	Wheat	Potatoes	Fresh coconuts
	Semolina	Sweet potatoes	Groundnuts
	Groundnuts	Groundnuts	Cashew nuts
	Millets	Gingelly seeds	Piyal seeds
	Almonds	Cashew nuts	Oilseeds
	Cashew nuts	Custard apples	Cream
	Fenugreek seeds	Sapotas	Cheese
	Poppy seeds	Bananas	
	Mustard seeds		
Fair	Gingelly seeds	Leeks	Avocado pears
	Pistachio nuts	Green plantains (veg)	Egg yolk
	Walnuts	Most fruits	Meat
	Green leafy vegetables	Drumstick leaves	Whole milk
	Fresh peas and beans	Onions	Pork
	Coconuts	Double beans	Fish
	Mushrooms	Coconuts	Chicken
	Maize	Carrots	Soya beans
		Walnuts	Poppy seeds
		Almonds	Rice bran

Rating	Proteins	Carbohydrates	Fats
Poor	Gelatin	Green leafy vegetables	Tender coconut
	Roots and tubers	Beetroots	Green leafy vegetables
	Most vegetables	Turnips	Roots and tubers
	Fruits	Radishes	Most fruits
	Fats and oils	Most vegetables	Most vegetables
	Sugar	Milk	Sago
	Honey	Tomatoes	Sugar
	Sago	Avocado pears	Honey
		Watermelons	Jaggery
		Muskmelons	Cereals
		Fish	
		Seafood	
		Meat	
		Egg	
		Poultry	

5.3   SCIENTIFIC TERMS FOR COMMON VITAMINS

Common Name	Scientific Name
Fat Soluble Vitamins	
Vitamin A	Retinol
	Carotene—Precursor of vitamin A or provitamin A
Vitamin D	Cholecalciferol
Vitamin E	Tocopherol
Vitamin K	Phylloquinone
Water Soluble Vitamins	
Vitamin C	Ascorbic acid
The Vitamin B Complex Group	
Vitamin B_1	Thiamine
Vitamin B_2	Riboflavin
Vitamin B_3	Niacin
Vitamin B_6	Pyridoxine
Folic acid	Folacin
Vitamin B_{12}	Cyanocobalamin
Pantothenic acid	—
Biotin	—

5.4   SOURCES OF FAT SOLUBLE VITAMINS

| Rating | Vitamin A | | Vitamin D or |
	As Carotene	As Retinol (Animal)	Cholecalciferol

Excellent	Radish greens
	Turnip greens
	Beetroot greens
	Drumstick leaves
	Fenugreek leaves
	Coriander leaves
	Mint
	Curry leaves
	Spinach
	Carrots
	Ripe mangoes
	Cape gooseberries
	Oranges
	Papayas
	Apricots
		Fish liver oil
		Liver
		Egg yolk
		Cheese (from whole milk)
		Whole milk
		Butter
		Cream
		Cottage cheese
		  (from whole milk)
		Whole milk solids
		Ghee
		Fortified hydrogenated fats
			Fortified milk
			Fortified butter
			Fortified margarine
			Fortified hydrogenated
			  fats
			Produced in human skin
			  when exposed to sunlight

Good	Pumpkin (orange
	  variety)
	Yam (orange variety)
	Sweet potatoes
	  (orange variety)
	Tomatoes
	Green chillies
	Capsicums
	Egg yolk
	Crab
		—	Fish liver oil

Fair	Pulses Lentils Jackfruit Drumstick (veg) Plums Musk melons Bitter gourds Some beans Palmolein	Meat	Egg yolk Liver Fatty fish in which the bones may be eaten
Poor	Pineapples Ladies fingers Peas Whole milk Fish	—	Processed cheese Butter Milk *As Ergocalciferol* Mushrooms Yeast

Rating	Vitamin E or Tocopherol	Vitamin K or Phylloquinone
Excellent	Wheat germ Rice germ Sunflower oil Cottonseed oil Safflower oil Corn (maize) oil Soya bean oil Oilseeds like gingelly Nuts	Spinach Cabbages Cauliflowers Green leafy vegetables Liver especially pork Manufactured by intestinal bacteria
Good	Groundnuts Legumes Whole grain cereals Green leafy vegetables Fish liver oil	Corn (maize) oil Soya bean oil
Fair	Fish Egg yolk Seafood Avocado pears	Whole milk Whole milk products Meat
Poor	Milk	Cereals Fruits

5.5 SOURCES OF WATER SOLUBLE VITAMINS

Rating	Vitamin C or Ascorbic Acid	Vitamin B Complex	
		B_1 or Thiamine	B_2 or Riboflavin
Excellent	West Indian cherries Indian gooseberries Guavas Cashew fruits Parsley Coriander leaves Drumstick leaves Radish greens Knol-khol greens Turnip greens Cabbages Capsicums Green chillies Drumstick (veg)	Wheat germ Yeast Whole grain cereals Pulses Gingelly seeds Groundnuts Pork Liver Nuts Oilseeds Dried peas and beans	Liver Kidney Wheat germ Yeast
Good	Citrus fruits Papayas Cape gooseberries Cauliflowers Knol-khol Bitter gourds	Beetroot greens Turnip greens Knol-khol greens Parboiled rice	Egg Milk Milk products Meat Green leafy vegetables Green chillies Garlic Mushrooms Crab

Rating	Vitamin C or Ascorbic Acid	Vitamin B Complex	
		B$_1$ or Thiamine	B$_2$ or Riboflavin
Fair	Sprouted pulses Potatoes Sweet potatoes Tomatoes Pineapples Musk melons Passion fruit Liver	Milk Milk products Potatoes Meat Clam Crab Shrimp Egg yolk Mushrooms	Cereals Pulses Groundnuts Chicken Fish
Poor	Meat Milk Fish Seafood Cereals Pulses Legumes Nuts Tamarind Jackfruit Bananas Woodapples Apples	Chicken Fish Fruits Root vegetables Tubers Vegetables Fats and oils Raw rice	Rice Pork Root vegetables Tubers Most fruits Most vegetables Fats and oils

Rating	Vitamin B Complex		
	B$_3$ or Niacin	B$_6$ or Pyridoxine	Folic Acid or Folacin
Excellent	Liver Groundnuts	Wheat germ Yeast Liver Pork Chicken Fish Meat Egg yolk Whole grain cereals Pulses Legumes Groundnuts Bananas Avocado pears	Yeast Wheat germ Egg yolk Liver Pulses Dried peas and beans Groundnuts Gingelly seeds Spinach Mint Parsley Ladies fingers

| Rating | Vitamin B Complex | | |
	B$_3$ or Niacin	B$_6$ or Pyridoxine	Folic Acid or Folacin
Good	Chicken	Dried fruits	Curry leaves
	Meat	Maize	Fenugreek seeds
	Milk and egg (as the	Carrots	Nuts
	precursor tryptophan,	Cauliflowers	Whole grain cereals
	an essential amino acid)	Cabbages	Cabbages
	Pork	Onions	Cauliflowers
	Fish	Potatoes	Colocasia
	Crab	Sweet potatoes	Beetroots
	Yeast	Spinach	Beetroot greens
		Parsley	
		Tomatoes	
		Mushrooms	
Fair	Whole grain cereals	Nuts	Tomatoes
	Rice flakes	Peas	Carrots
	Mushrooms	Seafood	Oranges
	Pulses		Fish
	Potatoes		Mushrooms
	Cauliflowers		Bananas
	Dates		Onions
	Nuts		Radishes
	Oilseeds		Coriander seeds
	Beetroot greens		Green chillies
	Seafood		
Poor	Maize	Milk	Milk
	Jowar	Fruits	Chicken
	Root vegetables	Coconuts	Meat
	Tubers		Potatoes
	Other vegetables		Fruits
	Fruits		
	Fats and oils		

Rating	Vitamin B Complex		
	B₁₂ or Cyanocobalamin	Pantothenic Acid	Biotin
Excellent	Liver Crab Shrimp Mussel Scallop Oyster Clam Prawn Sardines Lobster Manufactured by intestinal bacteria	Yeast Liver Egg yolk Wheat germ Chicken Avocado pears Dried peas and beans Cow-peas Groundnuts Mushrooms Cauliflowers Manufactured by intestinal bacteria	Egg yolk Liver Yeast Manufactured by intestinal bacteria
Good	Egg yolk Meat Other fish Cheese	Meat Pork Crab Fish Whole grain cereals Potatoes Sweet potatoes Pulses	Pulses Legumes Nuts
Fair	Chicken Pork Milk	Milk Milk products Cabbages Bananas Carrots Oranges Tomatoes Ladies fingers Fresh peas Fresh coconuts Corn (maize) oil Spinach	Milk Meat Whole grain cereals
Poor	—	Onions Fruits	—

5.6　FOOD SOURCES OF MINERAL ELEMENTS

Rating	Calcium	Phosphorus	Sulphur
Excellent	Milk Milk products Green leafy vegetables Curry leaves Fish with soft bones Crab Shrimp Gingelly seeds Poppy seeds Carum seeds Cumin seeds Cinnamon	Fish Meat Chicken Pork Milk Milk products Nuts Oilseeds Groundnuts Yeast Wheat germ	Meat Fish Egg Chicken Pork Milk Cheese Cereals Pulses Dried peas and beans Drumstick leaves Fenugreek leaves Jackfruit seeds Cauliflowers Nuts Oilseeds Knol-khol Drumstick (veg)
Good	Ragi Fenugreek leaves Drumstick leaves Mint Coriander leaves Dry coconut Slaked lime consumed 　with betel leaf Bengal gram Dried French beans Soya beans Jaggery Black gram dhal Oilseeds	Egg *Whole grain cereals (often in 　the form of unavailable phytin) *Pulses Carrots Coconuts Garlic *Cumin seeds Poppy seeds *Fenugreek seeds Coriander seeds *See text—Nutrient Inhibitors 　and Phosphorus	Maize Fresh peas Mint Coriander leaves Bitter gourds
Fair	Mutton Chow-chow marrows Dried fruits Yeast Tamarind Groundnuts	Colocasia Dried fruits Mushrooms Woodapples Tamarind Drumstick (veg) Beans	Fruits Most vegetables Potatoes Beetroots Spinach
Poor	Cereals especially rice Cabbages Potatoes Carrots Ladies fingers Fresh coconuts Garlic Fruits	Green leafy vegetables Potatoes Tender coconut water Fruits Fats and oils Honey	Root vegetables Tubers Cabbages

Rating	Calcium	Phosphorus	Sulphur
	Chicken		
	Meat		
	Egg		
	Sago		
	Mushrooms		
	Honey		

Rating	Magnesium	Iron	Zinc
Excellent	Wheat germ	Liver	Seafood especially oyster
	Yeast	Crab	Meat
	Whole grain cereals	Fish especially dried	Chicken
	Rice flakes	Meat	Egg yolk
	Pulses	Pork	Liver
	Green leafy vegetables	Seafood	Pork
	Betel leaves	Egg yolk	Wheat germ
	Nuts	Chicken	Processed cheese
	Dried peas and beans	Green leafy vegetables	
	Cow-peas	Rice flakes	
	Cumin seeds	Wheat germ	
	Fresh ginger		
	Green chillies		
	Ripe mangoes		
	Plums		
	Hard drinking water		
Good	Most spices and	Dried fruits	Crab
	condiments	Whole wheat	Fish
	Milk	Bajra	Oilseeds like gingelly
		Ragi	Nuts
		Millets	Whole grain cereals
		Pulses	Pulses
		Dried peas and beans	Poppy seeds
		Turmeric	Dried peas and beans
		Mango powder	Coriander seeds
		Asafoetida	Fenugreek seeds
		Tamarind	
		Poppy seeds	
		Black pepper	
		Cumin seeds	
		Cloves	
		Nuts	
		Oilseeds	
Fair	Cabbages	Green plantains (veg)	Mushrooms
	Potatoes	Watermelons	Pomegranates
	Bananas	Jaggery	Custard apples
	Fresh peas		Green leafy vegetables
	Red gram dhal		Root vegetables
	Tamarind		Tubers
	Crab		Other vegetables

Rating	Magnesium	Iron	Zinc
Poor	Carrots Cauliflowers Brinjals Fruits Fish	Brinjals Cabbages Root vegetables Tubers Most fruits Mushrooms Other vegetables Milk	Most fruits Milk

Rating	Iodine	Copper	Manganese
Excellent	Shellfish Salt-water fish Seafood Plants grown in iodine-rich soils Iodized salt	Liver Shellfish Raw oyster Yeast Wheat germ Whole grain cereals Pulses Dried peas and beans Nuts Betel leaves Mushrooms Green chillies Oilseeds like gingelly	Ragi Whole grain cereals Pulses Dried peas and beans Betel leaves Nuts Oilseeds Mustard seeds Gingelly seeds Fresh and dried ginger Condiments Spices
Good	Egg Cabbages Cheese Pork Potatoes	Groundnuts Fish Fresh water chestnuts Parwar Spices	Coriander leaves Mint Spinach Pineapples Pomegranates Sapotas Custard apples
Fair	Meat Milk Apples	Turmeric Tamarind	Drumstick leaves Fenugreek leaves
Poor	Fats and oils	Meat Milk Rice Fruits Green leafy vegetables Root vegetables Tubers Most vegetables	Fruits Vegetables Root vegetables Tubers Fish Meat Liver Poultry Milk Egg

Rating	Molybdenum	Selenium	Chromium	Cobalt (as Vitamin B_{12})
Excellent	Organ meats Pulses Dried peas Coriander leaves Fenugreek leaves Groundnuts Gingelly seeds	Meat Seafood Liver Fish like mackerel Ragi	Liver Yeast Meat Betel leaves Nuts Oilseeds Spices Condiments Poppy seeds Cheese	Liver Crab Shrimp Mussel Scallop Oyster Clam Prawn Sardines Lobster Manufactured by intestinal bacteria
Good	Ragi Whole grain cereals Green leafy vegetables	Whole grain cereals Pulses Dried peas and beans Salt-water fish Parboiled rice	Pulses Bottle gourds Green leafy vegetables Whole grain cereals Pineapples Pomegranates Custard apples Tomatoes	Egg yolk Meat Other fish Cheese
Fair	Green chillies Potatoes Cucumbers	Avocado pears Butter Milk Milk products	Vegetables Fruits Root vegetables Tubers Jaggery	Chicken Pork Milk
Poor	Spices Spinach Root vegetables Tubers Fruits Fish Meat Poultry Egg Milk	Fruits Vegetables Raw rice	Milk Chicken Fish	—

5.7   FOOD SOURCES OF ELECTROLYTES

Rating	Sodium	Potassium	Chloride

Excellent	Wheat germ
	Egg white
	Liver
	Knol-khol
	Lychees
	Musk melons
	Spinach
	Most green leafy
	  vegetables
	Cumin seeds
	Table/Cooking salt
	Baking powder/
	  Baking soda
	Preservatives
	  (Sodium benzoate/
	  Sodium citrate/
	  Sodium propionate)
	Monosodium
	  glutamate (MSG)
		Meat
		Milk
		Fish
		Chicken
		Sword beans
		Coriander seeds
		Cumin seeds
		Fenugreek seeds
		Green chillies
		Turmeric
		Jaggery
		Most fruits
		Pulses
		Legumes
		Bael fruit
		Colocasia
		Tree tomatoes
		Avocado pears
		Dried fruits
		Brussels sprouts
		Mushrooms
			Table/Cooking salt
			Drumstick (veg)
			Curry leaves
			Drumstick leaves
			Fenugreek leaves

Good	Shellfish Fish Meat Chicken Milk Dried peas Carrots Beetroots Radishes Most other vegetables Pulses Tender maize Wholemeal wheat flour Semolina	Seafood Coriander leaves Drumstick leaves Cereals especially whole grain Carrots Potatoes Onions Cauliflowers Cabbages Tomatoes Brinjals Drumstick (veg) Ladies fingers Nuts Oilseeds	Cereals Pulses Musk melons Green leafy vegetables
Fair	Cereals Egg yolk Dried fruits Jaggery Coriander seeds Turmeric	Fenugreek leaves Papayas Pineapples Pears Bananas Apples Guavas Egg Most vegetables	Vegetables Fruits Fish Meat Chicken Milk

Rating	Sodium	Potassium	Chloride
Poor	Sugar	Sugar	Nuts
	Mint	Curry leaves	Oilseeds
	Cabbages	Mint	
	Curry leaves	Sago	
	Drumstick leaves	Rice	
	Fruits	Semolina	
	Sago	Beetroots	
	Rice	Radishes	
	Dried French beans	Knol-khol	
	Onions	Snake gourds	
	Potatoes	Round gourds	
	Capsicums	Cucumbers	
	Nuts	Chow-chow marrows	
	Oilseeds	Custard apples	
	Groundnuts	Jackfruit	
	Mushrooms	Grapes (green variety)	
	Cucumbers	Honey	

5.8 SOURCES OF DIETARY FIBRE

Rating	Insoluble (Cellulose/Hemicellulose/Lignin)	Soluble (Pectins/Gums/Mucilages)
Excellent	Whole grain cereals and their products Green leafy vegetables	Legumes Pulses Fenugreek seeds Maize Carrots Dried fruits Flea (falooda) seeds Psyllium seeds and their husk (isabgol)
Good	Legumes Pulses Maize Carrots Dried fruits	Whole grain cereals Onions Potatoes Ladies fingers Nuts Oilseeds Bananas Mushrooms Fruits Vegetables
Fair	Root vegetables Tubers Nuts Fruits Vegetables	Refined cereals
Poor	—	—

Note: Animal foods such as milk and milk products, fish, meat, egg and poultry have no fibre.

5.9   CHOLESTEROL IN FOODS

Very High	High	Moderately High
Brain	Shrimp	Lean meat (Beef/Mutton/Pork)
Kidney	Prawn	Cheese
Heart	Squid	Cream
Sweetbreads	Sardines	Chicken with skin
Liver		Crab
Gizzard		Lobster
Egg yolk		Clam
Butter		Oyster
Ghee		Fish like mackerel
Lard (pig fat)		
Beef fat		
Fish roe		
Fish liver oil		

Fair	Low	Negligible	Absent
Whole milk	Skimmed milk	Nuts	Egg white
Other fish	Buttermilk	Oilseeds	All vegetable sources of food
		Maize	except nuts, oilseeds and
		Soya beans	their oils
		Vegetable oils	
		Margarine made from vegetable oils	
		Vanaspati	

5.10 NUTRIENT INHIBITORS

Rating	Oxalic Acid (Oxalates)	Phytic Acid (Phytates)	Goitrogens
High	Green leafy vegetables	Whole grain cereals	Radishes
	Curry leaves	Pulses	Turnips
	Drumstick leaves	Dried legumes	Cabbages
	Rhubarb	Nuts	Cauliflowers
	Plantain flower (veg)	Oilseeds	Brussels sprouts
	Green plantains (veg)	Spices	
	Drumstick (veg)		
	Indian gooseberries		
	Indian olives		
	Nuts		
	Oilseeds like gingelly		
	Kesari dhal		
Moderate	Green chillies	Turmeric	Groundnuts
	Beetroots	Dried red chillies	Oilseeds like mustard
	Potatoes	Tender maize	Soya beans
	Radishes	Rice	Legumes
	Plums		Lentils
	Dried fruits		

Rating	Oxalic Acid (Oxalates)	Phytic Acid (Phytates)	Goitrogens
	Chocolate		Maize
	Cocoa		Ragi
	Tea		Tapioca
Fair	Pulses	Refined cereals	
	Legumes	Bitter gourds	
	Fruits	Drumstick (veg)	
		Jackfruit seeds	—
		Curry leaves	
		Drumstick leaves	
Poor	Cereals	Green leafy vegetables	
	Fish	Root vegetables	
	Milk	Tubers	—
	Meat	Meat	
	Egg	Fish	
		Milk	
		Egg	

Trypsin Inhibitors	Tannins	Niacytin	Avidin	Thiaminase
Soya beans	Seed-coats of	Cereals	Raw egg white	Raw clam
Legumes	legumes	especially maize		Raw shrimp
Raw egg white	Spices	untreated		Raw crab
	Tamarind	with alkali		Raw betel-nut
	Ragi			Raw red cabbage
	Bajra			
	Tea			
	Coffee			

5.11 MEAN HEIGHT AND WEIGHT CHART FOR INDIAN BOYS AND GIRLS OF UPPER SOCIO-ECONOMIC STATUS AGED 5 TO 18 YEARS (1992)

Age in years	Boys				Girls			
	Height in cm		Weight in kg		Height in cm		Weight in kg	
	(1992)	(1972)	(1992)	(1972)	(1992)	(1972)	(1992)	(1972)
5.0	107.1	—	17.4	—	106.0	—	17.0	—
5.5	110.4	108.9	18.4	17.0	109.4	106.6	17.9	16.1
6.0	113.7	—	19.2	—	113.0	—	18.7	—
6.5	117.5	113.8	20.6	18.7	115.4	112.6	19.6	18.1
7.0	118.6	—	21.0	—	118.2	—	20.5	—
7.5	121.6	119.7	22.4	21.0	120.2	116.3	21.7	19.7
8.0	124.1	—	23.5	—	122.7	—	23.0	—
8.5	126.4	123.9	24.5	22.0	126.2	122.8	24.9	21.6
9.0	130.4	—	26.5	—	128.6	—	25.8	—
9.5	131.5	128.4	26.8	24.7	131.9	127.1	27.5	23.6
10.0	134.7	—	28.7	—	134.8	—	29.6	—
10.5	137.6	135.4	30.8	25.9	137.9	132.5	31.9	26.7
11.0	139.6	—	31.9	—	141.3	—	34.3	—
11.5	142.3	139.6	33.8	31.0	144.3	140.6	36.8	31.0
12.0	144.7	—	35.4	—	146.7	—	38.7	—
12.5	147.9	142.8	37.9	32.5	149.9	145.5	41.9	35.2
13.0	150.3	—	39.4	—	151.4	—	42.6	—
13.5	154.9	152.9	43.2	39.9	153.2	149.0	45.2	39.3
14.0	158.0	—	44.7	—	153.6	—	45.7	—
14.5	161.4	159.9	48.1	44.5	154.8	152.4	46.6	41.6
15.0	164.3	—	51.0	—	155.0	—	48.0	—
15.5	165.5	162.0	52.4	45.7	155.4	153.1	48.9	43.4
16.0	167.1	—	55.0	—	155.1	—	49.2	—
16.5	167.9	163.3	54.9	49.6	156.0	153.7	49.6	45.4
17.0	168.6	—	56.6	—	157.1	—	49.0	—
17.5	169.4	164.5	56.9	52.1	—	154.0	—	44.6
18.0	168.9	—	59.7	—	—	—	—	—
18.5	—	165.6	—	52.7	—	—	—	—

In preparing the above chart, relevant portions have been taken from the study, *Physical and Sexual Growth Pattern of Affluent Indian Children from 5 to 18 Years of Age,* by Agarwal, D.K., Agarwal, K.N., Upadhyay, S.K., Mittal, R., Prakash, R. and Rai, S., published in Indian Pediatrics (Journal of the Indian Academy of Pediatrics), Vol:29, October 1992, No:10, pp 1203–1282.

In 1972, a study by the Indian Council of Medical Research (ICMR) established the first indices of heights and weights for Indian children. These guidelines were reviewed in 1992 when it was felt that arriving at these parameters by examining a cross-section of the Indian population was hardly representative of ideal health. Today, the health status of boys and girls who enjoy better nutrition has found acceptance as the basis for setting a health standard for Indian children, though standard height and weight charts for adult Indians still have to be established.

5.12 NORMAL LEVELS OF FREQUENTLY TESTED CONSTITUENTS OF BLOOD

Blood Constituent	Normal Levels	
Haemoglobin	Male	13 to 18 g per 100 ml of blood
	Female	12 to 16 g per 100 ml of blood
	Newborn	18 to 22 g per 100 ml of blood
Haemoglobin Per Cent	Calculated at	
	Male	15.5 g = 100 per cent
	Female	14.5 g = 100 per cent
Red Blood Cell (RBC) Count	Male	4.9 to 5.5 million per cu mm
	Female	4.4 to 5.0 million per cu mm
White Blood Cell (WBC) (Leucocytes) Count	Male and Female 5,000 to 11,000 per cu mm	
Differential Count		
Neutrophils or Polymorphs	3,000 to 6,000 per cu mm	(60–70% of WBC)
Eosinophils	150 to 400 per cu mm	(2–4% of WBC)
Basophils	0 to 100 per cu mm	(0.5–1% of WBC)
Lymphocytes	1,500 to 2,700 per cu mm	(20–25% of WBC)
Monocytes	350 to 800 per cu mm	(3–8% of WBC)
Blood Platelets	2,50,000 to 5,00,000 per cu mm	
Total Plasma Lipids	300 to 800 mg per 100 ml	
Serum Cholesterol	120 to 200 mg per 100 ml	
High-density Lipoproteins (HDL)	45 to 72 mg per 100 ml	
Low-density Lipoproteins (LDL)	60 to 130 mg per 100 ml	
Very Low-density Lipoproteins (VLDL)	Up to 40 mg per 100 ml	
Serum Triglycerides	30 to 140 mg per 100 ml	
Serum Bilirubin	0.2 to 1.0 mg per 100 ml	
Serum Creatinine	0.7 to 1.5 mg per 100 ml	
Blood Urea	16 to 50 mg per 100 ml	
Serum Uric Acid	1.6 to 5.0 mg per 100 ml	
Total Serum Protein	6.0 to 8.0 g per 100 ml	
Serum Albumin	3.5 to 5.5 g per 100 ml	
Serum Globulin	1.5 to 3.0 g per 100 ml	
Albumin:Globulin Ratio	1.5 to 2.1	
Oral Glucose Tolerance Test (GTT)—Blood and Plasma Sugar Levels		
Fasting	Whole Blood	Less than 100 mg per 100 ml
	Plasma	Less than 115 mg per 100 ml
1/2 to 1 to 11/2 hours	Whole Blood	Less than 180 mg per 100 ml
	Plasma	Less than 200 mg per 100 ml
2 hours	Whole Blood	Less than 120 mg per 100 ml
	Plasma	Less than 140 mg per 100 ml

5.13 NORMAL LEVELS OF FREQUENTLY TESTED CONSTITUENTS OF URINE

Urine Constituent	Normal Levels (grams per 24 hours)
Creatine	None
Creatinine	1.0 to 1.5
Protein	None
Urea	20 to 35
Uric Acid	0.5 to 0.7
Bile	None
Glucose	None

5.14 HOME REMEDIES

Allergy

(1) Soak a few pieces of dried kokum, *Garcinia indica,* (no English equivalent), in 1 cup (250 ml/8 fl oz) water for a few minutes. Bring to the boil, then squeeze out. Drink the extract mixed with a pinch of salt and 1 teaspoon sugar. Soothe the areas affected by the allergy by rubbing the spent kokum over them. The sooner this treatment is administered, the more effective. *Caution*: Do not use this remedy for severe allergies.

Kokum syrup is sold commercially in some parts of the country, particularly in Western India. Stir 1 tablespoon of the syrup in a glass of water and drink immediately the allergic symptoms become manifest for the same effect.

(2) Curds are a natural antihistamine and are better tolerated than milk. Consumption of curds should be encouraged especially among people who claim allergy to milk.

Antibiotics, Offset Effects of

(1) Cook 1 tablespoon sago in 1 cup (250 ml/8 fl oz) water. Add the juice of 1 lime and 1 tablespoon sugar. Drink during antibiotic treatment. Lines the stomach and prevents damage.

Arthritis

(1) Every morning, eat a 1" (2.5 cm) piece of fresh ginger crushed and mixed in 1 teaspoon sugar. The pain, swelling and stiffness should be reduced from about the third month after the start of treatment.

(2) Include ginger and onions as much as possible in cooking.

(3) Add 1/2 tablespoon vinegar and 1 teaspoon honey to a glass of hot water. Stir well. Take at bedtime.

Asthma

(1) Bring 1 cup (250 ml/8 fl oz) milk to the boil with 1 cup (250 ml/8 fl oz) water. Add 2 generous handfuls (approximately 180 g/6 oz) peeled garlic and cook until

soft. Mash well. Dissolve 250 g/8 oz jaggery (preferably palmyra) in 1/2 cup (125 ml/4 fl oz) water over low heat. Strain and add to the mixture on the fire. Cook until the mixture thickens and begins to leave the sides of the pan. Add 1 tablespoon pure ghee and 2 teaspoons powdered dried ginger. Mix well. Bottle and store in the refrigerator. Eat 1 teaspoon every day.

Dried ginger is added as a cough preventive. Though this garlic "halwa" or *lehiyam* will not impart unpleasantness to the breath, as a measure of abundant caution, eat at bedtime.

Blood Cholesterol, Elevated

(1) Lightly roast, without oil, 1 tablespoon fenugreek seeds, powder, and consume with a glass of water, first thing every morning. A larger quantity may be roasted, powdered, and stored for use every day.

(2) Use turmeric and garlic as much as possible in cooking.

Blood Sugar, Elevated (Diabetes)

(1) Lightly roast, without oil, 1 tablespoon fenugreek seeds, powder and swallow with a glass of water every morning, 1 hour before any other food is consumed. Roast, powder and store a larger quantity for regular consumption. (Insulin-dependent diabetics *must* inform their doctor that this remedy is being used.)

(2) Grind 1 bitter gourd to a smooth paste with a little water. Squeeze out and drink the extract every morning. Do not store the juice. It has to be freshly prepared each time.

(3) Include onions as much as possible in cooking.

(4) Eat jambu fruit when in season. It rejuvenates the pancreas.

(5) Eat a fresh Indian gooseberry every day.

Body Ache

See Fever.

Bronchitis

See Asthma.

Chest Congestion

(1) Mix 1/4 teaspoon turmeric powder and 1 teaspoon honey in 1 cup (250 ml/ 8 fl oz) hot milk. Drink at bedtime, preferably on an empty stomach (at least 4 hours after the last meal).

(2) Crush together 2 whole garlic cloves, a 2" (5 cm) piece fresh ginger, 1 teaspoon black peppercorns and 1 teaspoon cumin seeds. Add 1 cup (250 ml/8 fl oz) water and 1 tablespoon powdered jaggery. Bring to the boil. Lower the heat

and simmer for 15 minutes. Strain. Drink the extract while still hot. This is called *kashayam*, one of the many forms that exist. (See also Influenza.)

(3) Bring a pot of water to the boil. Simultaneously, heat a piece of iron or steel until red hot. Crush 1 tablespoon carum seeds. Add to the water kept boiling on the stove together with 1 teaspoon turmeric powder and a few drops of eucalyptus oil. (If eucalyptus leaves are used—blue gum only—bring to the boil in the water from the beginning.) Cover immediately and turn off the heat.

Sit comfortably on a low stool, and place the covered pot on the floor in front of you. Draw a blanket completely over your head and shoulders until it touches the floor. Open the pot quickly, and gently lower the piece of heated iron or steel into the water. Inhale the rising steam, holding the blanket firmly down against the floor so that no steam escapes. Get someone to help to minimize the loss of steam and to prevent accidents. Best done at bedtime.

Colic

See Indigestion.

Conjunctivitis

(1) Soak cotton wool in a solution of turmeric powder and boiled water (1 teaspoon turmeric powder boiled in 2 cups/500 ml/16 fl oz water until reduced by half). Place over both eyes and rest for 30 minutes. (Unless absolutely foolproof, do not use commercial powders as they might contain other spices and condiments, and even artificial colours. Whole dried turmeric powdered at home is best. Turmeric stains.)

(2) Soak cotton wool in chilled rose water and place over both eyes. It will bring relief to itchy eyes and soothe tired ones.

Cough Mixture for Children

(1) To 1 cup (250 ml/8 fl oz) water, add 2 teaspoons carum seeds, 2 teaspoons linseed seeds, 1 tablespoon powdered jaggery and 1 small, green cardamom. Bring to the boil, reduce the heat and simmer over low heat for 15 minutes, or until reduced by half. Strain. Stir 1 teaspoon honey, and, a pinch each of turmeric powder and salt into the extract. Give twice a day for 2 days. (See also Asthma.)

Cough, Persistent

See Chest Congestion.

Cuts

(1) To staunch the flow of blood from a cut, first wash in running water, then press ice and turmeric powder into the wound. (As much as possible, use turmeric

powdered at home, as commercial powders might contain other spices and condiments too. Turmeric stains.)

(2) After a fall or injury (particularly to the head), eat 1 teaspoon sugar mixed with a pinch of turmeric powder every 3 hours for about 4 days.

Dehydration (from Diarrhoea /Vomiting/Bleeding/Strenuous Exercise)

(1) Oral rehydration therapy (See text).

Diabetes

See Blood Sugar, Elevated.

Diarrhoea

See Stomach Upset.

Earache

(1) Remove the stalk, and scrape out the seeds of a long, whole, dried red chilli with the tip of a long needle. Skewer it with the needle and fill it with mustard/ gingelly oil. Hold it over a flame (a candle is ideal) until the oil begins to bubble. Do not let the chilli burn. Cool until comfortably warm, then pour the oil into the affected ear. Plug the ear with cotton wool. Can be used for animals too.

Epileptic Fits

(1) Consume large amounts of fresh coriander leaves. Coriander chutney is one means of doing so. *Do not discontinue prescribed medication.*

Fever

(1) Boil 1 cup (250 ml/8 fl oz) water with 1 tablespoon fenugreek seeds until reduced by half. Take three times a day until the fever subsides.

Flatulence (Gas Trouble)

(1) Swallow 1/2 teaspoon mustard seeds with some warm water every morning 30 minutes before any other food or drink.

(2) Add a pinch of asafoetida powder and 1/2 teaspoon cumin seeds to pulses (dhals) during cooking.

Gallstones

(1) Eat plantain stem, prepared as a vegetable, as often as possible.

Gout

(1) Increase consumption of onions, garlic and bitter gourd. Avoid mushrooms and meat.

Haemorrhoids (Piles)

(1)   Include elephant yam as often as possible in one's diet.

Headache (Migraine)

(1)   Remove the large veins from cabbage leaves. Crush the leaves and place them in a cloth. Roll up and tie across the forehead. The headache will disappear as the leaves turn dry. (See also Toothache.)

Hepatitis

See Jaundice.

Indigestion (Stomach Gripes)

(1)   Add 1 teaspoon carum seeds to 1 cup (250 ml/8 fl oz) water and boil for 5 minutes. Strain and drink the extract.

(2)   Chew 1 tablespoon fenugreek seeds and swallow. Alternatively, lightly roast the fenugreek seeds without oil, powder and swallow with a glass of water.

Influenza

(1)   Mix 1 teaspoon holy basil leaves and 1 teaspoon dried ginger together. Add 1 cup (250 ml/8 fl oz) water and boil until reduced by half. Strain and divide the decoction into three doses. Take three times a day.

Itchy Eyes

See Conjunctivitis.

Jaundice

(1)   Roast 1 tablespoon black peppercorns until almost burnt. Set down from the fire and carefully add (as it will boil up) the water from 1 tender coconut, preferably the red-skinned variety. Let it cool, strain and drink the extract. Repeat for 3 days.

(2)   Boil a few guava leaves in sufficient water to cover them for 5 minutes. Strain and drink the decoction. Repeat several times until the symptoms disappear.

(3)   Chew on sugar cane sticks. The juice is just as good but the sticks are more beneficial.

(4)   Snack frequently on raisins, the blacker the better.

(5)   Raw bitter gourd juice rejuvenates the liver and spleen. (See Blood Sugar, Elevated.)

Kidney Stones (Renal Calculi)

(1)   Soak 1 handful whole bengal gram in sufficient water overnight. The next

morning, on an empty stomach, eat the rehydrated bengal gram uncooked and drink the soaking water.

(2) Plantain stem, cooked as a vegetable, helps to prevent the formation of kidney stones.

(3) Cook 1 handful ladies fingers (about 8 to 12) in sufficient water to cover them. Strain and drink the filtrate once a day. (The cooked vegetable may also be eaten to relieve constipation.)

(4) Limit consumption of tea and spinach.

Laryngitis

(1) Grind a 1" (2.5 cm) piece fresh ginger, 1 teaspoon cumin seeds, 1 tablespoon sugar-candy and 1/4 teaspoon turmeric powder together to a paste with a few drops of lime/lemon juice and honey. Smear the back of the throat with the paste. Repeat as often as relief is sought.

Pimples

(1) A special variety of turmeric called *kasturi/jangli* with a characteristic fragrance is to be used. Powder the dried turmeric and use like soap. Wash off with water. To avoid any yellow staining of the skin, mix the turmeric powder with either powdered green gram or bengal gram flour. The mixture of equal parts of turmeric powder and bengal gram/green gram flour *by weight* can be made in advance and stored in an airtight container.

If *kasturi* turmeric is not available, rub fresh turmeric root moistened with a little water on a smooth stone to get a paste. Mix with green gram/bengal gram flour and use instead of soap. Prepare paste before each application.

Prostate Problems

(1) Eat pumpkin seeds as often as possible.

Char maghaz or dried mixed seed kernels, used as a topping for Indian sweetmeats, is a good alternative if pumpkin seeds by themselves are not available.

(2) Avoid smoking.

Rancidity, Cooking Oil

(1) Add a marble-sized lump of tamarind to rancid oil and boil over steady heat until it is charred. Strain. The oil will be as fresh as ever.

Rheumatism

See Arthritis.

Sore Throat

(1) Swallow 1 tablespoon gingelly oil.

(2) Suck on sugar-candy made from palmyra sugar syrup.

(3) In a glass of hot water, dissolve 2 tablespoons salt and gargle every 4 hours. Rock salt/solar salt is preferred. (See also Laryngitis.)

Stomach Upset (Non-infectious)

(1) Lightly roast 1 tablespoon poppy seeds without oil. Eat mixed with 1 teaspoon sugar.

(2) Chew 1 tablespoon fenugreek seeds and swallow. Alternatively, lightly roast the fenugreek seeds without oil, powder and swallow with a glass of water.

(3) Drink a glass of water into which is stirred 1 tablespoon flea seeds.

(4) Nibble at the rind of a pomegranate. Alternatively, boil a few pieces of pomegranate rind in 1 cup (250 ml/8 fl oz) water for 10 minutes. Strain and drink the decoction. (See also Indigestion.)

Tonsillitis

(1) Mix 1 heaped tablespoon turmeric powder with 1 tablespoon rock salt/solar salt. Smear over the inflamed tonsils at bedtime. Leave overnight.

Toothache

(1) Clove oil is a time-honoured remedy for toothache. Alternatively, chew on a whole clove if a tooth proves troublesome until a dentist can be reached.

(2) Grind a 1" (2.5 cm) piece fresh ginger and 1/4 teaspoon salt together to a paste. Apply over the affected tooth to relieve toothache.

(3) Allow guava leaves to dry in the sun. Burn them and keep the ash in an airtight container. To prepare tooth powder, mix with mustard oil to make a paste and use to clean teeth.

(4) For toothaches (and headaches), rub castor oil (the cruder the better) at the back of the neck. Cools and soothes.

Trauma

See Cuts.

Warts

(1) Grind raw (mature) papaya and squeeze out the juice. Apply the juice (not white milk) directly to the wart(s) and allow to dry. Try to avoid contact with water. (Bedtime is best.) Repeat daily and as often as possible until the warts disappear.

Fresh raw papaya should be used every time. However, if a piece is removed from the same papaya for every application, it must be remembered its potency will be drastically reduced by the second day.

Whitlow

(1) Roast a small, whole brinjal over an open fire until the skin is black and charred. Cut into two and enclose the affected finger between the halves. Bandage to keep in position until the brinjal cools.

Worms

(1) Curry leaves are believed to help eliminate threadworms. They are particularly beneficial if consumed raw as in the form of a chutney.

(2) Grate 1/4 raw areca nut and mix with 1 teaspoon butter. Take at bedtime. Easily fed to children and pets.

Wounds

See Cuts.

Section 6

Index

Abbreviations of
Common Measures

C	:	Celsius
cal	:	calorie
cm	:	centimetre
F	:	Fahrenheit
fl oz	:	fluid ounce
g	:	gram
IU	:	international unit
J	:	joule
kcal	:	kilocalorie
kg	:	kilogram
kJ	:	kilojoule
l	:	litre
lb	:	pound
mcg or µg	:	microgram
mg	:	milligram
ml	:	millilitre
oz	:	ounce
ppm	:	parts per million
RE	:	retinol equivalent
tbsp	:	tablespoon
tsp	:	teaspoon